gun wgt p. 190

other wgts. p. 249

Gun 132#
petrol 74#   } 226
oil 20#

Engine 334# - 250# = 84

$$310 \times 1.25 = \frac{}{388\# \doteq 64 \text{ gal}}$$

Wing incidence p. 201
Box Beam p. 209
Struts p. 328
FII wing spars p. 370
D7 undercarriage p. 294
Tubing p. 229

VG p. 258, 275

Fokker:
The Creative
Years

A R Weyl

Edited by J M Bruce

Fokker: The Creative Years

A R Weyl

PUTNAM

ISBN 0 85177 817 8

© A. R. Weyl 1965

Printed and bound in Great Britain for
Putnam, an imprint of
Conway Maritime Press Ltd,
24 Bride Lane, Fleet Street,
London EC4Y 8DR
at the University Printing House, Oxford

Set in Monotype Times New Roman

First published 1965
Reprinted 1987

EDITOR'S NOTE

THE EDITING and preparation of this book for publication were performed after the author's untimely death. Not only were his personal and authentic advice and guidance on the text itself lacking: there was no clue to the sources of most of the material on which he drew in compiling this history.

One is thus unable adequately to acknowledge the author's indebtedness to those who contributed information and material: this is something that he himself would have done with the scrupulous care that was characteristic of him. He would, without doubt, have given pride of place to Reinhold Platz, that most modest man whom he persuaded to disclose so much about the early days of the Fokker empire at Schwerin and without whom the name of Fokker could scarcely have survived after Kreutzer's death.

Other contributions of documents and reminiscences came from Ernst Ditzuleit; photographs from the collections of Egon Krueger, Peter M. Bowers and Peter M. Grosz are reproduced as many of the illustrations.

To these names should be added several others. One hopes that those who helped in the making of this book but cannot now be identified will understand why only this general acknowledgment of their contributions can be made.

J. M. BRUCE

CONTENTS

CHAPTER I

UNWILLINGLY TO SCHOOL

ONE DAY early in 1910, among the passengers aboard a Rhine steamer was a disconsolate young Dutchman. His name was Anthony Herman Gerard Fokker; his destination was Bingen; and his immediate future lay in Bingen's Technical College. If young Fokker seemed preoccupied and oblivious to the splendours of the scenery it was because he viewed with extreme distaste the prospect of a return to the atmosphere and discipline of the classroom. He had had what he regarded as his fill of academic education in the elementary and secondary schools at Haarlem; now his interests lay in new and more practical fields.

Fokker was never happier than when tinkering with motor-cars and their engines. His was the enthusiasm of the mechanic, for he affected a strong dislike of all paperwork and theoretical engineering, largely because he lacked the ability to understand it. He had seen an aeroplane at an exhibition in Brussels in 1908, and had followed developments from the time of Wilbur Wright's visit to France. Aviation beckoned young Fokker alluringly: here was a fresh world in which he would—for he had supreme confidence in himself—achieve practical success.

Fokker's first aeronautical experiments were with model gliders cut from paper and celluloid, and he later designed a man-lifting kite. Perhaps fortunately, this was never built, for he was called upon to perform his year's conscription just after buying the materials. Fokker regarded his military service as an intolerable interference with his aeronautical experiments; he malingered without scruple and ultimately succeeded in bribing a doctor to declare him unfit for military duty.

Fokker's father, a well-to-do retired coffee planter, became increasingly insistent that the young man should lay the foundations of a career. Although appalled at his son's desire to fly, Fokker senior did not try to deflect Tony from his technical interests; he insisted, however, that if Tony wanted to be an engineer he must learn engineering thoroughly and obtain a diploma. Herman Fokker may also have entertained the hope that the training might turn the unruly spirit that was his son into a respectable citizen. He was wrong. Tony was perfectly certain that his father would have done better to buy him a flying machine; that was all he needed in order to become world-famous—not classrooms and examinations. As it turned out, the young man was right.

9

Thus it was that Tony Fokker came to be aboard a Rhine steamer early in 1910, bound for Bingen. Little did he know that, only eight years later, he would flee from Germany a multi-millionaire, owner of an engineering empire, a world-famous personality—and a criminal; that his name would be one of the most familiar in aviation and be bandied about in politics the world over; that honours would be heaped upon him; that the world's press would describe—and vilify—him as a most patriotic German. And all because he went the way of his own, not his father's, choosing.

The Bingen Technical School did not have the status of a university, but it had an excellent reputation for producing practical engineers. Ordinarily students were expected to have served an apprenticeship before entering the school, but it seems that in the case of Tony Fokker an exception was made, perhaps on the strength of his experiments with unpuncturable tyres and other practical work.

Despite this concession the Bingen school was not to enjoy the privilege of enrolling Mynheer A. H. G. Fokker. Before he reported to the school he learned that, some twenty miles away at Zalbach, near Mainz, there was a training establishment for automobile engineers that was advertising a course in aviation with prospects of flying tuition. A carefully worded letter that avoided any mention of the aviation course secured the ready agreement of Fokker *père* to his son's transfer from Bingen to Zalbach.

When Tony Fokker arrived at the Erste deutsche Automobil-Fachschule, Mainz, he discovered—so he alleged in his autobiography—that no-one at the school knew much more about aeroplanes than he did. That statement needs to be taken with a pinch of salt. At that time Tony Fokker could not have known much about aircraft or flying: the one and only aeroplane he had seen had been on static display in an exhibition; he had never seen anyone flying, nor had he met anyone who was working in aeronautics. The Zalbach establishment actually possessed a small laboratory with engines, airscrews and aircraft components, and at the time of Fokker's arrival an aeroplane was under construction. Someone on the staff must, therefore, have known something about the subject.

In point of fact the Erste deutsche Automobil-Fachschule had opened its aviation department on October 15, 1909. The school's advertisements had begun to appear in German technical journals as early as June 1909; they included illustrations of a workshop with wing structures and control surfaces for a biplane under construction. Also illustrated was an engine test-bed with a 30-h.p. water-cooled engine driving a two-bladed airscrew by a chain; equipment for the measurement of thrust and torque was available. None of this looked like ignorance or incompetence, nor did it suggest false pretences.

Modesty was never one of Tony Fokker's failings, and he habitually disparaged contemporary people and institutions. In the light of fact his later attempts to belittle the Mainz school and the grave doubts he cast upon the honesty of its management were absurd. Fokker was probably

10

more deeply indebted than he cared to admit to the Fachschule for his rapid advance in German aviation; indeed it is not impossible that the school may have provided the spiritual and material origin of the first Fokker aircraft, which Fokker claimed to be his own work.

The aviation course provided by the Fachschule was not intended to provide *ab initio* instruction: according to the prospectus it was intended to help men with engineering experience or apprenticeships to enter aviation. Fokker, of course, did not qualify, but the school welcomed his guilders and a place was found for him; he was promised that he would be considered for flying tuition if and when it became possible to do so.

The Automobil-Fachschule did not possess an aeroplane at the time of Fokker's enrolment: the students themselves had to design and build the aeroplanes on which they would learn to fly. In 1910 the school erected an aeroplane shed on the military training ground at Dotzheim near Wiesbaden. Flying pupils were invited to join; the tuition fee was modest but, as was customary at that time, a deposit was required as a cover against crash damage caused by the pupil.

Work proceeded on the construction of the school's first aeroplane, work in which Fokker participated eagerly. As he had neither served an apprenticeship nor had any craft training, his contribution can hardly have amounted to more than that of any interested, enthusiastic beginner. He spent little or no time in attending classes or drawing exercises: such activities he regarded as mere theory; and theory, in his opinion, never led to anything.

The Automobil-Fachschule aeroplane was a pusher of the then-familiar Farman configuration. Some thirty problematic horse-power were provided by a converted motor-car engine, with which the aircraft was considerably underpowered. It was abandoned in favour of a tractor biplane which, although of lighter construction than the first, yet retained the tail booms. This second aircraft was fitted with a 50-h.p. Argus aero-engine, the property of one of the students at the Fachschule.

As test pilot and flying instructor the school engaged Bruno Buechner, a burly, jovial Bavarian whose seventeen stone promised to tax the little Argus engine severely. Buechner's weight was not his only handicap, however: he himself had not yet learned to fly. He was a racing driver of great repute, but his flying experience was confined to a few tentative hops in a monoplane that he acquired and all too quickly wrecked.

Buechner viewed the prospect of flying the Automobil-Fachschule biplane with trepidation; he therefore did all he could to postpone its take-off and, with Fokker as human ballast, taxied the aircraft at various speeds. This exercise was detrimental to the undercarriage, but Fokker acquired experience in the behaviour of an aeroplane on the ground.

When Buechner could no longer postpone an attempt at flight he succeeded in wrecking the aircraft irreparably. Fokker's selfish wrath at this thwarting of his personal desire to fly is reflected in his sarcastic

11

description of the event. For Buechner Fokker had no word of sympathy: his sole concern was at the fact that the Fachschule had neither an aeroplane nor an instructor. He considered he had been swindled and said so.

Among the other would-be pilots whose hopes were shattered by Buechner's crash was Franz von Daum, an ex-officer of the German army, about fifty years of age and of independent means. He was so keenly interested in aviation that he was willing to help finance the construction of an aeroplane. This was Fokker's opportunity, and he and von Daum entered into an informal partnership: Fokker would construct an aeroplane to their ideas; von Daum would put up most of the money and provide the engine; both would learn to fly on the completed aircraft. Such seems to have been the general nature of their agreement. Von Daum apparently gave up his interest in aviation after the abrupt ending of his collaboration with Fokker; we therefore have only Fokker's account of the whole affair, and this, of course, is somewhat one-sided.

Von Daum provided a 50-h.p. Argus aero-engine, Fokker 1,500 marks of his father's money and his services as an aircraft constructor. Fokker implies that he designed the aircraft as well: this is doubtful, and probably only partly true. There are grounds for believing that von Daum had ideas of his own, and that the engineers of the Automobil-Fachschule, and perhaps Jacob Goedecker too, contributed constructive advice and design ideas.

Study of the contemporary aviation journals provides support for the belief that the design of the Fokker–von Daum monoplane was not entirely Fokker's. Published reports described this monoplane as an aeroplane of the Automobil-Fachschule, Mainz. An illustration depicted the aircraft standing between two biplanes of the Automobil-Fachschule, and the caption stated that all three were the training aeroplanes of the Fachschule. Fokker could be seen in the pilot's seat of the monoplane but his name was not mentioned, either in the caption or in the accompanying notes. This seems to leave little doubt that the Fachschule had contributed substantially to the aircraft. If such descriptions had been inaccurate Fokker, and probably his partner too, would certainly have protested to the publishers concerned, the more so because Fokker had demanded the return of his 500-mark deposit from the Fachschule and must have regarded his personal connexion with its aviation course as severed.

However, there is little doubt that the general arrangement of the aircraft came from Fokker, for it was similar in general configuration to his paper models. It was a tractor monoplane with pronounced dihedral on the mainplanes; the centre of gravity was fairly high above the wing. A small tailplane lay immediately behind the mainplane, but there was neither elevator nor rudder. Control was to be maintained by warping the mainplanes, differentially for lateral and directional control, and in the same sense for control in the looping plane.

Construction of the machine began in the autumn of 1910; the work seems to have been done in the Wiesbaden workshop of the Automobil-Fachschule. In his autobiography Fokker states that the steel-tube frames of the mainplanes were made from rough drawings by "a Frankfurt company"; the wooden components were made in "a neighbouring carpenter's shop". Fittings and other metal parts were produced in the Mainz workshops of the Fachschule. There is also the evidence of Jacob Goedecker's testimony that his workshop contributed, but it seems that the extent and nature of that contribution will never be known.

The "fuselage" consisted of two parallel wooden beams; this idea obviously came from Goedecker, for the contemporary Goedecker monoplanes had the same feature. The influence of Goedecker could also be seen in such details as the tailplane design, seat mounting and engine installation.

For one who had such a high opinion of himself, Fokker was remarkably vague about the part he himself played in the making of this first aircraft. A possible explanation for this vagueness might be that, thanks to his lack of the theoretical knowledge that he so ostentatiously despised, he was incapable of any structural design work.

The Fokker–von Daum monoplane was completed by October 1910. The date is determined by the fact that a photograph of the aircraft in its original form, taken on the Wiesbaden-Dotzheim parade ground, was published in *Flugsport* for November 2, 1910. The partners seem to have contrived to remove their "training" monoplane from its attachment to the Automobil-Fachschule: before the end of 1910 it was at the airship ground of Baden-Oos, where its testing continued.

Like all experimental aeroplanes of that period, the monoplane was repeatedly modified as its trials proceeded. An essential addition was a conventional rudder: without it the aircraft was virtually uncontrollable on the ground, for no other provision for steering had been made. It was found that warping both wings in the same sense was totally ineffective as a means of control in pitch, consequently the trailing edge of the tailplane had to be made flexible (as on the Goedecker monoplane) to serve as an elevator. This proved effective, but the aircraft's response when taxied at higher speeds indicated a disconcerting degree of instability. Stability was at that time regarded as perhaps the most desirable attribute an aeroplane could have; that it could be obtained by giving the wings pronounced sweep-back had been conclusively demonstrated in England by J. W. Dunne. Details and drawings of the successful Dunne biplane had appeared in *Flugsport* for July 6, 1910, and cannot have escaped Fokker's notice. The Fokker–von Daum monoplane therefore acquired an appreciable degree of sweep-back.

Fokker himself did all the testing of the aircraft; indeed, he virtually prevented von Daum from trying to fly it. Selfish though this action was, it is perhaps well that it was so: Fokker was twenty, slim, wiry and agile, and had exceptionally quick reactions. Although he had no more flying

13

experience than von Daum he was, by virtue of being thirty years younger, more likely to achieve early success in flying their aeroplane, with its new and untried features.

Real success was not achieved until December 1910 when, after all the modifications described above had been made, Fokker succeeded in making a hop of about 100 yards in the monoplane. His labours had been crowned with success, and he was naturally elated and greatly pleased with himself.

As was his wont when immersed in developmental work Fokker had not spared himself. He never indulged himself with personal luxuries; he was a lifelong abstainer from alcohol, and he did not smoke; his sole weakness was sugar in every form. In his endeavours to get the Fokker–von Daum monoplane into the air Fokker had worked long and strenuously in the open. He contracted a severe chill, and went home to spend Christmas at Haarlem, to rest and recuperate.

Not unnaturally, Franz von Daum had come to resent the way in which his younger partner monopolized their jointly-owned aeroplane. Fokker's absence gave von Daum his first opportunity to try his skill on the aircraft. Unfortunately he taxied into a tree and damaged the machine extensively. Von Daum was honest enough to tell his partner of the mishap at once, and a furious Fokker hurried back from Haarlem—once again his personal flying ambitions had been thwarted by what he regarded as the ineptitude of another.

The monoplane was so extensively damaged that there was little point in trying to repair it. In any case, Fokker had come to realize that it had been too heavy, complicated and unpractical; its destruction brought an opportunity to produce an improved aircraft. This idea Fokker put to von Daum who, chastened by his experience with the original machine, readily agreed. Fokker suggested that this time Jacob Goedecker should build the new monoplane to their ideas. Goedecker was also to help with the detail design.

Goedecker's name has already been mentioned. He was one of the few qualified engineers who took an early interest in German aviation. He had devoted five years of university study to engineering and naval architecture and had done post-graduate research in the laboratory of Professor Junkers at Aachen University. His scientific work had been of a high standard. Goedecker's interest in flying started in 1902 with the study of the infant science of aerodynamics. Thence he progressed to practical experiments, and in 1909 he constructed his first monoplane at Gonsenheim, near Mainz.

Fokker had made friends with this approachable, frank and helpful Rhinelander who had neither ambition to become a pilot nor the business acumen to make money out of aviation.

The first Goedecker monoplane had a cantilever wing that could be swivelled about a vertical axis for steering. Fokker and von Daum knew this aircraft well; several of its features influenced their ideas. It proved

14

itself capable of making short hops but was not conspicuously successful; it was therefore abandoned.

Early in 1910 Goedecker designed a *Taube*-like monoplane powered by a 50-h.p. Argus engine. *Taube* was the name of a very stable monoplane developed by Etrich and Wels with the guidance of Professor Ahlborn. The *Taube* wing was shaped like the seed leaf of *Zanonia Macrocarpa*, which gave perfectly stable glides; and the Etrich–Wels monoplane was remarkably stable. The name *Taube* was quite widely applied to other aircraft having a wing generally similar to that of the original Etrich–Wels machine.

On April 24, 1910, the Goedecker Taube made a complete circuit of the Grosser Sand parade ground near Gonsenheim. It was flying while Fokker was working on the clumsy pusher biplane of the Automobil-Fachschule; it was, in fact, the first aeroplane he saw flying.

Later in 1910 Goedecker built an improved model of his Taube; it incorporated more steel-tube construction than its predecessors, and probably gave Fokker and von Daum the idea of using steel tubing in their aircraft. Instead of exploiting his talent as an aircraft designer, Goedecker was content to remain in the comparative obscurity of Mainz, where, during 1911, he built three more Taube-type monoplanes and opened a flying school.

Fokker had much to thank Goedecker for. From him he learned more about technical matters than from anyone else during his long career in aviation. If Fokker had had a real grounding in engineering he might have learned enough from the modest Rhinelander to become an aircraft

Fokker on his second monoplane, completed in the spring of 1911.

15

Eleven years later, Fokker sits in the pilot's cockpit of a Fokker F.III (360-h.p. Rolls-Royce Eagle).

designer himself. Instead he was compelled throughout his career to depend upon the engineering abilities of others to design the aeroplanes that he falsely claimed to be his brain-children.

Goedecker was willing to build the new Fokker–von Daum monoplane.

16

He agreed to design its structure and have the components made in his workshop; Fokker would work on the assembly of the machine.

In the new aircraft the ineffective and complicated wing-warping control was abandoned, and conventional elevator and rudder surfaces were fitted. Although Fokker might have found that models with swept-back wings and marked dihedral needed no lateral control, Goedecker knew that even the stable Zanonia plan-form could not do without it. The monoplane therefore had ailerons. The undercarriage, which differed from the type Goedecker had favoured up to that time, was a simpler, cleaner structure than that of the first monoplane. Power was provided by von Daum's same 50-h.p. Argus engine, which had apparently survived the crash of the earlier machine.

The new monoplane was kept at the Dotzheim parade ground. It was a great improvement over its predecessor: it was lighter and its controls were effective.

Fokker, more than ever resolved to keep his partner from flying this precious monoplane, made progressively longer flights. As his experience increased so did his great natural talent for flying develop. On May 5, 1911, he succeeded in making a shallow turn at a height of about fifty feet. With this proof that "his" monoplane could fly and be controlled in flight, Fokker took and passed the tests for the pilot's certificate on May 16. He was granted German Licence No. 88, issued on June 7, 1911, by the Deutsche Luftfahrer-Verband. Fokker had achieved his aim.

But if Fokker had attained his goal, von Daum had not; and he insisted that he would now learn to fly on the monoplane. Fokker's counter-arguments were unavailing. Although von Daum made quite a good start, he crashed and damaged the aeroplane beyond repair. He was unhurt physically, but the blistering tirade that the unfeeling Fokker delivered against him killed his enthusiasm for flying. He sold his share in the aircraft to Fokker—which was exactly what the shrewd Dutchman wanted.

The Haarlem Spider in its original form with ailerons. It proved to be so stable that the ailerons were dispensed with and no lateral control of any kind was provided.

CHAPTER II

THE SPIDERS

THE MOST important asset Fokker gained from the dissolution of this incongruous partnership was the 50-h.p. Argus engine, which had survived the second crash with little damage. This remarkably durable power unit was installed in another monoplane, which was built by Goedecker. The new aeroplane was a refined development of its predecessor; it was smaller, lighter and simpler. The span was reduced from 43 to 36 ft. and, in accordance with Fokker's ideas, there were no ailerons.

Fokker took an enthusiastic part in the building of the aircraft. He became competent in the simple structural methods that Goedecker had developed; but he never acquired the skill of a craftsman.

This third monoplane was completed in August 1911. With its lower weight and smaller span it had a better performance than its predecessors: it could carry a passenger and fuel for twenty minutes at full throttle.

By this time Fokker's father was aware of the nature of Tony's activities. Apparently he had become resigned to the fact that his son was not going to settle down in a conventional career, for he became a member of the committee that organized a flying demonstration given by Tony Fokker at Haarlem. Thanks to Fokker's skill as a pilot, the demonstration was a resounding success.

The monoplane had necessarily to travel by rail to Haarlem, and the ease with which it was dismantled and reassembled testified to the soundness of Goedecker's structural design. Fokker appreciated this advantage; all subsequent Fokker types were designed to be easily transportable.

In flight the third monoplane, which became known as the Haarlem Spider, proved to be as stable as Fokker had intended, and no lateral control was required. Although by no means the first two-control aeroplane, the Fokker Spider was the most practical one that had been constructed up to that time.

This did not mean that the Spider was particularly easy to fly, nor was it so completely stable as the Etrich Taube. Later experience showed that the Spider could be difficult in gusty weather, particularly if a take-off or landing were made slightly out of wind.

About twenty-five Spiders in all were made by Goedecker and assembled in the Fokker workshops at Johannisthal. They were flown extensively during 1912 and 1913 and remained in use as primary trainers until late in 1914.

Fokker, who was not a sentimental man, preserved one of the earliest Spiders. After the First World War it was kept at Amsterdam as a museum piece. In 1924 it was fitted with a 70-h.p. Renault (the power unit of a few of the 1912 Spiders) and exhibited at the Paris Aero-Salon; in the following year Fokker demonstrated it in flight. This specimen had the stick control of the 1912 production version. In 1941 it was stolen by the Germans and transferred to the Berlin Air Museum, where it was later destroyed by Allied bombing.

In 1936 a replica of a Spider was built in Holland to celebrate the twenty-fifth anniversary of the date of Fokker's pilot's licence. It had a 90-h.p. Argus engine. This replica was flown by Fokker on June 6, 1936,

The Goedecker monoplane of 1911, as flown by Fokker, who is leaning against the airscrew in this photograph.

19

at Schiphol where it is preserved to this day as part of an aeronautical museum.

When Goedecker received Fokker's order for the third monoplane, Fokker was appointed works pilot and flying instructor of the Goedecker school. In this capacity he flew the Goedecker Taube-type monoplane, which was larger and heavier than his own machine. The Goedecker monoplane was stable and flew well; its rate of climb was poor, however, and it was not very manoeuvrable. It had a hand-wheel control similar to that of the Etrich Taube. This control arrangement became a standard requirement laid down by the German military authorities.

Fokker flew the Goedecker monoplane with skill, and became a good instructor. In the summer of 1911 he flew a new Goedecker on reconnaissance flights during the autumn manoeuvres of the XVIII Army Corps in the Taunus mountains. These flights were highly successful; Goedecker was decorated for the achievement of his aircraft, and the publicity benefited his flying school; Fokker earned high praise and a £25 fee for his part.

Fokker's basic design was protected by his German patent D.R.P. 265,515, which was applied for as late as January 25, 1912, and granted in 1913. It is not clear why Fokker waited so long after his separation from von Daum before applying for the patent: his aeroplane had been publicly exhibited and widely publicized months before the date of application.

The essence of Fokker's patent was that automatic stability in an aeroplane was produced by the combination of dihedral, sweepback, and a centre-of-gravity position above the centre of pressure: when one of these factors was absent inherent stability could not be obtained.

Fokker had first achieved the combination of these factors in the first Fokker–von Daum monoplane after its wings had been given sweep-back, but the true prototype of the Fokker Spider type was the Haarlem Spider, the third Fokker monoplane. In its essentials this aircraft was similar to the monoplanes built in 1912 and 1913, but had these differences of detail:

(1) The Haarlem Spider had a wheel control; when rotated, the wheel actuated the rudder; fore-and-aft movement of the control column actuated the elevator. From the next monoplane (the A-1912 type) onwards a stick control on a universal pivot was used: sideways movement of the stick operated the rudder; fore-and-aft movement the elevator.

(2) On the Haarlem Spider the two cabane pylons were in line with the wing spars. On production Spiders, beginning with A-1912, the rear pylon was moved aft to the leading edge of the tailplane.

(3) The Haarlem Spider's ignition switch was on the rim of the control wheel, on the starboard side.

The Haarlem Spider shared with many of its descendants the stark simplicity of its crew accommodation. Pilot and passenger sat in total exposure on exiguous seats between the two longitudinals that did duty as fuselage. Two large flat radiator elements were attached to the longitudinals. A small gravity tank was mounted between the forward cabane struts; a stand-glass on its starboard side indicated its contents.

Each wing had two spars of seamless-drawn steel tubes; each spar consisted of three tubes of progressively smaller diameter, bolted together at their ends to produce a tapered spar. The bolts also provided anchorage points for the wing bracing. This method of forming tapered spars was evolved by Goedecker. The ribs were also of his design: each consisted of a short length of steel tube bent to produce the pronounced camber of the wing; into this rib nose a length of bamboo was fitted and formed the

This Spider is believed to be the aircraft that was fitted with a 70-h.p. Renault engine in 1924 and exhibited at the Paris Aero-Salon of that year.

remainder of the rib. All ribs were identical and were sheathed in pockets sewn into the strong fabric covering of the wing. The wing was therefore single-surfaced at a time when such contemporary machines as the Etrich–Wels Taube had double-surfaced wings.

The Goedecker–Fokker wing section was too shallow to enclose the spars. The front spar ran under the ribs at the leading edge; the rear spar ran over the ribs and was faired over by a narrow strip of fabric. The ribs were attached to the spars by clamps bolted through the spar tubes. There was no drag bracing between the spars. The wing tips of the early Spiders and those of all training variants were square-cut, but some competition machines had the refinement of slightly rounded tips.

The bracing of the wings was originally effected by wire but, following Goedecker's example, steel cables were later adopted. The cables were attached to the tall cabane struts above the wings and to the undercarriage skids below, both of which anchorages gave favourable bracing angles.

This Goedecker-designed wing could be easily dismantled, easily

21

assembled, and easily repaired. By the same token it was easy for Fokker's small workshop to assemble new Spiders from the components supplied by Goedecker. It was also a simple matter to vary the sweepback, dihedral or incidence of the wings: all that was necessary was to fit appropriate sockets to the ends of the central spanwise wing-spar connecting tubes.

This simple wing was so successful at the low air speeds attained by the Spider that Fokker became convinced that there was no need to bother about the aerodynamic refinements that the "theorists" regarded as desirable. The shape of a wing section did not seem to matter; camber was all that was needed. Fokker failed to understand why critics of his Spider wing found fault with it: later, when the Prussian Army took an interest in his products, he was to learn that some of the constructional features that Goedecker had embodied in the Spider did not meet with the approval of structural experts. Fokker remained averse to theory and aerodynamic refinement, and his designers always had to fight whenever a new idea was to be incorporated in a Fokker aeroplane.

Construction of the tailplane was similar to that of the wings, but the ribs were wholly of bamboo. Elevator control was provided by warping the rear portion of the surface. That considerable physical force was required to flex the bamboo rods may be deduced from the substantial size of the stick that replaced the pilot's wheel control. The advantage of the stick control lay in its greater simplicity and lower weight. The rudder consisted of two triangles of steel tube hinged to the aft bracing pylon, one above and one below the tailplane.

The fuselage had only two longerons, strong ash beams of rectangular cross section, partly spindled out to save weight. They were about 13·2 ft. long and about 34 in. apart. Attached to the longerons were the two inverted-V cabane struts, the undercarriage struts, and the central rear skid.

The undercarriage struts formed an integral part of the wing structure. Not only did they provide anchorage points for the flying wires, but near their upper ends they carried the transverse steel tubes that interconnected the mainplane spars.

The undercarriage proper incorporated two long ash skids that projected forward in order to protect the airscrew. The axle was bound to these skids by rubber shock-absorber cord; it consisted of two steel tubes telescoped one inside the other over their entire length. Two wheels of motor-cycle type were usually fitted, but the 100-h.p. military Spiders had two pairs of such wheels to prevent digging in on soft ground. The whole undercarriage structure was liberally braced with piano wire.

The rear support of the undercarriage was an extraordinary device that gave Spider pilots much trouble. It was rather close to the wheels and made ground handling tricky, for the small rudder was the only means of steering. The unwary pilot might easily find himself travelling in directions he never intended. This troublesome rear support consisted of a long central skid attached to the centre of the axle and having a "scraper" or a claw brake at its rear end. The rear of the skid was sprung via a vertical strut the top of which was connected by rubber cord to the fuselage at a point immediately behind the pilot's seat. The arrangement was primitive in the extreme, and any competent engineer would have replaced it by a simpler and more practical device. Fokker stuck to it, however: he loved primitive things and disliked tidying up.

No part of the Fokker Spider was welded. Goedecker was opposed to that method of jointing, consequently every tube connexion was made by bolts passed through the tubes; U-bolts threaded on both legs were used as anchoring fitments. The structure was nowhere reinforced to compensate for the loss of strength at the bolt holes. Cast aluminium fittings attached the undercarriage struts to the longerons and formed the sockets for the cabane struts. The flying wires or cables were also attached to cast aluminium fittings bolted to the skids.

Most of these crude joints would be quite unacceptable nowadays, but in their time they were satisfactory and were not considered unsafe.

Fokker held the view that low weight and simplicity mattered more than crew comfort; he therefore set his face against the provision of such refinements as cockpit fairings. His only voluntary concession to luxury in later Spiders was the fitting of bucket seats. Ultimately, however, he had to provide cockpit fairings, to add a faired bottom to the fuselage and finally to fit a complete fuselage shell with windscreens. Army requirements accelerated his change of outlook. Fokker, who hated long flights and could scarcely read a map, did not readily appreciate the importance of providing military crews with enough protection to enable them to handle maps and write messages or sketch enemy positions. The seat fairing fitted to privately owned or competition versions of the 1912 Spider was of the type fitted to the Goedecker monoplane. It was supplied by the Frankfurt car-body manufacturer Georg Kruck. Trainer versions of the Spider had no seat fairing whatever.

One advantage that Fokker could claim for his Spider was that the view from both its seats was as good as could be had from a tractor monoplane. The wide gap between the wings and the fuselage, although inefficient aerodynamically, gave a better field of vision than could be obtained on any other German monoplane of the time.

The power unit of the Haarlem Spider and many of its descendants was an Argus engine, which was bolted directly to the two longerons. During 1912 and 1913 Fokker rejected all suggestions that he should fit other engines to his competition aircraft. This might mean that he had an agreement with the Argus firm to sponsor their products.

The Argus and Daimler-Mercedes companies were then the leading makers of aero-engines in Germany, and Daimler-Mercedes made great efforts to capture the market with their series of water-cooled in-line engines specially designed for use in aeroplanes. Various smaller firms competed, but with little success.

The Argus Motoren G.m.b.H. was one of the oldest aero-engine firms

Fokker Spider with cockpit fairing, 1912.

in the world. It had been founded in 1902 by Henri Jeannin,[1] Klingen-
berg and Rathjen, and had been supplying airship engines since 1906.
The 50-h.p. aeroplane engine was developed in 1909, and from 1911 the
firm concentrated its efforts on the production of aero-engines. The
50-h.p. version was followed by a 60-h.p. engine that had its cylinders
cast in pairs and a camshaft located in the crankcase, actuating the valves
by push-rods; the gear drive was at the rear and was not enclosed. In
1912, 70-h.p. and 100-h.p. engines were produced; all were four-cylinder
in-line units. These engines had a good reputation but from 1913 the
Mercedes engines began to show superiority.

The original arrangement of the cooling system, in which two large
flat radiators were attached to the longerons, was not completely satisfactory. Later Spiders had a single smaller radiator block mounted
athwartships behind the engine. Fokker found these radiators something
of a nuisance; for this reason he tried the air-cooled Renault engine and
liked it.

The Spider's engine had neither exhaust stubs nor silencers, and pilots
willy-nilly inhaled a mixture of exhaust fumes, soot and lubricating oil.
The fuel system was generally of the simple gravity type already described.
At a later stage a larger tank was fitted: mounted between the longerons
just in front of the pilot, it was a pressure tank; a hand pump was fitted
to the starboard longeron.

The precise identity of Fokker's first airscrew is uncertain: it may have
been made by Goedecker, or it may have been one of the French Chauviere
Integrale airscrews that could be had from Frankfurt. As soon as Fokker
had settled at Johannisthal the new A-1912 type Spider was fitted with a
Garuda propellor, the blades of which were inclined slightly forward.
This unusual airscrew was designed by Bruno Jablonsky, who became a
well-known industrialist in Britain.

[1] Henri Jeannin's brother Emile was, during 1910–11, Germany's most successful
competition pilot of the Aviatik aircraft of his native Alsace. In 1912 he set up his own
aircraft works at Johannisthal. There, his activities influenced the fortunes of his
neighbour Fokker.

Ernst Ditzuleit, who was one of the first flying instructors to be employed by Fokker and flew the Spider type extensively, has kindly recorded these impressions of the two-seat versions powered by the 70-h.p. and 100-h.p. Argus engines.

"The Spider was inherently stable. In the air it was perfectly simple to handle. When the engine was throttled down or switched off, the aircraft automatically assumed the correct gliding attitude; for landing one had only to flatten out. Take-off and landing were far from easy, however. The saying among aviators then was that anyone who could take-off and land a Spider could fly anything."

The difficulties were no doubt largely attributable to the arrangement of the undercarriage already mentioned.

In December 1911 Fokker moved to Johannisthal, at that time the centre of German aviation. Goedecker was sorry to lose him, for he had been a sound pilot and a good if somewhat impatient instructor. Fokker hoped to win some of the substantial prizes offered in the Johannisthal competitions, to teach flying, and possibly to obtain some orders for the Spider.

At Johannisthal the representative of the new aero-engine branch of the Fahrzeugfabrik Eisenach Dixi motor-car firm offered Fokker the use of a shed. Fokker accepted with alacrity. The Dixi company had redesigned their four-cylinder car engine as an aero-engine and had formed a subsidiary company, Dixi Luftfahrt und Bootsmotoren Verkaufs G.m.b.H., to market it. This subsidiary had rented the shed for the use of customers.

Fokker assembled his monoplane in the Dixi shed. He later tried a Dixi engine. Reports in German periodicals stated that the engine had been very successful both in a Goedecker monoplane and in Fokker's machine, but it seems Fokker found fault with it. He moved out of the Dixi shed after sugar had been put into his monoplane's petrol tank one Saturday afternoon, preventing him from competing for that part of the gate money shared out among pilots who made flights before the visitors. Fokker rented his own shed and reverted to using the Argus engine.

Fokker and his monoplane were at first looked upon as freaks by the Johannisthal habitués. The aeroplane looked rough and unfinished, and so did its pilot and designer. The absence of any form of lateral control on the monoplane was regarded as final proof that its designer was slightly insane. Fokker was regarded as an aviation maniac who worked hard on a useless and ill-conceived flying machine in preference to entering into the friendly social life of the Johannisthal community.

But Johannisthal changed its opinion of Fokker and his monoplane when he began to fly it: it was obvious that the Spider flew well; it was equally obvious that its pilot knew his trade. The more serious-minded among the mixed crowd of aviators and hangers-on came to realize that

25

the young Dutchman with the deplorable manners was not only the best pilot at Johannisthal but was determined to go into business in aviation. Although he came from a wealthy family and did not need to earn a living, he was no sportsman merely seeking thrills.

When he was not working, Fokker virtually lived in the Café Senftleben, for that establishment was an excellent place for making useful connexions and gathering information.

His immediate objective was the establishment of a flying school; for this he needed a business partner with capital. He had the good fortune to find the partner he was seeking in Hans Haller, a man of independent means who owned, and occasionally flew, a biplane at Johannisthal. Haller never took his pilot's certificate and indeed gave up flying soon after joining forces with Fokker. To the partnership he brought £500 (at pre-1914 value) and undertook to look after the business side of the venture.

Another valuable acquaintance of Fokker's was Dr. Walther Lissauer,[1] a Berlin-born physicist of repute, who had decided to make a career in engineering after studying several subjects. This quiet, cultured man had become a skilled pilot of the Otto Aircraft Works. At Johannisthal he was in charge of the aircraft division of the Berlin motor-body and coach-building firm of Kühlstein. Fokker found that he could gain a great deal of technical information from this older, experienced man.

At a time when most of the aeroplane constructors at Johannisthal were obliged to work on insufficient financial means, young Fokker was particularly fortunate in being able to count on financial help from his family: from them he received a total of over £15,000 at pre-war value. This subsidy enabled him to outlive many of his early contemporaries; without it he could hardly have made the grade in industry.

The shed that Fokker rented after leaving the Dixi shed was one of eight 50 ft. × 50 ft. sections in a long rectangular building. It had formerly been occupied by the Automobil und Aviatik A.G., a Strasbourg firm that built Farman box-kite biplanes and Hanriot monoplanes under licence. The Automobil und Aviatik concern was connected with the Argus engine company. Fokker soon found that for a flying school with facilities for assembly and repair more space was needed, so he rented the adjoining section of the building as well.

Other compartments in the same long building were occupied by the Rumpler company (for housing training aircraft); the Berlin patent agent Haefelin with an interesting but unlucky monoplane of his own design; the A.G.O. firm, then still a branch of the Munich aircraft works of Gustav Otto; and O. Trinks, a Berlin manufacturer of aeronautical components, who had built a twin-fuselage monoplane.

Johannisthal in Fokker's time was not altogether ideal as an aerodrome. It had been opened by an enterprising syndicate late in 1909. It lay

---

[1] Pilot's Certificate No. 22, gained on September 7, 1910, on a Grade monoplane; now (1962) living in the U.S.A. as a director of a research laboratory.

between the boroughs of Johannisthal and Adlershof, beside the Berlin–Goerlitz railway; on the other side of the aerodrome, west of the railway, was the Teltow canal. This canal, although only a narrow waterway, produced unexpected turbulence on occasion, and beginners were not encouraged to fly over it. During the war, certain ex-cavalry officers who had no aviation experience held positions of command at Johannisthal, and one of them achieved a kind of immortality by issuing a strict order that the Teltow canal was to be flown over only where there were bridges: this, he declared, would avoid crashes caused by gusts.

The flying ground proper was large (2,450 yd. in the N.E.–S.W. direction of the prevailing wind and 1,450 yd. across) but not very even. In fact, soon after the First World War a professor described its sandy surface as a most interesting formation of dunes. Care had therefore to be exercised in selecting areas for take-offs and landings—as Fokker discovered at the cost of a dislocated shoulder.

Nor was the flying area reasonably free from obstacles. A few hundred yards west of the building that housed the embryo Fokker company stood two airship sheds. The smaller and older of these was 265 ft. long, 110 ft. wide and 82 ft. high; it housed the non-rigid Parseval airships that regularly flew over Berlin by night bearing illuminated advertisements for toothpaste. The larger shed could accommodate two Zeppelins and was at that time the largest airship shed in Germany. It was four times as large as the Parseval shed, and much higher. To the underpowered aeroplanes of the time with their poor climbing ability, it was a great obstacle; moreover its bulk produced unexpected and unwelcome gusts and eddies.

Other hazards were the narrow belt of tall and scraggy pine trees that lay along the eastern side of the aerodrome between the flying ground proper and the railway line, and an adjoining pine wood in the direction of Johannisthal railway station.

The flying ground was encircled by wooden railings which served the dual purpose of protecting the public from unmanageable aeroplanes and the aeroplanes from the unmanageable public. The precaution was essential, especially when there was a crash, for the souvenir-hungry Berliners were capable of dismantling aircraft and pilot with impressive speed.

A thirteen-foot high fence enclosed the whole aerodrome with all its many sheds, grandstands, offices, refreshment kiosks and other buildings. Its primary function was to keep out gatecrashers, but it was also intended to deny non-paying visitors the pleasure of seeing the flying. It did not succeed completely in doing so, however, for large parts of it were occasionally spirited away by determined aviation enthusiasts.

Aloof, and apart from the bustle of that part of Johannisthal where Fokker worked, stood the sheds of the Flugmaschine Wright company. The Wright school was a branch of the first aeronautical enterprise in Germany, sponsored by His Majesty the Kaiser and his powerful friend

Dr. Walther Rathenau (later Foreign Minister and an early victim of the Nazis). Although the Wright biplanes were obsolescent the school throve on its own exclusiveness: distinguished visitors paid their respects first to the Wright establishment; and its pupils and staff did not mix with the rest of the Johannisthal fraternity.

Not far from the aerodrome, work was proceeding on a building that was to house the new Deutsche Versuchs-Anstalt für Luftfahrt (German Aeronautical Research Establishment), better known as the D.V.L. Its chief was Dr.-Ing. Bendemann, a good-looking, kindly man of great ability.

In charge of the aeroplane department was Dr.-Ing. Wilhelm Hoff, who had worked with Professor Dr. Hans Reissner at Aachen Technical University, and with Major Professor Dr. von Parseval in the construction of the Parseval seaplane. Hoff was himself a pilot and one of the very few people who had done full-scale research work at that early date.

The engine expert of the D.V.L. was E. Seppeler, a fair-haired man with a lively personality, a quick temper, and many good ideas. He was never without his notebook, in which he jotted down notes of events and ideas as they occurred.

Little did Fokker guess, in that December of 1911, how many bitter hours he would have to spend in this home of theorists and (as he chose to call them) "slide-rule pushers".

During January 1912 Fokker flew a great deal, trying to earn gate money and to improve his monoplane. The Spider, still Argus powered, had been improved by the addition of the seat fairing; the original primitive radiator had been replaced by one of the block type mounted just behind the engine.

Fokker's flying skill increased daily. His turns became neater and were executed so close to the ground that disaster seemed inevitable. His flying won him much admiration and he soon came to be regarded as one of the most daring and skilful pilots at Johannisthal.

Fokker was not the only daredevil at Johannisthal at that time. He had two rivals: the Stuttgart engineer Kurt Rosenstein, who was Rumpler's chief pilot, and the Russian Abramowitch, chief pilot of the Wright company. Fokker never liked competition, and he heartily disliked Rosenstein and Abramowitch. The more sophisticated mid-century may find it amusing to learn that Rosenstein's stunt flying consisted of shallow dives and zooms, and flying low with both hands off the controls—the Etrich Taube's stability permitted the latter exercise and made it impossible to do anything more spectacular than the dives and zooms. Abramowitch flew a Wright biplane—large, heavy, somewhat underpowered with 55 h.p., and fitted with a peculiar system of control. But the Wright controls were powerful and effective, and Abramowitch could throw it about low down, near the spectators, and in winds that grounded other pilots.

Photographic evidence proves that Fokker's steep turns on the Spider, often described as "over the vertical", never exceeded an angle of about 45 degrees; nevertheless they were steep enough to make Rosenstein give Fokker best, and his admission of defeat gave Fokker immense satisfaction.

Early in February 1912 Fokker made one of his few cross-country flights. He landed on the frozen Mueggelsee about five miles from the aerodrome; on the return journey he climbed to 7,000 ft., a good performance for that time. By that time the Spider had acquired the 60-h.p. version of the Argus engine; later, the 70-h.p. Argus was fitted.

As soon as all the formalities of the Fokker-Haller partnership were settled, two more Spiders were ordered from Goedecker. By this time a modest workshop had been established in Fokker's sheds, and two mechanics were employed. The two new machines arrived as parts and components; on arrival they were assembled, and the flying school began to function.

In those days, opening a flying school was just as simple as that: there were no licences, no regulations, no applications, approvals nor refusals, no examinations, no inspections. Anyone could open a flying school and teach people to fly.

Fees were high, and profits could be large. The comprehensive fee was between £60 and £100 (at pre-1914 value), and the pupil had to put down the crash-indemnity deposit mentioned earlier. Most schools took good care to see that no part of this deposit was ever returned. In many cases the instructional facilities were of questionable quality: obsolete aircraft of doubtful airworthiness and inexperienced instructors were by no means uncommon, and techniques of instruction seemed to be designed to extract as much money as possible from the students.

A sorely-needed corrective was applied by the German Army's insistence that its pupils—until 1913, exclusively commissioned officers—must receive adequate flying training from competent pilots and on safe aeroplanes. The tuition fee granted to flying schools was generous: the Prussian Army always paid the industry well. Even Fokker had to admit that.

Fokker hoped to get pupils from the Army. This meant he had to provide good training and adequate facilities. It also meant that he had to operate his school successfully for some time before he could approach the Doeberitz flying centre with a request to be considered.

His training technique was simple but effective. He gave the would-be pupil a few flights in a two-seater. At an early stage Fokker would do several steep turns and then ask the pupil to climb out of his seat and on to the wing. If the pupil showed fear or hesitation Fokker rejected him. After these familiarization flights the pupil was given a low-powered single-seat aircraft. In this he practised taxying, progressed to making short hops, thence to longer straight flights. Further dual instruction was then given, the pupil was taught to turn, and he was then on his own.

The B-1912 variant of the Fokker Spider. This version had a belly fairing under the cockpits, and was powered by a 100-h.p. Argus.

Solo training was not uncommon in those days, and it produced good pilots at little cost to the school.

While two further Spiders were being assembled a group of Army officers visited Fokker's shed and examined his monoplane. They liked its simplicity and were impressed by the fact that it was inherently stable: at that time inherent stability was regarded as a desirable characteristic of a military aeroplane, which almost universally was looked on as a reconnaissance vehicle.

The army wanted 100-h.p. two-seaters capable of carrying enough fuel for several hours' flying. The seats had to have adequate protection against wind and weather, and—magnificent requirement—there had to be accommodation for an officer's hat. In view of the Army's demands, Fokker installed a 100-h.p. Argus in one of the next Spiders and added a shallow fairing underneath the seat bearers. The structure was not strengthened to take the more powerful engine, but the span was increased slightly and a large supplementary fuel tank was fitted. The aircraft was known as the type B-1912 and was successful. It could lift a greater load, had a better rate of climb, and was appreciably faster than its predecessors.

It seems probable that Fokker engaged a design draughtsman to deal with these modifications, for it was about this time a man named Palm became associated with Fokker. Palm remains one of the unknown men of aviation: the annals of the industry contain no mention of his name; where he came from, where he went to, his Christian name—all are unknown. Yet exist he undoubtedly did: his activities were well-known among Fokker employees, with whom he appears to have been popular. He was probably a draughtsman with a flair for aircraft design. Whatever or whoever he was, he was an indispensable member of Fokker's organization until their ways parted, late in 1914.

In May 1912 the existence of the newly-formed Fokker Aeroplanbau G.m.b.H. seemed to be placed in jeopardy by an official warning against the formation of new aircraft firms. The Prussian War Ministry pointed out that the money devoted to military flying was insufficient to keep the existing firms going.

Fokker was already working hard to impress the military visitors who dropped in at his shed with increasing frequency. On May 14, 1912, when the Bavarian prince-regent was a spectator, he flew the 100-h.p. monoplane with three passengers and 265 lb. deadweight aboard, a total of 880 lb. But this impressive performance was to have tragic consequences: Fokker had flown with this overload in severely gusty weather, and the structure of the Spider had been strained. Ten days later, again in gusty weather, Fokker was climbing to 2,000 ft. with Leutnant von Schlichting as a passenger, when a lift wire snapped. Deprived of its bracing, the front spar tube bowed upwards. Fokker throttled back and glided down carefully; von Schlichting tried gallantly to comply with Fokker's request to climb out on to the good wing; but near the ground the wing failed and von Schlichting was killed in the crash.

Fokker was shaken but uninjured. He fainted, and on coming round bewailed his personal misfortune without saying a word about von Schlichting.

This accident made Fokker realize that his Spider would have to be improved before it could be acceptable to the military authorities. As an immediate consequence, the wire bracing of all Spiders was replaced by steel cables.

Not long after this disaster a well-built young man applied for a job as a mechanic; he said he had experience in gas welding. Up to that time no Fokker aeroplane had had any welded joint; Goedecker did not trust them. Fokker's partner Haller had been impressed by the extensive use made of welded joints by the Frenchman G. Poulain, who had even made a welded steel-tube fuselage. At Haller's suggestion Fokker bought welding equipment and had made up his mind to have a set of Spider rudders welded up from steel tube.

With this in mind Fokker asked the young man to make a specimen weld for him. After this brief test he engaged him, the whole interview having taken only a few minutes.

Fokker can hardly have imagined that this young welder-mechanic was to stay with him for nearly twenty years and make Fokker's name world-famous—that he was in fact the future technical director of the Fokker company.

The young man was Reinhold Platz. In 1905, when the Fouché acetylene-oxygen process of fusion welding was introduced in Germany, Platz had just completed his apprenticeship with an oxygen-producing firm in Berlin. He quickly learned the technique and went on to experiment with new applications of it. His employers exploited his skill, and sent him as a demonstrator to industrial undertakings in Germany, Switzerland and Russia.

In this way Platz acquired an experience of gas-welding that was unique at that time. Moreover, his experience was not confined to the welding

31

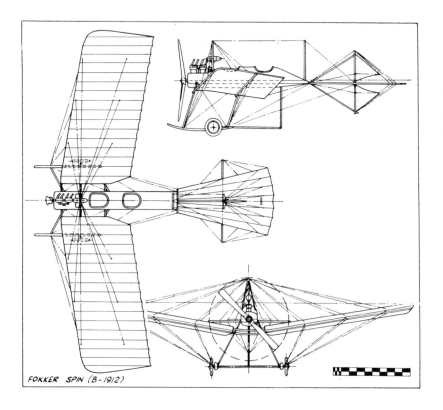

FOKKER SPIN (B-1912)

of steel: he had successfully welded aluminium without the use of flux to produce motor-car bodies and petrol tanks.

In the course of his travels Platz had had contacts with the infant aircraft industry. The tricky welding jobs he did at Johannisthal for such pioneers as G. Poulain and H. Dorner convinced him that there was great scope for welding in aircraft structures—particularly the steel-tube structures favoured by Fokker.

Much sooner than Fokker had dared to hope, in view of the crash in which von Schlichting died, his energy and drive were rewarded. In June 1912 the Royal Prussian War Ministry ordered a 100-h.p. Spider. Conditions of supply were that the aircraft had to fly for at least one hour at an altitude greater than 1,000 metres, and that it must be delivered by air to Doeberitz without landing en route.

Although the route from Johannisthal to Doeberitz is easy to follow on a clear day, Fokker, a poor map reader and navigator, soon became lost on the delivery flight. While he was trying to get his bearings a burst water pipe compelled him to land. The repair effected, Fokker was told how to get to Doeberitz, and he reached his destination without further mishap. So masterly was his demonstration of the Spider that no-one had the heart to ask him to make a trouble-free delivery flight, and the aircraft was accepted. Fokker, with an eye to the future of his flying school, made the most of the opportunity to make a favourable impression at Doeberitz.

Fokker lost no opportunity to seek business. He became friendly with A. Gruenberg, a Russian engineer who had taken his pilot's licence at the Albatros flying school, in the hope that this new contact might lead to orders for the Fokker flying school. When Gruenberg told Fokker that the Russian government was organizing an international competition for aircraft, Fokker was keenly interested, for the winning aeroplane was to be ordered in substantial numbers.

Accompanied by his friend I. W. E. L. Hilgers, Fokker went to St. Petersburg with one of the new Spiders. There they found some fifteen other competitors, all of whom were amply provided with the means to bribe their way past the multifarious Government offices and authorities. Fokker did as much palm-greasing as he could afford, and he and Hilgers demonstrated the Spider in daring fashion: Hilgers flew for six minutes with his hands raised above his head; Fokker climbed to 1,500 ft. in seven minutes with a load of 445 lb. and came down in a spectacular spiral glide, making startlingly steep turns; between them the two pilots left no doubt about the Spider's stability and performance. But it was all in vain; the Spider placed third and received no orders.

Among the Russian pilots who flew the Spider at St. Petersburg was Miss Ljuba Galantschikoff. She went to Johannisthal, where she bought a Fokker Spider. This aircraft had a 100-h.p. Argus engine driving a Garuda airscrew and was fitted with the neat seat fairing. On September 30, 1912, Fokker climbed to 10,000 ft. in this Spider and won a £20 prize for doing so.

At St. Petersburg Fokker had been impressed by the performances of aircraft powered by the Gnôme rotary engine. He installed a borrowed 50-h.p. Gnôme in one of the school Spiders, but the monoplane was not suited to the light rotary, lost manoeuvrability and reacted sluggishly to the controls, lateral control being particularly ineffective. This was probably attributable quite as much to the rearwards shift of the centre of gravity as to the torque reaction. Take-off was prolonged and the aircraft could not be held straight during the ground run. Discouraged, Fokker discarded the Gnôme.

As another experiment Fokker fitted ailerons to one of the Spiders. These proved to be ineffective and useless and, like the Gnôme engine, were discarded.

By the end of 1912 the Fokker flying school was flourishing; on suitable days the Spiders were flying from dawn to dusk. At this time the first two Army officers were attached to the Fokker school. They were Leutnant A. Muehlig-Hofmann and Leutnant Reincke. Reincke soon left, after an early crash: Fokker thought him unlikely to qualify as a pilot, and another officer took his place.

The crude wing structure of the Fokker Spider type can be seen in this photograph of a wrecked aircraft. Probably a training machine, this Spider had a four-wheel undercarriage.

Muehlig-Hofmann had a natural aptitude for flying and passed his pilot's test on November 19, 1912, after a very short period of training. He found Fokker a good teacher and a pilot of unusually fine "feel". Muehlig-Hofmann liked the Spider. When he was posted back to Doeberitz he flew the two Spiders there extensively, and acquired a reputation as a Fokker specialist—so much so that, during the next two years, whenever Fokker submitted a new type for testing by the Army, Muehlig-Hofmann was detailed to report on it.

According to Muehlig-Hofmann's recollection the Spider with 100-h.p. Argus had a speed of about 44 m.p.h. and could climb to 6,600 ft. with minimum load; it was very stable.

By the end of 1912 the Fokker school was outstanding. Six Spiders were available for instruction—few firms at Johannisthal had as many in use—and no time was wasted, whereas other schools left pupils hanging about idle for long periods, especially when Army pupils had to be given preference. Fokker and Haller had succeeded in introducing an exemplary standard of efficiency into what had been something of a racket. Fritz Cremer, Fokker's old friend who had learned to fly at the Fokker school in September, 1912, became chief instructor and set the pace of the school. On days of good weather he would often make as many as seventy instructional flights: his maximum was eighty-three, during a short February day in 1913. Quick training was the rule. Franz Kuntner, a mechanic from Vienna, passed his pilot's tests after only three days of instruction. He later became one of Fokker's works pilots.

On December 7, 1912, the Fokker Aeroplanbau G.m.b.H. was officially registered at the company-registration office of the Coepenick District Court of Law. Its capital was 300,000 marks (about £15,000 at pre-1914 value); the manager was stated to be the engineer A. H. G. Fokker; Hans Haller was recorded as confidential clerk.

At about this time Fokker offered the Spider to the British Government.

Fokker (wearing top hat) and Bernard de Waal beside a Spider of the Fokker flying school, 1913.

In his autobiography he gives a somewhat melodramatic account of this episode, but the result was that his offer was declined. The British Government had made a hesitant and belated entry into aviation and was not particularly interested even in contemporary British stable aircraft, such as the Handley Page and Valkyrie monoplanes. It was not interested at all in stable aircraft of foreign origin.

Fokker had no better luck in his attempts to sell his aeroplane to his native Holland. He thought that aircraft might help to resolve the transport problems of the Dutch East Indies, so he sent Hilgers, with two Spiders, to give demonstrations to the Dutch Army authorities. One of the monoplanes had a 100-h.p. Argus, the other a 70-h.p. Renault. But all Hilger's efforts were in vain: the Dutch were quite uninterested. The two Spiders did not return to Johannisthal: they were probably sold locally.

The "cockpit" of one of the 1913 Spiders.

CHAPTER III

THE BUSINESS GROWS

BY EARLY 1913 Fokker had twenty-five employees and his flying school was doing well—so well, in fact, that he needed someone to run it while he devoted all his time to instructing. Fokker found the man he wanted in Bernard de Waal, his successor as instructor at Goedecker's school. De Waal agreed to join Fokker, and Goedecker parted with him regretfully.

De Waal started work at Johannisthal in March 1913 and soon proved to be an excellent flying instructor. Like Fokker, de Waal was Dutch, but he was more human than his employer: de Waal was even-tempered and had a great sense of humour; as a man he was well liked by everyone; as an instructor he was patient, imperturbable, yet swift to react. He stayed with Fokker until his untimely death, from illness, on July 28, 1924. He was usually the first after Fokker himself to test a new aircraft or modification and he frequently gave Fokker valuable practical advice on development problems. But so reticent and modest was de Waal that he was not known outside the Fokker concern.

Soon after joining Fokker, de Waal went, with Kuntner, on a second attempt to persuade the Dutch military authorities to buy Fokker aircraft. Flying a Spider with a 100-h.p. Argus, they covered the 580 km. to Utrecht and The Hague in about $6\frac{1}{2}$ hours' flying time. The Dutch army had sent Lieutenant van Heyst to the Fokker school in January 1913, and he had

36

reported favourably on the Spider, on which he made thirty flights. But the Dutch Army Aircraft Purchasing Commission advised against the acquisition of Fokker monoplanes, and no order was placed.

At the end of 1912 it was clear to Fokker that he could expect no orders from the Prussian Army. He therefore turned his attention to the needs of the Reichsmarine, the Imperial Germany Navy. The Navy wanted aircraft. In 1912 they had organized a seaplane competition at Heiligendamm, but excessively difficult technical conditions were imposed and no worthwhile result was achieved. Official designs for flying-boats were constructed by selected manufacturers: the Albatros works built a flying-boat designed by the naval constructor H. Wahl, and other officially-sponsored flying-boats were built by the D.F.W. and Rumpler concerns.

Fokker was so impressed by the official desire to secure seaplanes that he decided to produce one of his own. His interest had been stimulated by the flying-boat that Goedecker had entered for the Heiligendamm competition. De Waal had flown the Goedecker boat.

Some mystery and intrigue and a hint of espionage attended Fokker's first seaplane venture. One of his pupils had been one Felix Schulz, who described himself as a captain in the merchant navy but was in reality a regular officer of the Imperial Navy, employed on discreet missions by the naval intelligence department. Schulz spent some weeks in England, during which time he "learned to fly" at the Avro school at Shoreham, displaying a remarkable degree of skill for a "novice". He may well have been the mysterious German naval "Lieutenant X" reported by the Press to have tested the Avro 503 seaplane at Southampton in August 1913 before its purchase by the German Navy.

It has been said on the one hand that Schulz was a spy, on the other that he was merely an agent for the German government in arranging the purchase of British seaplanes.[1] Whatever he was, Schulz contrived to acquire for Fokker the drawings of a new British seaplane. Unfortunately the identity of the British machine remains unknown. Fokker in his autobiography unhesitatingly describes Schulz not merely as a German spy but a British spy as well. (This had not troubled Fokker when he asked Schulz to act as his agent in England with a view to interesting the British Admiralty in Fokker aircraft.) Schulz was never able to refute or confirm Fokker's statement: he was killed in a crash at Johannisthal on September 26, 1913.

It is probable that the general design of the unidentified British seaplane had little influence on the first Fokker seaplane, for the aircraft that appeared on the River Dahme near Coepenick on February 9, 1913, bore no resemblance to any contemporary British aircraft.

The Fokker W.1 was a flying-boat. It is not known who designed it or who made it; it simply appeared. Neither Palm nor Goedecker had any hand in its design, and Fokker himself could not have designed it.

[1] In addition to an Avro 503, Germany bought a Sopwith Bat Boat flying-boat and a Wight pusher seaplane.

No components were made in Fokker's workshop; Goedecker neither supplied materials nor made parts. Fokker, as usual, offered no explanations, but he let it be known that construction began on January 2, 1913. A contemporary advertisement announced confidently but prematurely that the Fokker-Aeroplanbau could supply Fokker Seaplanes . . . without giving further details.

The W.1 was an unequal-span biplane, quite unlike the Spider landplanes. The hull might have been made by one of the many boat wharves along the waters near Berlin, but the maker of the wings has never been identified. One cannot exclude the possibility that the German Admiralty may have been responsible for the aircraft and may have financed its construction, but it seems that the truth about the Fokker W.1's origin will never be known.

The only part of the flying-boat that bore any semblance of a relationship to its landplane predecessors was the upper wing: it had pronounced sweep-back and dihedral, and was without any form of lateral control. There was no other common feature. Both mainplanes had two wooden spars and double-surface fabric covering; the upper spanned about 54 ft., the lower about 23 ft. The upper centre section was left open; the 70-h.p. Renault[1] engine was installed as a pusher on the rearward extensions of the two parallel ash beams to which the upper wings were attached. The lower wing was attached directly to the upper longerons of the hull, and had a small plywood float under each wing tip.

The shallow hull was a wooden structure and had obviously been made by a boat builder. The basic framework of longerons and bulkheads was planked with narrow strips of cedar; there was a single step just forward of the centre of gravity. The step was adjustable, consisting of a piece of strong fabric held stretched by spring-loaded levers. It was a

[1] In "Flying Dutchman" Fokker himself wrongly states that the engine was the 100-h.p. twelve-cylinder Renault.

The Fokker W.1.

38

device for which Fokker held a patent (D.R.P. 267071), although it is unlikely that he was the actual inventor. The patent was for self-adjusting elastically deforming planing bottoms for floats and hulls; it was claimed that the device would soften the impact of alighting and would give broader planing surfaces.

There was no fixed tailplane: the elevator was supported above the stern of the hull by a braced framework of steel tubes. The balanced rudder was in two parts, one above, the other below, the elevator.

As required by the Reichsmarineamt, the engine could be started from the cockpit. A crank handle behind the passenger's seat turned a shaft that was connected by chain and sprockets to the engine. With the 70-h.p. Renault the Fokker W.1 was underpowered, and Fokker intended to fit to a second version the 100-h.p. twelve-cylinder engine that he later wrongly attributed to the W.1 itself.

Fokker may have suspected that the centre of gravity was too far aft, for he took a mechanic and 130 lb. of ballast on board for the flight trials. A few low hops showed that the W.1 was in fact tail heavy, and some modifications were made. Fokker then attempted a flight. With the engine running full out the aircraft was not unmanageably tail heavy, but it was not apparent that the elevator was too small, for the slipstream kept it effective. As soon as Fokker throttled back the tail dropped alarmingly and the machine stalled in spite of Fokker's full use of the elevator. He opened the throttle fully to regain control and attempted a landing, trying to make a series of stalled descents with stick fully forward and cautious use of the throttle. His efforts were unavailing, however: the final stall was too low; the bows caved in when the hull struck the water, and Fokker was thrown clear. His mechanic had more difficulty in getting away from the wreckage and narrowly escaped decapitation by the propeller when he surfaced—the engine was still running.

The crash was a blow to Fokker's pride and a disappointment, for he had entered the W.1 in the great international Monaco seaplane competition and it would have been the only German entrant. In March 1913 Fokker announced that a new flying-boat was under construction for the Monaco competition, but there is no evidence that work was ever started on a successor to W.1. In the following month the firm announced that "owing to urgent commitments on military orders" it was too busy to take part in the Monaco contest. And that was that.

There was some truth in Fokker's statement that his firm's preoccupation with orders for Army aircraft prevented the continuation of the flying-boat experiments. Rather unexpectedly the Prussian War Ministry ordered two more Spiders, one with a 100-h.p. Argus, the other with the new 95-h.p. six-cylinder Mercedes engine.

In Germany, as elsewhere, no aircraft manufacturer troubled to name his products in any systematic fashion. By the spring of 1913, however, the tidy Prussian military mind required that Army aeroplanes should have a manufacturer's type designation, both for convenience of reference

The first Fokker M.1, with the 100-h.p. Argus engine.

and to signify compliance with current Army specifications. The two Spiders were therefore known as type M.1, the M signifying "Militär", or military. The W.1, with W signifying "Wasser" (water), had begun the parallel series for seaplanes. Spiders built for civilian use retained the earlier letter-and-year designations.

Of the two M.1s the machine with the 100-h.p. Argus was completed first: flown by Lt. Muehlig-Hofmann it was delivered by air to Doeberitz on March 2, 1913. When tested by Fokker the M.1 climbed to 2,000 ft. in nine minutes with a total load of 442 lb.; this included fuel for three hours. The measured take-off run was 67 yd.

The 95-h.p. Mercedes version (Army number A.38/13) was held up by delay in delivering the engine, which was then a new design and in great demand. The power unit arrived at the end of March and the completed aircraft was tested by Fokker. He himself flew the machine on its delivery flight to Doeberitz, taking only twelve minutes, thanks to a strong tail wind.

Fokker made no real profit from the sale of these two M.1s, for he had priced them reasonably in the hope of obtaining further orders. But the

The second M.1 wearing its military number A.38/13 on the lower half of its rudder.

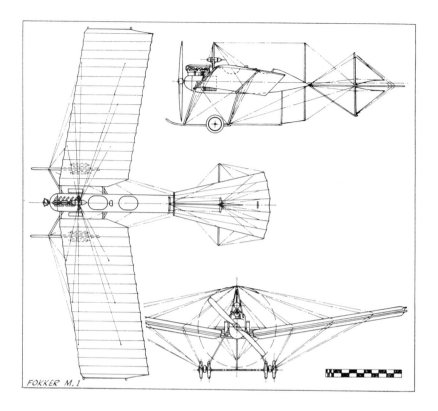

FOKKER M.1

two-control system of the Spider did not find favour with the Army pilots, and the machine had little to commend it for serious operational use. It could perform quite well from a prepared aerodrome in calm conditions, but it was risky to try to fly it from small fields in a cross-wind: its lack of lateral control was then acutely felt. In gusty air it wallowed so much that its observer could observe little, and a structural disadvantage was the method of anchoring the lift bracing cables to the undercarriage. In the Army's eyes these disadvantages outweighed the Spider's simplicity and robustness, and no further order was placed.

But official interest in Fokker did not wane. He impressed the authorities by supplying what was ordered, and supplying it quickly; he did not dazzle the military pilots with technical mumbo-jumbo, but listened to what they had to say without arguing. Besides, his flying school was unquestionably efficient, and earned the praise of those officers who were sent there.

The Fokker school was not only efficient but the firm's bread and butter. Some measure of its efficiency—and an interesting impression of flying performances of the period—may be gained from the following list

Little is known about this development of the M.1. It had a 70-h.p. Renault engine, a modified fuselage and simplified cabane bracing.

of flying times for the month of February 1913. The list includes flights by works pilots and visiting test pilots.

Kuntner	$2\frac{1}{4}$ hours in 27 flights
Lt. Reinke	2 hours in 47 flights
von Arnim	$1\frac{1}{2}$ hours in 18 flights
Felix Schulz	$1\frac{1}{2}$ hours in 20 flights
Muehlig-Hofmann	$1\frac{1}{4}$ hours in 4 flights
Cremer	$13\frac{1}{2}$ hours in 194 flights
Fokker	$3\frac{3}{4}$ hours in 45 flights
Schwarz	1 hour in 5 flights
Fr. Galantschikoff	$\frac{1}{2}$ hour in 5 flights
Dr. Ringe	$\frac{1}{4}$ hour in 3 flights
A. Gruenberg	$\frac{1}{4}$ hour in 2 flights
Rentz	$\frac{1}{4}$ hour in 2 flights

Flights were made on twenty-three out of the twenty-eight days in the month; three pupils (Kuntner, Schulz and von Arnim) qualified for their pilots' licences; there were three crashes (by Dr. Ringe, Lt. Reinke, and Gruenberg). For the time of year, these results were decidedly better than those achieved by other flying schools, including those operating under strict military discipline.

In March de Waal took over the responsibility of managing the flying school. Cremer carried on as chief instructor, although de Waal certainly had more experience of instructing. During that month ten pilots put in a total of twenty-six hours' flying in 286 flights.

By this time Johannisthal had become overcrowded. Several collisions occurred; anxiety grew in official circles; forthright questions were asked in the Reichstag. Such was the background to the offer, made to Fokker by Oberleutnant Franz Geerdtz of the Inspektion der Fliegertruppe (Flying Corps Inspectorate, usually abbreviated to *IdFlieg*), of a three-year contract to undertake flying training for the Army. Profits and turnover would be guaranteed, on condition that the Fokker flying school was removed from Johannisthal. Geerdtz suggested the little-used aerodrome at Goerries, near Schwerin, as the school's new home. The military authorities would use their influence to ease Fokker's negotiations with the aerodrome company and to secure favourable terms and conditions for the establishment there of a Fokker military flying training school. It was as fair an offer as any ministry could make, and Fokker accepted readily.

The aerodrome at Goerries had been opened in June 1912. The town of Schwerin had granted 25,000 marks (about £1,250 at pre-1914 value) towards its establishment. It was close to the lake of Schwerin in beautiful wooded and agricultural country. Few people had actually flown at Goerries, however. The Freiherr Albrecht had courageously tried to establish a small aircraft works and flying school but was soon compelled to give up. His sheds on the aerodrome and all tools and equipment, including welding apparatus, were put up for sale: Fokker acquired most of these assets for a song.

The Fokker school was now divided into two parts: a military establishment and a smaller civilian school. The former was gradually transferred to Schwerin, where it proved to be a greater success than ever. The training of civilian pupils continued on the Johannisthal aerodrome.

Spiders of the Fokker flying school at Schwerin, November 1913.

At Johannisthal the Fokker concern had expanded to occupy four compartments of the big building: Fokker had taken over those formerly occupied by Trinks and the Allers flying school. The removal of the greater part of the Fokker school made more workshop space available.

The Fokker Military Flying School at Goerries came into official being on June 1, 1913, under a profitable three-year contract with the Prussian War Ministry. The school was set up and subsequently run by Dr. Walther Lissauer, who had become Fokker's adviser in such matters: he acted as a consultant, and also helped Fokker re-organize his workshop.

Like all other commercially-managed military flying schools of the time, the Fokker school was a civilian establishment. To maintain military discipline among the pupils an army captain was appointed as commandant. He had no authority to interfere with the flying tuition, but he was responsible for ensuring that the training syllabus was strictly adhered to. Up to August 1914 only commissioned officers were sent to Goerries.

The Goerries school started with six Spiders, two of which were low-powered machines for solo exercises. Fokker ordered more Spiders from Goedecker. Some were erected in the new workshops at Goerries, work that might be said to mark the beginning of the great Fokker factory at Schwerin, which was to grow into an undertaking that employed 3,000 workers.

The first officer to pass his pilot's test at Goerries was Oblt. E. Denk, who gained his certificate on July 11, 1913. A few days earlier, Fokker's mechanic Paul Weidner fulfilled the more stringent requirements of the test for the field-pilot's brevet.

Weidner flew an Argus-powered Spider, but the *IdFlieg* later stipulated that field-pilot brevets could be acquired only on aeroplanes fitted with the standard military control. To meet this requirement Fokker acquired two old Rumpler Taube monoplanes; they served faithfully until the outbreak of war.

In 1913 the Prussian Army held a competition for military aeroplanes. The object was to find the best aircraft that could be easily and quickly assembled and dismantled in the field, and transported speedily from place to place by road. At that time the assembly of existing aircraft was usually a time-consuming process: much rigging, truing-up and test flying were needed before a machine could be operational. The worst offenders were the Taube monoplanes with their elaborate wing bracing; the biplanes were better, but still far from practical as operational military vehicles. None of the German military aeroplanes was robust enough to withstand the kind of road transport to which they would be subjected in the field.

Germany had another reason for seeking a more practical military aeroplane than she then had. France had evolved the concept of the light, fast, tactical scout aeroplane, capable of being readily transported by road and being easily and quickly assembled and dismantled. In war, these single-seaters would operate from fields close to the fighting line, making short-range reconnaissance flights in place of or as an adjunct to the cavalry. This idea appealed to the more far-sighted German pilots but found no favour with the General Staff, who held that a fighting troop of cavalry was the most reliable means of tactical reconnaissance. In the opinion of the brass-hats the military value of aircraft was still problematical and the only function they might be able to perform was strategic observation.

The terms of the competition stipulated that each aeroplane, dismantled and with spares, a tent and repair facilities, must be transported on a single trailer or lorry: the design of the vehicle was left to the competitor.

The Kühlstein Torpedo monoplane, which influenced the design of the Fokker M.2.

Time limits of two hours for assembling the aeroplane and one hour for dismantling were imposed. A journey of 250 miles had to be made along prescribed roads, punctuated by flights and assembling-and-dismantling exercises. All had to be performed within a set time and under strict supervision. The winner would receive an order for ten aircraft at 45,000 marks apiece (£2,550 at pre-1914 values).

If simplicity of structure and ease of assembly had been the sole criteria for assessing the quality of the aircraft, the Fokker Spider would have had a good chance of winning the competition. Fokker realized, however, that the Spider's appearance and performance placed it at a disadvantage: he needed a faster aeroplane.

One of the fastest aeroplanes at Johannisthal at that time was the Kühlstein Torpedo monoplane, which had been designed by Max Court. The design was taken up by the Berlin carriage-building firm of Kühlstein, who took Court into their employ. The Torpedo had an elegant fuselage of good streamline form, and its external bracing was kept to a minimum. The fuselage structure consisted of round wooden hoops with a number of stringers acting as longerons; its cross-section was polygonal, and a

45

good aerodynamic entry was provided by a shapely spinner on the airscrew. Construction was of wood and, as Fokker learned, this type of fuselage was not too satisfactory: it was neither light nor simple, and was susceptible to deformation.

Fokker wanted something better for his competition entry. He soon had an idea.

Behind the building in which the Fokker Aeroplanbau was housed, Emile Jeannin had his workshops. Jeannin made extensive use of steel tubing with welded joints in the construction of his monoplanes; wood was used only for the wing spars and ribs and secondary components. His first monoplane was not successful: unstable, prone to stalling, and affording its observer little view, it was not acceptable to the Army. The Army saw merit in the durable steel-tube method of construction, however, and suggested to Jeannin that he might build a Taube-type monoplane embodying his steel structural methods. The resulting Jeannin Stahltaube proved to be one of the sturdiest of these stable monoplanes, and a few examples remained in service until 1915.

In some mysterious way Fokker contrived to obtain one of Jeannin's welded steel-tube fuselages. Reinhold Platz found it one morning in the workshop. When he asked Fokker where it had come from, Fokker mumbled something about someone in town having made it for him, and left it at that. Platz told him that he could weld up such a structure just as well. Fokker was non-committal.

This Jeannin welded fuselage was made the basic structure of the streamlined fuselage of the Fokker M.2 monoplane. Wooden hoops fitted over the steel-tube structure bore numerous light wooden stringers to give the fuselage a circular cross-section; the covering was of fabric. The aluminium engine cowling had neat lines and faired smoothly into the fuselage contours. The cylinder heads of the 95-h.p. six-cylinder Mercedes engine remained exposed, but the two radiators were shaped to fit neatly into the streamlined shape of the fuselage. The pilot sat in the rear cockpit, but the observer was so close in front of him that intercommunication was not difficult.

The Fokker M.2 in its original form with divided elevator and single rudder surface.

46

The Fokker M.2 on its transporter.

Four sockets were welded to the lower longerons to provide attachment points for the wing spars. The spars were of wood, partly spindled out and with piano-wire drag bracing. The ribs had wooden webs with elongated lightening holes; the aerofoil section was similar to that of the Nieuport monoplane. The wings were fabric covered; all structural members were wholly enclosed, the only protuberances being the four attachment points for the bracing and control cables. The wing tips were slightly rounded, and lateral control was by warping.

In the tail unit the flexible bamboo tailplane/elevator surface of the Spiders was replaced by a conventional fixed surface and movable elevators. All the tail surfaces had welded steel-tube frames. The balanced rudder was wholly above the fuselage; there was no fin.

The undercarriage was much the same as that of the Spiders and the M.1, and retained the primitive central rear skid. There was a true tail skid but it was a protective device, not a real part of the undercarriage. Another unsatisfactory feature of the earlier Fokkers repeated on the M.2 was the attachment of the lift-bracing cables to the undercarriage skids.

No record of the M.2's performance seems to have survived, but it must have been little slower than the Kühlstein Torpedo which, with 100 h.p., is believed to have attained a speed of about 145 km./hr. (90 m.p.h.).

Whether the M.2's performance was good or not, Fokker did not depend on the aircraft alone and kept his ear to the ground. He always regarded good intelligence as indispensable to industrial success, and it was vital that he should know what his rivals were doing about the competition.

The object of Fokker's greatest interest was Franz Schneider, the

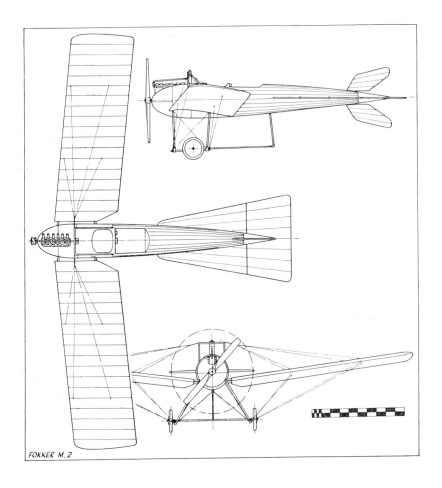

FOKKER M. 2

technical director of the Luft-Verkehrs-Gesellschaft, better known as
L.V.G. Schneider was a Swiss and a competent engineer. He had contributed to the design of the Nieuport monoplane of 1910, an aeroplane
remarkable for its clean lines, its simple, robust construction, and good
performance. In the following year a Nieuport monoplane with the first
100-h.p. nine-cylinder Gnôme engine won the keenly contested military
competition in France.

After this success Schneider was approached by the L.V.G. and subsequently joined the German company as technical director. He produced
a monoplane design generally similar to the successful Nieuports; it was
about the fastest aircraft then flying in Germany, its only serious rival
being the Kühlstein Torpedo monoplane. Schneider's L.V.G. monoplane did not find immediate favour with the Army, however: several
of the best military pilots crashed while testing the type; it was said to

lack stability; and its observer was even more badly placed than in the Taube.

However, the monoplane that Schneider designed for the German competition had perhaps the best chance of winning. The L.V.G. machine, powered by a 70-h.p. Mercedes, was relatively small; it was robustly built; and it could be assembled and dismantled quickly. For the competition Schneider designed a special road-transport vehicle that could carry the monoplane's fuselage with its tail unit and undercarriage assembled and in place; a retractable ramp facilitated loading and unloading of the fuselage. Under the fuselage supports were shelves for spares and tools, and there was space for repairs to be made. The wings formed the side walls of the vehicle and the whole was covered by a tarpaulin. Schneider applied for patents to cover several of the features of his vehicle.

Fokker knew some of the L.V.G. mechanics, and he managed to learn all about Schneider's preparations and the details of his ingenious transporter. Fokker's transport vehicle resembled Schneider's sufficiently closely for the L.V.G. designer to warn Fokker, before the competition, against infringement of his patents. Fokker did not heed the warning: the competition was not held in public and, as the patent law then stood, Schneider would not be able to prove infringement.

Schneider's monoplane had little to commend it as a military aircraft, but it was never put to the test. A daring and skilful Russian pilot, Elia Dunetz, had been engaged to fly the L.V.G. in the competition. On April 24, 1913, the monoplane's wing broke up in flight; it crashed and Dunetz was killed.

The M.2 in the 1913 military aircraft competition. Fokker is standing to the right of the airscrew, wearing a scarf.

With his most dangerous rival eliminated, Fokker's chances were considerably enhanced. When the competition began he raced his aircraft-laden vehicle over the prescribed route as quickly as he could. His team organization was excellent and gained him valuable time at the assembly and dismantling periods. He won the competition hands down.

Yet it is doubtful whether Fokker really got the promised order for ten aeroplanes, for no record of the aircraft can be traced. Surviving military pilots of those early days are sure there were never as many as ten Fokker monoplanes of any 1913 type in Army service. It is also certain that no Fokker aircraft built in 1913 was ever scheduled for mobilization (all earlier Spiders supplied to the Army were training aircraft never intended for operational use).

The Fokker M.2 with its revised tail unit.

The answer may rest in the report on the M.2 made by Leutnant Muehlig-Hofmann. He had tested the aircraft at the request of the Doeberitz establishment, and found it to be directionally unstable, lacking adequate rudder control, and useless for military purposes.

These criticisms may have been responsible for the modifications that were made to the M.2's tail unit. The original divided elevator was replaced by a single long-chord surface, the single rudder by a two-piece unit disposed above and below the fuselage. Even after modification the M.2's career was brief, and it participated in no other competition.

CHAPTER IV

THE DEVELOPMENT OF THE M.5

IN JULY 1913 Fokker had the opportunity of studying closely one of the most advanced monoplane designs of the time. The French pilot Léon Letort landed unexpectedly at Johannisthal. He had flown non-stop from Paris on a Morane–Saulnier monoplane. The distance of 920 km. (570 miles) had been covered in $8\frac{3}{4}$ hours; the Morane's 80-h.p. Le Rhône rotary engine had consumed 155 litres (34 gallons) of petrol and 49 litres (10·8 gallons) of oil; Letort still had 80 litres (17·7 gallons) of petrol left when he landed.

Two aspects of the Fokker M.3.

The light and graceful monoplane created a sensation at Johannisthal; it had put up a performance that no contemporary German aeroplane could equal. The Morane–Saulnier was a revelation to Fokker: he saw for the first time what a well-designed light monoplane with a good engine could do. He was even more impressed by the implicit confidence that Letort had in his engine. Between the time of his landing on July 13, 1913, to that of his return flight to Paris on July 27, the French pilot gave not the slightest attention to his aircraft. This afforded a good opportunity, missed by few interested people, of studying the aeroplane at close quarters.

But Fokker already knew a good deal about the Morane–Saulnier monoplane. The celebrated Swiss pilot Edmonde Audemars, who had made the first flight from Paris to Berlin in 1912, wanted to be the first man to fly from Berlin to Paris. For this flight, made in 1913, Audemars had chosen a Morane-Saulnier Type H monoplane in which he installed an 80-h.p. Gnôme in place of the usual 50-h.p. engine; the aircraft was a single-seater with a span of 8·5 metres (27 ft. 10½ in.). The Morane-Saulnier was sent by road from Vienna (where Audemars had been flying) to Johannisthal. Audemars knew his compatriot Schneider well, and had his aircraft housed in the L.V.G. sheds for assembly.

Fokker used his connexions among the L.V.G. mechanics to good purpose, and contrived to get into the L.V.G. sheds after working hours. It appears that he took with him someone who could make sketches. By chance, Schneider found Fokker there and sent him packing, but not before he had secured valuable technical details of the Morane–Saulnier. Audemars learned of this incident and told Raymond Saulnier, the designer of the monoplane, about it during the Paris Aero Salon of 1913. When Audemars met Fokker twenty years later he reminded him of the incident. Fokker merely grinned and said that all was fair in war . . . the Morane–Saulnier was, after all, the best aircraft of its day . . . it had interested him and he had wanted to study it. . . .

The appearance of Letort's and Audemars' Morane–Saulnier monoplanes at Johannisthal influenced German aircraft development. Various attempts were made to copy the design or to reproduce its main features. These attempts were probably helped by the publication in *Flugsport* of a technical description of the Morane–Saulnier. Few such descriptions were published; the leading French aviation journals of the day seemed to overlook the progressive features of the aircraft.

Fokker's aeronautical education was further advanced in October 1913 by another Frenchman flying another French aeroplane. The man was Adolphe Pégoud, his aircraft a Blériot monoplane, and his aerobatic performances made a profound impression on Fokker. Fokker realized the capabilities of a manoeuvrable, robust aeroplane. He also realized that his own moderately steep turns and zooms could no longer be described as daring artistic flying. Like many of the German pilots who saw Pégoud's performance, Fokker resolved to imitate the Frenchman's feats as soon as he could obtain a suitable aeroplane. Some of the Johannisthal pilots immediately placed orders for Blériot monoplanes.

The failure of the M.2 led Fokker to conclude that streamlining did not pay: it increased weight and complicated construction. If slab-sided fuselages were good enough for the fast L.V.G. monoplane and for the Jeannin aircraft, they would do for him too. The next Fokker, basically

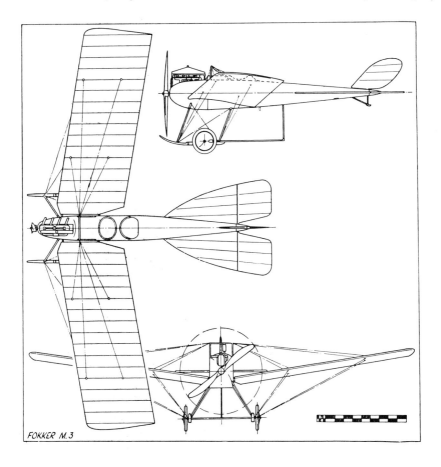

FOKKER M.3

similar to the M.2, therefore, had an unfaired fuselage with a rectangular cross-section.

The new monoplane was the Fokker M.3, and it was built at Johannisthal. In structural design its fuselage was generally similar to the Jeannin fuselage but was welded by Platz. A short top decking was added about the cockpits. The 95-h.p. Mercedes engine was fitted with one of the new Windhoff overhead radiators. This was light, compact, and less affected by the vibrations of the engine, being mounted directly on it; it was considerably better than the heavy, leaky side radiators of the M.2, but restricted the forward view from the cockpits.

The wings, tail unit and undercarriage were generally similar to those of the M.2, and the main lift bracing was again anchored to the undercarriage skids. The leaf-shaped, balanced rudder had ribs of light steel tubing.

The M.3 was the last type to have Fokker's two-control system: the rudder was actuated not by a rudder bar but by the control column. The stick had two convenient hand grips to accommodate both hands, and this feature was retained on all subsequent Fokker aeroplanes.

The Fokker M.3 was first flown on September 26, 1913, at Johannisthal. Fokker flew it during the autumn week of flying at Johannisthal but had little success with it. It is doubtful whether he ever submitted it for trial by the Army.

A second machine, designated M.3A, was built. It was powered by the 70 h.p. Renault salved from the crashed W.1, and had a divided rudder. The mainplane was mounted lower than that of the M.3: on the M.3A the rear-spar anchorage passed wholly below the fuselage.

The M.3 was sent to Schwerin for use as a trainer but survived only until November 1913, when P. Weidner crashed it in a heavy landing while instructing. Fokker managed to sell the M.3A to a wealthy Russian named Worobieff. It seems that the purchaser never flew the aircraft, however—a fortunate omission on Worobieff's part, for the machine was dangerous. At the beginning of the war, Ernst Ditzuleit was given the M.3A for training purposes and found it abominable. When flying straight it was laterally unstable, rocking from one wing to the other. In turns it refused to bank properly, and skidded. The gliding angle was tolerable but the aircraft would float for some distance before settling down some-

The Fokker M.3A, photographed at Johannisthal.

This illustration of the M.3A shows the divided rudder.

what abruptly. The M.3A was not successful as a trainer. Finally, and to everyone's relief, Ditzuleit crashed it on September 7, 1914.

The Doeberitz flying centre took a sympathetic view of Fokker's attempts to produce a practical military monoplane. They suggested that he might be more successful if he were to abandon his two-control system and follow the Zanonia-seed principle of the Taube monoplane.

Fokker knew he had to produce something fundamentally different from the Spider if he was to stay in business. The profit made by the flying schools was not enough to maintain his growing organization and finance new developments. His Dutch backers wanted to see existing aircraft types making some profit before committing themselves further: they pointed out that other German aircraft manufacturers seemed to be doing well out of the substantial Army orders that were being placed.

A completely new design was wanted, and Palm was instructed accordingly. The new aircraft was designated M.4, and in it the original and characteristic features of the Fokker-Goedecker design were completely abandoned. The wings had moderate dihedral and no sweepback; their raked tips and the shoulder-wing arrangement suggested Taube influence, but the Fokker M.4 differed from the Etrich–Wels machine in having ailerons. These control surfaces had oblique hinge lines, and their pronounced wash-out gave them a characteristic upward twist. The mainplanes were braced by cables.

The wings were made entirely of wood. The main spars were of ash, spindled out for lightness; the front spar was 80 mm. (3·15 inches) aft of the leading edge, along which a pre-formed strip of plywood was placed to preserve the aerofoil section. The wing section had more camber than that of earlier Fokker types. Fokker hoped that this would provide more lift: it may have done so, but only at the expense of longitudinal stability. A gap was left at each wing root to improve downward vision.

The Fokker M.4, the so-called *Stahltaube*.

The tailplane was attached to the upper longerons of the fuselage and had two separate elevators. The balanced rudder was somewhat similar to that of contemporary Morane–Saulnier types.

The M.4 fuselage was a welded steel-tube structure of plain rectangular cross-section. It was of original design and incorporated some detail suggestions made by Platz. The engine was a 100-h.p. six-cylinder Mercedes with a Windhoff overhead radiator. The seats were farther apart than on earlier Fokkers; this gave the observer more room. The pilot occupied the rear cockpit, and had stick control.

The undercarriage was sprung by rubber rings at the upper ends of the main struts; it incorporated a nose-wheel at the forward end of its central member; and there was a conventional tailskid in place of the primitive and awkward skid amidships that had been fitted to all predecessors of the M.4. The nosewheel had been included at the request of the Army, who regarded it as a better safeguard against nosing-over than the skids of the earlier Fokker types. The lift bracing cables of the mainplanes were attached to the central member of the undercarriage, which was rigidly attached to the fuselage and consequently thought to be immune to the shocks sustained on landing and during taxying. Platz thought this undercarriage rather an impossible structure, and in fact it had to be modified several times.

Although the M.4's wings were made entirely of wood, it was given the name Stahltaube. At that time, the Jeannin Stahltaube (which also had all-wood wings) was highly thought of in Army circles and was much sought after by Service pilots.

The M.4 was built at Schwerin, and its first flights were made during November 1913. It proved to be a disappointment. Various modifications were made in an endeavour to make it acceptable to the Army, but they were unavailing and the M.4 remained unpleasant to handle. Doeberitz detailed Leutnant Muehlig-Hofmann to test the new Fokker. He found it unstable and in performance decidedly inferior to contemporary German aeroplanes. It could not be used as a trainer, and few of

In this rear view of the M.4 the skewed hinge lines of the ailerons can be seen.

the Fokker pilots tried it. It was broken up after a brief existence, and Fokker dismissed Palm its designer.

It was perhaps regrettable that Fokker acted so hastily, both in demonstrating that he had no use for inferior designers and in having the M.4 scrapped. The aircraft had been a step in the right direction and might have been developed successfully. The gap at the wing roots was a bad feature; the wing camber was excessive and impaired stability; the centre of gravity may have been too far aft (as it often was on Fokker types); the undercarriage needed tidying up. All this could have been put right without disproportionate expense.

Before Palm left, late in 1913, he and his assistant, Martin Kreutzer, designed a new seaplane to Fokker's instructions. The directions given by Fokker were his interpretation of the Admiralty's requirements and suggestions. German naval opinion now favoured twin-float biplanes for coastal defence and reconnaissance purposes, and the Admiralty encouraged German aircraft manufacturers to produce suitable designs. A naval aircraft competition was announced, to be held in August 1914. Substantial prizes were offered for the aircraft with the best performance, and the winner could reasonably expect to receive a naval order for his aircraft. The sponsored projects designed by official naval constructors had been abandoned.

The new Fokker seaplane was designated W.2. Like the W.1, it was a sesquiplane: the span of the upper wing was twice that of the lower. The long extensions were braced by cables, and the landing wires were attached to two tall king-posts above the upper wing. The whole structure looked too frail to stand up to naval use. Ailerons were fitted to the upper wing only. To improve the crew's field of vision the upper and lower centre sections were not covered.

The steel-tube fuselage was mounted in mid-gap. Its rear half was uncovered, Blériot fashion. The engine was a 100-h.p. Mercedes,

57

The Fokker W.2.

with two large radiators mounted on the fuselage sides. The main floats were of the pontoon type, and a broad, flat tail float was fitted.

The W.2 was entered, not for the Warnemünde contest, but for the Nordischer Seeflug, an oversea flight of about 1,030 km. The route was from Schwerin to Christiania in Norway, now Oslo, and the competition was due to start on August 21, 1914. It was announced that de Waal would fly the W.2.

However, after a few short flights on Schwerin Lake, Fokker decided that the W.2 was no good. No attempt was made to modify or develop it: it was quietly dismantled in spite of the firm's advertisements that it could offer full facilities for training on seaplanes. The fuselage and floats were converted into a hydroplane, in which a 70-h.p. Renault replaced the 100-h.p. Mercedes. This contraption, of course, did not fly and did not qualify for the designation W.3.

Despite the failure of the Fokker W.2, Fokker's initiative in building it seems to have attracted the attention of the German Admiralty. They decided to put the Fokker Aeroplanbau on the list of manufacturers eligible to receive contracts for prototypes. Thus the W.2 effort was not entirely wasted.

When Palm left, he was succeeded by Kreutzer.[1] Kreutzer had come into Fokker's employ by answering one of Fokker's advertisements for young engineers to work in a technical office, but it is possible that he met Fokker in 1911 while undergoing engineering training at Bingen or Mainz. He had worked well with Palm, and now, at the age of 22, he became chief designer of the Fokker works, a position he held until his death in a crash in the summer of 1916.

Although Kreutzer had been through a technical school his engineering knowledge was confined to mechanical engineering. He knew little about aeronautics and he had no experience of aircraft design. His workshop experience was limited, and he came to rely more and more on Platz's

[1] Born July 12, 1891, at Cologne; died June 28, 1916, at Schwerin. Pilot's certificate No. 725, dated April 8, 1914.

advice. They became friends and within a year Platz was Kreutzer's right-hand man in the design work on new types. Kreutzer fitted in well with Fokker's staff and was well liked. Early in 1914 he began to learn to fly on Spiders at Goerries; he passed his tests, became a competent pilot, and often helped in making the acceptance tests of production aircraft. But he did no test flying: that job remained in Fokker's hands, assisted by de Waal. And no-one could have done it better.

From October 1, 1913, all workshops of the Fokker Aeroplanbau were transferred to Schwerin. Fokker retained only two of his former four compartments in the big building at Johannisthal; they housed a branch

Martin Kreutzer.

59

of the flying school for civilian pupils, and a repair shop. Fokker, Nischwitz and de Waal occasionally instructed there. August Nischwitz, one of Fokker's mechanics, learned to fly in 1913 and was retained at Johannisthal as resident instructor and to look after the repair shops. A taciturn and retiring man, he soon gave up instructing and went into the production workshop. As production engineer he later accompanied Fokker to Holland, and served in his post-war Dutch undertaking. The Fokker Aeroplanbau now had some thirty-five men on its strength. At Schwerin, Lissauer had helped Fokker to organize the workshops, which were in the charge of Fokker's first mechanic, Kahl. Lissauer had left the ill-starred aviation department of the Kühlstein Wagenbau company after the failure of the Court-designed Torpedo monoplane. He had more confidence in Fokker's Spider, which he flew quite often.

Lissauer did not find it easy to persuade Fokker to adopt rational methods of organization. Fokker would have preferred to stick to his haphazard workshop practices. He had no proper understanding of economy: to him it meant investing as little as possible in equipment. He thought that everything ought to be improvised: if an item of equipment was required it had to come from the scrap heap or must be, at best, dirt-cheap worn-out machinery. His ideal seemed to be the obtaining of something for nothing. Lissauer tried to convince him that such a primitive attitude was incompatible with achieving economy in production costs and quality in the finished product. When Fokker finally made Lissauer responsible for setting up and equipping the Military Flying School he did it efficiently and in an amazingly short time. The military authorities were so impressed by Lissauer's achievement that they asked him to undertake the same task at Doeberitz, and consequently he left Fokker's employ in 1914.

At the end of 1913 Fokker was in a difficult position. His enterprise was in debt. He owed considerable sums to relations and friends of his father in Holland. Their promised repayments and ample dividends had failed to materialize, and their disappointment was the greater because they knew that all the major German aircraft manufacturers had substantial orders, and larger contracts for aeroplanes were predicted. Fokker's backers could not understand why the Fokker Aeroplanbau failed to get more orders from the Army.

The dismal failure of all the Fokker prototypes had diminished the confidence that his Army friends had had in his designing ability. This seemed to be emphasized by Muehlig-Hofmann's condemnation of the M.4. Even the military flying school was no longer so profitable as it had been. Some training was still being given on the Spiders, but the *IdFlieg* had already indicated that to facilitate transition to operational types they would prefer instruction to be given on more conventional aeroplanes. The *IdFlieg* did not like Fokker's two-control system, and had compelled him to buy two Rumpler Taube monoplanes because they insisted on tests for the field-pilot's brevet being taken on aircraft with military type controls. Sooner or later they would probably ask him to give *ab initio* instruction on aircraft with conventional controls.

Civilian pupils were also becoming fewer. The National-Flugspende training scheme had led to an expansion of training facilities, and more and better flying schools were available. Pupils preferred to be taught on up-to-date aircraft with standard military controls.

As a novelty, the Fokker Aeroplanbau tried to attract pupils by advertising training on seaplanes on Lake Schwerin. At that time the firm had neither a seaplane of any kind nor any instructor with seaplane experience, so it was perhaps fortunate that no would-be seaplane pilot tested the validity of the advertisements.

The activities of the Johannisthal branch were so reduced that it almost ceased to function. Fokker retained his shed space at Johannisthal, however. The firm re-registered as having its offices at Schwerin. Hans Haller was the business manager, and the name Fokker-Aeroplanbau was retained.

The design department under Kreutzer consisted of one technician and three draughtsmen. None of them had any special design qualifications or experience in aeronautics. Such was Fokker's faith in his own technical intuition and in his skill in ferreting out details of other people's technical developments that he confidently believed that these talents of his would carry him to success. He was partly correct, but he would have been better equipped to compete with his rivals had he followed Lissauer's advice and engaged the best-qualified technical men. Fokker did not do that: such technicians might have found out how little technical knowledge he himself had, so he employed only what he called "practical people". To him, these were bench-workers who had no real engineering knowledge.

In May 1914 Fokker let it be known, through the technical press, that he was building a new flying-boat at Schwerin. It was said to be a sesquiplane with a span of 16·2 m. (53·4 ft.) and a length of 9·5 m. (31·3 ft.), powered by a 100-h.p. engine driving a pusher airscrew. It seems to have been a development of the W.1, and intended for the Warnemünde competition. But no more was heard of it. It may have been abandoned at the design stage; certainly no components passed through the workshops.

With his new and inexperienced designer, Fokker was faced with the need to produce an aeroplane that would not go wrong and would yield quick rewards; he had to make money, and quickly. The best thing was to copy an existing successful type, preferably one capable of aerobatics: there was money in that. The cavalry-scout aeroplane was much talked about. The French, with the advantage of their light rotary engines, had such aircraft. He had seen the amazing performances of these little machines when Audemars and Letort flew at Johannisthal. The Morane–Saulnier was such an aeroplane; it was, indeed, one of the best examples of its class.

The Morane–Saulnier monoplane has already been briefly referred to

61

Robert Morane and Raymond Saulnier in a Morane–Saulnier monoplane, 1913.

earlier in this chapter. It was the product of a happy collaboration between the brothers Morane and the experienced aircraft designer Raymond Saulnier. Léon Morane was an eminent pilot who had begun his aviation career with the Blériot firm, where Saulnier was a leading designer. Morane and Saulnier separated from the technically unadventurous Blériot and set up a new firm in partnership with Borel. Towards the end of 1911, Léon Morane and Saulnier started a firm of their own, and exhibited three monoplanes at the Paris Aero Salon in December 1911. These aircraft achieved several successes in sporting events during 1912.

Late in 1912 a much improved monoplane was developed. This was a highly successful design, typically French, and with many interesting detail features. It was exceptionally light, at least by German standards, but structurally perfectly safe.

In its general arrangement, the Morane–Saulnier monoplane resembled the successful Nieuport monoplane. But the Morane–Saulnier was the more practical of the two; it had a more efficient aerofoil section, a better plan-form of the wings, and gave its pilot a wider field of vision.

In common with many of its contemporaries, the Morane–Saulnier owed much of its success to the rotary engine. For their monoplane Morane and Saulnier selected the 80-h.p. Le Rhône, which was decidedly better than the Gnôme of equal nominal power.

The Morane–Saulnier monoplane enjoyed a number of successes in 1913, not only in France but elsewhere. These successes inspired a number of German attempts to copy the design. One of the first was made late in 1913 by H. Zahn at Würzburg, but his aircraft was written off in a serious crash and he became bankrupt. The AGO company produced their "cavalry" monoplane, which was more or less a Morane–Saulnier imitation but had a tailplane and a water-cooled engine.

Bruno Hanuschke, one of the Johannisthal enthusiasts, appeared in the autumn with a new monoplane that externally resembled the Morane–

An early Hanuschke monoplane, a copy of the Morane–Saulnier design.

Saulnier. Hanuschke's machine differed from the French original in having a steel-tube fuselage and an unorthodox control system. A wheel actuated the rudder and a foot lever operated the wing warping, as on the Nieuport monoplane; only the elevator control was conventional. This arrangement was not a success: skilled pilot though he was, Hanuschke damaged his monoplane in several landing incidents.

A more sensible line of action was followed by the Pfalz-Flugzeug-Werke of Speyer, a Bavarian firm that came into operation late in 1913. They acquired a licence for the manufacture of the Morane–Saulnier design and in addition the parasol monoplane of the same *marque*. Little publicity was given to this agreement.

Fokker's close study of the Morane–Saulnier monoplanes brought to Johannisthal by Audemars and Letort has already been mentioned. Despite his examination of the aircraft and the sketches that he had made, Fokker did not have enough information to enable him to make a good copy of the French machine. And Hanuschke's crashes were proof enough that surreptitious inspections and measurements were a poor

A later Hanuschke monoplane in military service.

basis for successful reproduction. No detailed, authentic description of the Morane–Saulnier had been published.

It became clear to Fokker that, if he was to make a sound copy of the Morane–Saulnier, he would first have to obtain an actual specimen of the type. The full story of how Fokker acquired cheaply—for 500 marks (about £25), as he told Ernst Ditzuleit with great pride—a dilapidated Morane–Saulnier monoplane is not known: several versions are told by people who were with Fokker at that time. What is known is that late in 1913 (or in January 1914) Fokker and Haller went to Paris, and when they came back they brought with them a Morane–Saulnier monoplane that was slightly damaged and in a state of disrepair.

It was a single-seater of Type H with a 50-h.p. Gnôme rotary engine and a 14-square-metre wing. Fokker's specimen seems to have been one of the earliest of the Type H Morane–Saulniers, but it was of the 1913 design with sprung undercarriage. With an aircraft of this type Legagneux had won the Pommery Cup contest in April 1913; Audemars had flown an identical machine from Villacoublay to Wanne in Westphalia on April 16, 1913, and the Type H that he flew at Johannisthal differed from standard only in having an 80-h.p. engine and increased tankage. Ordinarily the Type H carried 30 gallons of petrol and oil in a divided tank in front of the cockpit; feed was by gravity. For competition purposes a supplementary tank was sometimes installed behind the cockpit, with air-pressure feed to the main tank. The normal loaded weight was about 400 kg. (880 lb.).

It is certain that Fokker did not buy his machine from the Morane–Saulnier firm; it must have been acquired "on the side", and seems to have been sold for scrap. No drawings, erecting or handling instructions accompanied it. Fokker had made no attempt to secure a licence for the construction of the Morane–Saulnier monoplane or any of its patented features.

On arrival at Schwerin, Fokker's bargain Type H was unobtrusively put into a remote shed where it was unlikely to arouse the curiosity of the flying-school pupils or the workshop staff. Only a select few of his staff knew about it and helped to restore it to serviceability. Even to them Fokker did not explain why he had bought the Morane: he simply said that he wanted to try out a light monoplane fitted with one of the French rotaries that were so popular.

During January 1914 the little monoplane was dismantled, overhauled and reassembled; it was rigged as well as might be in the absence of a copy of the manufacturer's instructions. The Gnôme engine was cared for and tuned by a foreman who had had previous experience of the type. Close acquaintance with the Morane–Saulnier showed Fokker and his associates how a light and simple structure could be achieved by sound design.

The restored aircraft was first flown by Fokker himself, with only de Waal, Richard Schmidt, Alexander von Bismarck, and a few trusted mechanics present. After a few tentative hops to accustom himself to the unfamiliar engine Fokker took off. Although the Morane–Saulnier— light, sensitive, with powerful controls—was the antithesis of the Spiders that Fokker knew so well, he quickly mastered the agile machine and soon took advantage of its great manoeuvrability. The Type H was then flown by de Waal, Schmidt and young von Bismarck, and all were unanimous in their praise of it. So delighted was von Bismarck that he immediately asked Fokker to make him a similar aircraft. Fokker asked for, and got, payment in advance.

Fokker in the Morane–Saulnier monoplane he bought cheaply and had rebuilt. Standing in front of the aircraft are (*l. to r.*): Oberleutnant W. von Beaulieu, Hans Schmidt (Fokker's personal mechanic), Bernard de Waal, Alexander von Bismarck, Hauptmann Walter (first commandant of the Fokker military flying school), and Hans Wunderlich (a flying pupil under the *National Flugspende* scheme).

Fokker was convinced that for military purposes the Morane–Saulnier monoplane was much better than any of the contemporary German stable aeroplanes, but it needed skilled pilots. Rotary engines were somewhat out of favour in the air service at that time, largely because the Gnômes of the early Farman-type biplanes had suffered from the sand of the Doeberitz exercise ground and the attentions of unskilled mechanics. Elsewhere the Gnôme had been so successful that Fokker did not doubt that it was more reliable than German officialdom believed it to be; he also knew that a firm near Frankfurt-am-Main had acquired a licence for the Gnôme and was making a batch of them.

Fokker was therefore in no doubt that he should copy the Morane–Saulnier monoplane, or at least use it as the basis for his next aircraft. Kreutzer and he decided which features of the French design should be reproduced and which should be modified. The machine was flown for a few days, after which it was carefully dismantled to provide the basis for the drawings of the new Fokker M.5. Platz, who was at that time in the workshop, saw no other drawings than those made direct from the Morane–Saulnier. Nevertheless, the M.5 embodied several characteristic

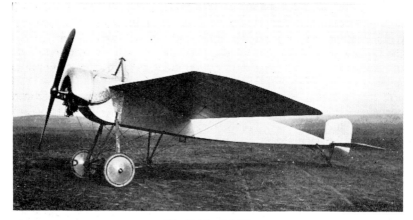

The Fokker M.5K.

differences from its French prototype; indeed, German friends of Fokker still maintain that, apart from a superficial similarity of outward shape, the M.5 was very different from the Morane–Saulnier.

And in truth the M.5 was different, though the differences were not immediately apparent. It was altogether more robust than the Morane–Saulnier: its fuselage was a welded steel-tube structure, superior in every way to the Morane's built-up wooden construction with its multiplicity of small fittings; its wings had deeper rear spars and embodied tubular compression struts whereas the French machine's only compression members were the ribs. The thickness of both spars was 5 mm. greater on the Fokker, and the deeper rear spar produced a different aerofoil section.

The Fokker wing was more efficient than that of the Morane–Saulnier, not merely because of its new aerofoil section but also because that

Front view of the M.5K.

section was more carefully preserved: the ribs of the Fokker were at a pitch of 340 mm.; those of the Morane were at 395 mm.: moreover the M.5 had riblets to preserve the upper-surface contour between the full ribs. Spanwise strips of tape were applied zig-zag fashion over and under the ribs to prevent the ribs from twisting sideways under the pressure of the doped fabric.

The Fokker M.5 retained the wing-warping lateral control that characterized the Morane–Saulnier. The compression struts had hinged end joints to allow them to flex during warping. Fokker retained stick control although he knew that the Army preferred wheel control, and he was right to do so.

Fokker with the M.5K.

This stronger wing imposed a weight penalty—all Fokker wings were 25% heavier than Pfalz-built Morane–Saulnier wings of the same area—but this was offset by the lower weight of the steel-tube fuselage. In the later Fokker fighting monoplanes the fuselage weighed about 45 kg. (100 lb.), whereas the Pfalz E.I fuselage weighed 62 kg. (137 lb.).

In its shape and size the M.5 fuselage resembled that of the Morane–Saulnier. At the point of maximum cross-section the Fokker fuselage was shallower by about 2 in. to improve the pilot's view. By a suitable re-disposition of the spacers the cockpit could accommodate a passenger behind the pilot on a sort of longitudinal bench seat. In the M.5 built for young von Bismarck this space was to have been occupied by a long-range tank, but this was never installed.

Kreutzer gave Platz full particulars of the shape and position of the fuselage attachments and left him to work out the design of the detail

Fokker in the cockpit of the M.5K.

features of the fuselage structure. This gave Platz his first experience in the design of a major component, and he and Kreutzer together created the classic Fokker-type fuselage which, with little modification, was not only to serve generations of Fokker aircraft but also to provide the fuselage-design basis for aircraft made by other manufacturers.

The four-longeron structure had diagonals in the forward bays where rigidity was essential; the remainder was cross-braced by wire. Platz formed the retaining lugs for the wire bracing by welding in small pieces

The M.5K undercarriage.

of bent steel tubing at all corner joints of longerons and spacers; through diagonally-opposite lugs a loop of wire was passed, its ends connected by a turnbuckle, thus saving two end connexions in each bracing. This form of fuselage bracing remained a characteristic of Fokker fuselages, including those of the large four-engined aircraft, up to the 1930s.

The M.5 fuselage was light and strong; it could be easily trued up; it allowed modifications and adaptations to be incorporated simply. The material was seamless mild-steel tubing. During the war it occasionally became scarce but Platz always insisted on the seamless quality and

The tail unit of the M.5K.

managed to get it. No great skill was required of Fokker welders. The fuselages were usually welded by men but most of the details were welded by girls. After welding, the longerons were usually found to be slightly distorted between the spacers; the degree of distortion depended on the welder's skill. The deformation could easily be remedied by hammering out, and this straightening-out process caused no failures in 100,000 welds in Fokker fuselages; nor did any Fokker fuselage fail structurally under air or ground loads within the design requirements. Platz would not reject a fuselage solely because of post-welding distortions, but he would never accept tubes of high carbon content nor pass defective welds: any suspicion of a crack meant rejection. From the production standpoint the Fokker fuselage presented no great problems. It was so simple and easily produced that it soon brought substantial profits in spite of low aircraft prices. Platz produced the first monoplane fuselages at piecework rates in about forty working hours. This labour time included collecting the material, cutting, shaping, bending and fitting the tubes, tacking them into place, welding all seams, bending and welding-in the tubular lugs, straightening the structure after welding, wire-bracing and truing-up the fuselage.

The Fokker M.5 engine mounting was copied from that of the Morane. The Gnôme rotary was installed in an overhung mounting, the rear bearing being bolted to the apex of a pyramid of steel-tubing. A cylindrical tank with compartments for castor oil and petrol was mounted between the engine and the cockpit, and fed the engine by gravity. An additional tank could be fitted behind the pilot's seat when required; it fed the gravity tank either by pressure feed or by pumping.

The engine cowling was an unabashed copy of that of the Morane–Saulnier despite the fact that the French firm had a valid German patent for this clever feature. In it the Morane company had neatly solved the problem of containing most of the liberal ejection of castor oil and petrol that characterized rotary engines without allowing it to collect where it could catch fire, and yet leaving the engine reasonably accessible.

Platz made the Fokker cowlings (for the Morane type was retained on all Fokker aircraft until late in 1916, so satisfactory did it prove to be) by welding wheeled or beaten aluminium sheet, using his fluxless welding technique. After the completed cowling and metal panels had been burnished the new aircraft was a splendid sight with its gleaming metalwork.

Like the Morane fuselage, that of the Fokker M.5 terminated in a horizontal knife edge at the tail: the tube that constituted the sternpost served as the bearing for the elevator hinge axis. The elevator itself was a cantilever, balanced surface. The rudder had originally belonged to the M.4 Stahltaube; there was no fin. The tail surfaces were made of welded steel tubing covered with fabric. They were generally similar to those of the Morane–Saulnier but Platz and Kreutzer made them more substantial at the cost of a small increase in weight. Their wisdom in doing so was later proved when the Pfalz monoplanes fell into disgrace after elevator failures at the front. Fokker monoplanes never suffered from this kind of trouble.

When he flew the Morane–Saulnier Fokker immediately noticed its tendency to swing on take-off and to ground-loop. The Fokker monoplane therefore had greater track (2 m. as opposed to the Morane's 1·5 m.), and the axle was further back to allow the tail to come up more quickly on the take-off run. Fokker later discovered that the tendency to ground loop could be cured by giving the wheels slight toe-out (i.e., opposite to the customary toe-in in motor cars). For this feature he took out a German patent (D.R.P. No. 300,181 of July 19, 1914).

To give the ground clearance stipulated by the military requirements, and to give more favourable angles for the lift-bracing cables, the Fokker undercarriage was made nearly six inches higher than that of the Morane.

Elevator detail of the M.5K. The control horn was on the starboard side only.

It differed in principle, too. The two bracing pylons under the fuselage were connected by a wood-reinforced tube which carried, at its ends, hinges for the axle frames. Each frame was a V-member consisting of a half-axle and a radius rod. From the wheel hubs a strut ran to the fuselage, its upper end sliding up and down in a vertical slot in the fuselage; within the fuselage this strut's fork-like end engaged the rubber rings that provided shock absorption. All the undercarriage struts were of steel tubing: the pylon struts were of elliptical cross-section; all the others were circular and had wooden fairings taped on.

The pilot could see the shock absorbers working and they were reasonably accessible for maintenance. The slots in the fuselage made the cockpit draughty, a point that mattered little to Fokker, who cared little about comfort in flight, but was criticized by pilots who flew operationally in the military machines at high altitudes or in cold weather.

In spite of all the care that had been taken to give the Fokker monoplane a sound undercarriage, it frequently failed to stand up to rough ground and rough pilots; so much so that *Fokkerbruch* became the recognized Service slang term for excusable damage following undercarriage collapse. On later Service monoplanes the axle had to be brought forward again after a series of crashes caused by overturning after landing on soft or rough ground.

The forward pylon provided the anchorage point for the lower ends of the lift cables attached to the front spars of the wings. To the rear pylon was attached the rocking lever that actuated the wing-warping cables. The upper bracing cables of the rear spars were continuous from one wing to the other, running over pulleys mounted at the apex of the top cabane struts.

The small metal fittings in the undercarriage and wing-warping system were similar to those of the Morane–Saulnier. But whereas the French machine had well-machined but expensive parts, the Fokker components were fabricated simply from welded steel sheet and were correspondingly cheaper.

The choice of an engine for the new type presented little difficulty. Von Bismarck wanted to make long cross-country flights; Fokker's thoughts were on the scouting single-seater that the Army wanted and on his desire to have an aerobatic aeroplane. The Army would of course insist on a German-built engine, so the 50-h.p. Gnôme would not do: it would have to be either the new Oberursel or the Schwade.

As already mentioned, space was provided behind the pilot's seat for the installation of an additional long-range petrol tank. Fokker intended to fit such a tank once the M.5 had completed its flight trials, but the opportunity was taken to put in a long seat that would accommodate a passenger. A removable back-rest half-way along this seat was provided for the pilot to lean against. This accommodation was cramped and uncomfortable, and would not have been acceptable for a military observer; the aircraft's climbing performance also suffered. However, this primitive expedient facilitated pilot familiarization: there was no dual control, but the passenger could get the feel of the stick and note the reaction of the aeroplane.

Fokker had great confidence in the M.5: aerodynamically it differed little from the Morane–Saulnier and extensive modifications were not likely to be needed. He was anxious not to lose time by delaying the construction of further M.5s until the completion of the prototype's trials.

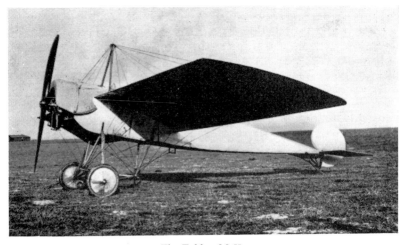

The Fokker M.5L.

72

He decided to build two prototypes simultaneously and to make a small batch of fuselages and other major components to enable him to promise early delivery against the orders he confidently expected. He made sure that Oberursel would supply the engines he wanted, for other manufacturers were also interested in this German-built Gnôme for competitions from which foreign-made engines were excluded. Parts for about five Fokker M.5s were put in hand at once.

It was originally intended that the two prototypes should be identical. However, soon after construction began, it was decided to fit one of them with a longer-span wing of much the same area as that of the Morane–Saulnier Type G two-seater. Fokker wanted to emulate the aerobatic performances of Garros, Hamel and others on Morane–Saulnier monoplanes; he therefore thought it advisable to fit a larger wing, which would, in addition, compensate for the greater weight of the Fokker and its bigger Oberursel. The long-span variant had three bracing cables to each spar, and a taller cabane was fitted to give the landing wires a more favourable angle in view of the greater loads imposed by inverted flight.

The two versions of the M.5 were called M.5K, with K signifying *kurz* or short span; and M.5L, with the suffix signifying *lang*, or long span. The M.5K was intended to be a high-speed military scout which would not be required to indulge in aerobatics; the M.5L was to be the aerobatic and long-range version of the design.

The two M.5 prototypes were completed during the latter half of April 1914. The M.5K was the first to fly. C. G. Henze recalls that no Oberursel had arrived in time, so the 50-h.p. Gnôme of the Morane–Saulnier was installed as a temporary measure.

Fokker had no difficulty in handling the new monoplane, but its climb was not spectacular and not up to the standard of performance required by the military authorities. The M.4 rudder was barely adequate and a larger surface was desirable: one was designed and the first was fitted to the M.5L, which emerged a few days after the M.5K's first flight.

The somewhat disappointing performance of the M.5K with the 50-h.p. Gnôme convinced Fokker that the M.5L would need a more powerful engine if it were to be flown before an Oberursel became available. Foreman Auer was sent to his old boss Gustav Otto, at Munich, and bought from him—cheaply—a 70-h.p. Gnôme of the older type, from a discarded aircraft. This engine was installed in the M.5L. With it, the new aircraft had quite a creditable performance; furthermore, the new comma-shaped rudder proved to be satisfactory.

When the first two 80-h.p. Oberursel-Gnôme engines arrived from Frankfurt they were installed in both prototypes. De Waal, Richard Schmidt, Kuntner, von Bismarck and other Schwerin pilots now tried the M.5s: they found the long-span version easier to handle, although slightly slower: all were delighted with it. The black-painted, well-finished M.5L was unanimously considered to be a success.

73

Fokker in the cockpit of the M.5L.

This opinion was shared by officers of the Army Flying Corps, among them von Beaulieu, who had acted as adviser to Fokker in the M.5 venture, and W. von Buttlar. The latter was so impressed that he immediately ordered an M.5L for his private use. It was perhaps the first time that a Prussian regular officer of the Flying Corps acquired an aeroplane of his own.

The little M.5K, although temporarily set aside, was to become the progenitor of the famous Fokker single-seat fighters of the 1915–16 period.

Early in May 1914 the news was allowed to leak out to the Press that Fokker was testing a new aircraft of his own design that was powered by a German rotary engine and showed great promise.

The Army's Inspectorate of Aviation (*IdFlieg*), wearied by other aircraft manufacturers' slowness to understand official operational requirements, showed interest in the new Fokker aircraft. Their interest grew when Fokker demonstrated the aerobatic capability of his new monoplane, and officers were sent to Schwerin to report on it.

The latest Army requirements stipulated that the strength of aeroplane wings and their bracing should be evaluated by testing them to destruction by sand loading. Fokker may have complied after a fashion with this strict (but to his mind, wasteful) requirement, but no-one can recall such a test being made on the M.5, nor is there any record of one. His stunt of having an impressive number of people to stand on the wings may have satisfied the more technically ignorant of the Army officers, but it cut no ice with structural engineers. For obvious reasons it could not be carried to the limit where the structure begins to fail, nor could deformations be observed and measured: its technical value was therefore nil. Fokker's

Of the men standing on the wings of the M.5L, de Waal is fifth from the left and Auer seventh from the left. Standing second from the right is Kuntner.

lack of technical understanding prevented him from appreciating the sound reasons for sand-loading tests. They were to be brought home to him rather forcibly at a later date.

In the case of the M.5L Fokker's demonstration apparently satisfied the *IdFlieg* officers by showing that the aircraft was strong enough for inverted flight. The illustration above shows eight people on each wing. Allowing for wing weight relief, this load would roughly correspond to a "safe" load factor of between 2·2 and 2·5, which could be deemed reasonable, though not wholly convincing, proof of adequate strength for mild aerobatics. But in fact the M.5L never gave cause for doubts about its structural strength.

It was on the M.5L that Fokker essayed his first loop, an event which he describes authentically in *Flying Dutchman*.[1] Once he had mastered the art of looping smoothly, Fokker fitted a venturi-type air-speed indicator to the M.5L, possibly the first installation of such an instrument.

Fokker showed young von Bismarck how loops were done, and trained Kuntner and Oblt. von Buttlar in the art. It was Kuntner's first loop, made after three days' instruction on June 18, 1914, in the presence of numerous Army officers, that assured the military future of the Fokker M.5 design. The officers were impressed, as Fokker wished them to be, and the type was recommended for adoption.

A small batch of some ten M.5L monoplanes were ordered for evaluation by the Air Service units. Experienced military pilots had flown both versions of the M.5, and the M.5L had seemed the better of the two for the Army's purposes.

By this time Fokker and his new monoplane were well known. Aerobatic displays were popular features at air meetings, and tempting fees

[1] Fokker was not, as he claims in that book, the first to loop in Germany. He was preceded by Roth, Breitbeil, Tweer, and possibly also by Jahn, Kueppers, Scherff and Hoehndorf.

75

were on offer to pilots who could emulate the feats of Pégoud. When Fokker was approached he agreed with alacrity to perform: apart from the immediate financial gain, the opportunity of advertising his new aircraft was too good to miss. His partner under the contract was to be Dr. Josef Sablatnig, a dashing pilot of great experience from Bohemia. Sablatnig had not done any aerobatic flying, nor did he have an aeroplane suitable for it; he was awaiting delivery of a Blériot.

Fokker's contract called for a first public exhibition at Frankfurt am Main. It took place during the Prinz Heinrich-Flug, a competition in which selected groups of Air Corps officers took part. Fokker gave a polished display of stunting on May 18, 1914, which was a rest day for the competitors; Hanuschke and Robert Sommer also flew.

Further demonstrations followed at other places, and Fokker's self-assurance and showmanship advanced in step with his experience. For four consecutive days, beginning May 30, he stunted at Johannisthal. His flying skill was undoubtedly at its height. He flew an uninterrupted sequence of daring and carefully planned manoeuvres at low altitude, showing off the new monoplane to the best advantage. His loops, now perfect, were executed at a dangerously low altitude; his turns were the steepest ever seen at Johannisthal: his dives seemed almost vertical; and he brought his M.5L down in parachute-like descents, semi-stalled, a manoeuvre made possible by the powerful wing-warping control. Even his take-offs were spectacular, so short did he make them; and his landings were made with consummate skill, ending with the shortest possible forward run.

On the last day, the Prussian War Minister, General von Falkenhayn, and his staff came to watch Fokker's exhibition. This was an unprecedented honour at Johannisthal. Fokker was decorated with a laurel wreath, and he was promised a bronze statue by the aerodrome's grateful management. This was quite a change from the days when he had come, cap in hand, to ask von Tschudi's clerk for the hire of a shed that was about to become vacant.

By now it was obvious that Fokker's mastery of aerobatic flying had made him one of the most accomplished demonstration pilots of the day. It was equally evident that his new M.5 monoplane was an unusually good aircraft. The tour had been the advertisement that Fokker had intended, and it had been accomplished without the slightest mishap. In view of the capriciousness of the Oberursel this was no mean feat and a high testimonial for Hans Schmidt, Fokker's personal mechanic.

An advertisement in *Flugsport* for June 6, 1914, justifiably described the new M.5 as an aircraft that "combined aerobatic capability with military usefulness". The advertisement also quoted a top speed of 127 km./hr. (79 m.p.h.), a climb to 1,000 metres (3,300 ft.) in 2 minutes 4 seconds, a take-off run of 12 metres (13 yd.), and a landing run of 21 metres (23 yd.).

Fokker had now definitely arrived. He had beaten his contemporaries among German manufacturers by building an aircraft that had good military prospects and was without a rival. He was ahead of Schneider, Hanuschke, and the A.G.O. concern; the Bristol monoplanes had been a failure at Halberstadt and the reorganized firm had gone over to making Taube monoplanes, which were no match for the M.5. The Aviatik firm's rotary-powered "light" biplane had in fact proved to be nearly as heavy as their ordinary two-seater. The Union works at Teltow had brought out a light biplane with swept-back wings and an 80-h.p. Schwade (Gnôme copy) rotary, but Fokker did not regard it as a serious competitor.

Although everything seemed to be running in the Fokker M.5L's favour, its introduction into the Army was not a particularly happy one. Late in June 1914 one of the first production machines was sent to the third Air Battalion at Cologne for evaluation. It was flown first by the unit's adjutant, Oblt. Hermann Kastner; he liked the aircraft immensely and thought it admirably suitable for scouting purposes. From his first acquaintance with the M.5L Kastner always had a preference for the light rotary-powered monoplane. His preference did much, a year later, to speed the introduction of the Fokker fighting monoplane.

Other officers tried the new Fokker after Kastner had flown it. About a week after its arrival at Cologne the aircraft crashed, killing its pilot, who had attempted an emergency landing near Cologne after the Oberursel had failed. The inference drawn from this unhappy occurrence was that military pilots who had trained on *Tauben* or biplanes with stationary water-cooled engines were insufficiently experienced to handle the light, fast and manoeuvrable Fokker. Conversion training was needed. It was therefore decided that unless a pilot had previous experience on monoplanes with rotary engines (e.g., by training on the original Bristol monoplanes of the military flying school at Halberstadt) he should be sent to Schwerin for instruction on the Fokker.

Fokker was asked to provide appropriate facilities at his military flying school. This meant the design of a proper two-seater with dual control, and the provision of a number of M.5Ls for instructional purposes. By the end of July, at least five and possibly more M.5Ls had been completed and supplied; but the total cannot have exceeded ten.

Alexander von Bismarck went to great pains to obtain dope of the light blue colour he wanted for his M.5L. In his effort to give his Fokker a high-gloss finish he applied a varnish which turned his beautiful blue to a rather unpleasant greenish hue. Von Bismarck's annoyance over this misfortune became the greater when his aircraft was nicknamed *Die Gartenlaube* (arbour)—the name of a respectable and somewhat Victorian family magazine well-known for sugary love-stories.

The other private owner, W. von Buttlar, specified a green finish for his machine. The choice of colour was inspired by the uniform of his regiment, the Marburg Jaeger. As will be told later, von Bismarck's and von Buttlar's M.5Ls were taken over by the Army when war broke out.

During the early months of the war the few M.5Ls that were with the

Fokker M.5L in Austrian service, numbered 00.13. (*Photo: Wolfgang B. Klemperer*).

German Air Corps rendered sterling service, and were much sought after by pilots. The Oberursel engine soon acquired a reputation for unreliability, however, and Fokker pilots were officially discouraged from venturing very far into enemy-held territory: during the first weeks a few experienced officers had been taken prisoner after emergency landings.

The Oberursel-built Gnôme's worst trouble was overheating of the cylinders. This could happen even when it was carefully nursed, but many of the regular officers did not take the trouble to handle the engine well, consequently it gave a great deal of trouble and was disliked by most mechanics. The cause of the overheating apparently lay in the obturator rings on the pistons: it was suspected that the Gnôme company had failed to tell their German licensees the correct material for these rings. The suspicion may not have been ill-founded, for other Gnôme copies (e.g., the 80-h.p. Schwade Stahlherz) suffered from precisely the same defect. Instead of moving freely in their piston grooves to maintain gas-tightness, the obturator rings of the Oberursel stuck fast in the grooves, letting the combustion mixture pass. To make matters worse, the Oberursel firm did not have a good enough engineering staff to ferret out the cause and provide an early remedy. This proved extremely unfortunate for the Fokker aircraft.

In February 1915, some fifteen M.5Ls and six M.5Ks were in operational service on all German fronts. They were used for reconnaissance and artillery-spotting duties.

The military versions of the M.5 had apertures in the wing roots between the spars; these were provided to improve the pilot's downward view for observation duties. Later, observation flaps were installed in the floor of the cockpit. These production machines also had the metal covering of the nose behind the engine cowling extended aft. This served as a protection against the engine's proneness to catch fire when started after overgenerous priming, or when a valve spring broke (a not-infrequent occurrence).

The French captured a few of these early birds. The span of the M.5L was said to be about 11 m. (36·1 ft.) and the length 6·9 m. (22·6 ft.).

A few more M.5Ls were supplied to the Army up to August 1915, but none were operational after June 1915.

The M.5L seems to have been known officially as the Fokker A.I, but the men who flew it talked of their Fokker E (*Einsitzer*—single-seater) to distinguish it from the M.8 two-seater artillery spotter. This has led to confusion with the later genuine Fokker E-types, which were armed fighters.

A similar confusion exists over the M.5K. Only two M.5Ks were in operational use in December 1914, and three in June 1915. They were used as flying dispatch riders, maintaining liaison with headquarters during campaigns of rapid movement, and were flown exclusively by selected regular officers. In spite of being single-seaters these aircraft were occasionally listed as Fok. A.III in official records. In other records they were (wrongly) described as Fok. E.II. Some M.5Ks were with aircraft parks, depots or schools behind the fighting zone. The type was less popular than other contemporary Fokker aircraft until its conversion to a fighter in May 1915.

At the time when the initial production order for M.5s was placed, the *IdFlieg* let Fokker know that in their opinion a two-seat aircraft would be preferable for military purposes. The emphasis in Germany, as in France, had shifted from the single-seat tactical scout to the light artillery spotter carrying an observer and able to operate from front-line fields close to the batteries. For this requirement an aircraft giving a good downward view and adequate room for the observer was essential: the cramped accommodation of the M.5 would not do. It was therefore suggested to Fokker that he should develop his monoplane into a proper two-seater while retaining its main characteristics.

Fokker and Kreutzer doubtless knew that some French designers had resorted to the parasol wing arrangement to provide a completely unobstructed downward view. Fokker also knew that the Pfalz concern

Fokker M.6.

had acquired a licence to build the Morane–Saulnier Parasol monoplane. One such Morane–Saulnier Parasol had been built at Speyer and had been demonstrated at Schleissheim to the Bavarian Army authorities.

Fokker did not like the idea of having an aircraft's centre of gravity below its wing, possibly because he had heard that parasol monoplanes could be subject to unpleasant slow oscillations. He did not go the whole hog with a true parasol monoplane but produced an aircraft with its wing slightly above the fuselage in a position roughly mid-way between those that characterized shoulder-wing and parasol monoplanes. This was the Fokker M.6.

The span and wing area of the M.6 were roughly the same as those of the M.5L. As on the single-seater, there were three bracing points on each spar and the bracing pylon was as tall as that of the M.5L fuselage. The cabane structure to which the wings were attached supported the front spars about 16 in. above the top longerons; the steel tube that connected the rear spars formed a sketchy division between the two cockpits. To facilitate access to the cockpits the centre-section was left uncovered, and the trailing portion of each wing was cut away.

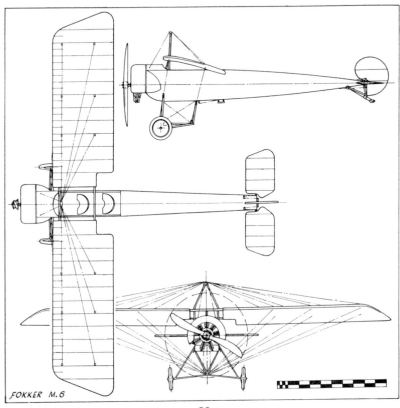

FOKKER M.6

Seated in the cockpit of the M.6 is Schmidt, Fokker's mechanic.

The M.6 fuselage was slightly longer than that of the M.5L. The seats were separate but still so close together that little more than a very small hand camera and a signal pistol could be accommodated. The M.6 differed from contemporary Service aircraft of the A and B categories by accommodating its pilot in the front seat. This gave him a good field of forward vision, but he and his observer were not otherwise comfortable, for the cockpits were excessively draughty.

The M.6 was a short-lived and unlucky aircraft. It was evaluated by air corps officers at Schwerin, and Fokker was urged to improve the downwards field of vision. While it was still undergoing its evaluation trials, Oberleutnant Kolbe tried it. It was his second flight in a Fokker monoplane, and he took Hauptmann Ruff, a pupil of the Goerries school, with him as passenger. While airborne Kolbe apparently misused a three-way fuel cock: when the engine stopped, deprived of fuel, he attempted an emergency landing in allotments near the aerodrome but the aircraft crashed. It was wrecked; the pilot died hours later from an unsuspected internal haemorrhage; Ruff escaped with a fractured thigh.

By now the clouds of war were massing and aircraft were urgently wanted. The Fokker M.8, an improved artillery spotter, was virtually ordered "off the drawing board"—the Army placed a provisional order for twenty, paying their usual one-third of the price in advance, before the prototype flew. The type number M.7 had been allocated to a light two-seat biplane, powered by the 80-h.p. Oberursel but having a longer range than its predecessors. This aircraft was designed to meet the requirements of the German Admiralty, who were also in a hurry to obtain aircraft and were willing to pay handsomely for them.

The Austro-Hungarian government, desperately short of aircraft because of their misguided policy of standardizing the faulty Lohner biplane, also came to Fokker seeking military aircraft for early delivery. They also offered to provide facilities for the licence production of suitable types in Austria and Hungary.

Fokker eagerly accepted all orders without considering whether he could fulfil them. The first orders for the M.5 and his success as an aerobatic performer had set his business on its feet and it was making a handsome profit. The Military Flying School was run in exemplary fashion by de Waal: it was working to capacity, had suffered few crashes, and was making good money. Fokker's Dutch backers began to receive worthwhile dividends from their investments and realized that aviation was a Good Thing; his family saw that their erstwhile black sheep was not such a fool in business after all. And the war made things even better.

A close-up of the M.6.

CHAPTER V

WAR

ON THE first day of mobilization, Fokker and all other German aircraft manufacturers were informed by telegram that all aviation material was subject to requisition by the Army. The Navy protested, for they had placed orders of their own with Fokker by arrangement with the War Ministry. Naval officers hastened to Schwerin and offered higher prices for anything with wings. Officers from operational units also came, bent on acquiring some of the coveted new Fokkers.

Fokker was delighted to find himself for once in a seller's market. He was only too willing to sell to anybody: had the Allies come for his aeroplanes he would have sold to them just as readily. For cash, of course.

So he sold whatever aircraft were at Schwerin to the highest bidder, and at prices he would never have dreamt of a few weeks earlier. He quickly got rid of all the junk that had accumulated for want of customers. He even sold aircraft that did not belong to him: for instance, von Bismarck's precious *Gartenlaube* and the M.3A that he had palmed off on Worobieff.

On the following day Leutnant von Buttlar came to fetch his *grüner Vogel* (green bird) M.5L for his squadron. Fokker had not dared to sell that.

Another visitor was Colonel von Eberhardt, who delivered a stern and pointed homily to Fokker. The Inspector found that production at Schwerin was lamentably inadequate. By accepting orders from the Army, the Navy, and from Austria, Fokker had undertaken far more than his factory could produce; he was messing about with experiments instead of getting on with the production of aircraft that the Army now needed so urgently; Fokker ought to realize that output was all that mattered, at the moment.

The rebuke was well merited. Fokker had rashly accepted every order offered to him, quoting impossible delivery dates, without considering how they could possibly be fulfilled. The Army had long-standing orders for M.5Ls and for a substantial number of two-seat artillery spotters developed from the M.6. The Navy had just ordered seven two-seat biplanes of a type (M.7) still to be built (Order No. B.1043 to 1049/14) at £825 per airframe, without engine and instruments—a very good price. No performance had been specified, and Fokker had promised delivery from October 1914. He had promised the Austrians all the aircraft they wanted; and they wanted more than his whole factory could produce in a year.

Fokker's works consisted of a pitiful collection of old huts and shacks, neither equipped nor manned for any kind of quantity production. The most that Fokker and his collaborators had ever produced were two of the simplest aeroplanes at a time. The greatest handicap of all was Fokker's lack of technical knowledge, for he did not know how to set about production in batches or series. His reluctance to invest in production equipment was fatal. Lissauer's advice had long been forgotten.

Fokker's business instinct told him that the *IdFlieg* now meant business: if he was not to be kicked out of his works he would have to come up to scratch. Moreover, as an alien in a country at war he could scarcely expect to be given special consideration. He therefore promised to give priority to the Army, to whom he was so much indebted, and to speed the delivery of Army aircraft. The M.7 biplane for the Navy and for the Austrians was set aside, and all efforts were concentrated on the completion and testing of the M.8 artillery-spotting monoplane. A strenuous day-and-night routine for the staff began; more workmen were engaged and the workshops were enlarged.

Glad to see the efforts of the Fokker team, Col. von Eberhardt decided to form an artillery-observation squadron equipped throughout with the new M.8. The order for this type was increased to more than forty aircraft; they were designated Fok. A, later Fok. A.I. They and the back-log of 24 M.5L were to be produced with all possible speed.

At the same time, thirty officers were attached to the Fokker school, most of them for conversion training. Unfortunately, the school had been left with very few aeroplanes, none of which had a rotary engine, and it was difficult for de Waal and his instructors to keep flying training going. Worobieff's M.3A, which the Service had returned as unsuitable, was pressed into use as a trainer. Unpleasant to handle and barely controllable, it was cordially disliked by every instructor. Fokker recognized it as a source of danger and suggested to Ditzuleit (whose exclusive training aircraft it somehow became) that he should put it out of its misery by crashing it. This was ultimately achieved, quite unintentionally, in the course of an emergency landing. Shortly afterwards Ditzuleit joined the Navy to become their Fokker pilot.

Fokker realized that the school needed more aircraft, and went on building up his labour force to meet the increasing demands. Fortunately the structural simplicity of Fokker aircraft enabled inexperienced workers to make a useful contribution to production in a short time.

From the fronts came news of the exploits of Fokker aircraft. Late in August, Hauptmann Goebel had to make a forced landing in French-held territory during a flight to Sedan from Air Depot No. 4 at Trier. Evidently the Oberursel had failed again. On August 30, 1914, Leutnant von Beaulieu, flying an M.5, made an impressive reconnaissance in the

Charleroi sector. Leutnant von Hiddessen had been over Paris in a Fokker. In September an M.5 had been forced to land near St.Omer and was captured intact. Allied pilots flew it up to 8,000 ft. and were quite impressed.

One of the pilots who made good use of the M.5L was Oblt. H. Kastner. He was with No. 38 Feldfliegerabteilung, stationed at Brussels and later at Ghent. Using his M.5L as a two-seater with Lt. Niemann as observer, Kastner made successful reconnaissances during the Dixmude fighting on the Yser. He later took the monoplane to the Eastern Front, where it ended its career during a forced landing, the Oberursel having been at fault again.

Kastner's notable successes on the Fokker made other squadrons eager to have similar aircraft. Among them was the squadron led by Oblt. Freiherr von Freyberg.

The Fokker M.8.

The M.8 (Fok. A)

Fokker kept his promise to make speedy deliveries of aircraft to the Army, for the first production M.8s were handed over in October 1914.

The M.8 was a true shoulder-wing monoplane, the wings being attached to the upper longerons. Large apertures were provided in the fuselage sides under the wings to give the occupants a good field of downward vision; side-mounted windscreens were fitted to the operational M.8s to

85

make downward observation more comfortable. The crew sat in close tandem in the single large cockpit.

The span and chord of the wings had been increased, and the area was now 20 sq. m. (216 sq. ft.); the wing loading was therefore about the same as that of the M.5L flown as a single-seater, consequently the take-off and climb were good. The spars were farther apart than those of the M.5 and the ribs were more widely spaced, to keep the weight down. The wing-bracing cables had quick-release devices for easy dismantling in the field. For road transport the wings were strapped along the sides of the fuselage. The M.8, like all Fokker aircraft, was eminently transportable. This was an important consideration, for German replacement aircraft were never as a rule flown to the front or to base formations.

The M.8 fuselage was about 40% wider than that of the M.5 and two slim people could even sit side-by-side in it. The main petrol tank, with a separate compartment for the castor oil, was mounted behind the engine and had a fuel gauge that could easily be seen by the pilot; the feed was by gravity. Behind the cockpit was a supplementary tank of the kind intended for von Bismarck's *Gartenlaube*. Both tanks were of brass

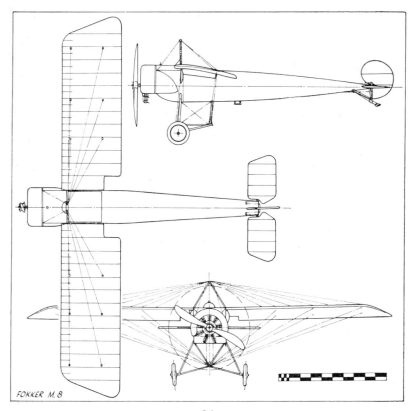

FOKKER M.8

Oberleutnant A. Muehlig-Hofmann photographed in January 1915 with his Fokker M.8 (Fok. A.I), A.195/14.

sheet and had an oval cross-section. The petrol feed from the rear tank to the gravity tank was by pressure. To provide the necessary pressure a hand pump was fitted in the cockpit; later, a windmill-driven fuel pump was fitted.

The M.8 incorporated several refinements of detail. The control column had a convenient two-handle grip with the blip-switch button between the handles. This feature was reproduced on all subsequent Fokker aircraft.

In their flying characteristics the Fokker M.8 and its relations differed

87

from the typical contemporary German B-types. The Fokkers did not automatically assume the correct angle of bank when turning: they had to be rolled with their powerful wing warping and held in the banked attitude while turning. The German pilots had to learn this difference in handling. They also had to learn that, in gusty weather, the M.8 flew best when the stick was held loosely so that the wings could flex freely under the gust loads. The M.8 then rode through gusts far more smoothly than other German aircraft with their great stability, and the strain on pilot and aircraft was much less.

The M.8 never passed a proper acceptance test, but it seems that strength demonstrations satisfied the authorities even though they were

Martin Kreutzer on the Fok. A.I, No. A.215/14 (Factory No. 15).

made in the usual Fokker manner with "live loads" standing on the wings of the inverted aircraft.

As planned by the *IdFlieg* in August, two Fokker squadrons of six aircraft each were formed for artillery spotting and tactical reconnaissance. These units, Feldfliegerabteilungen 40 and 41, flew Fokker M.8 monoplanes exclusively until late 1915. In the Service the M.8 was designated Fok. A (later Fok. A.I) to distinguish it from the M.5K and M.5L.

Individual Fok. A's were allocated to various other field squadrons and to the newly formed B.A.O. and B.A.M.[1] formations for target reconnaissance. All the Fok. A's were flown by selected pilots. One of the earliest of these was Lt. Parschau of B.A.O. who had previously managed to get one of the few M.5s in the Service. He had become friendly with Fokker, who appreciated his splendid airmanship.

[1] B.A.O.—Brieftauben Abteilung Ostende, B.A.M.—Brieftauben Abteilung Metz (Carrier Pigeon Sections, Ostend and Metz): these were security code names for the first German bombing squadrons.

On November 11, 1914, Parschau landed his Fok. A at Pontfaverger in the Rheims sector, having come from the base aircraft park at Rethel. By chance he met the young Lt. Oswald Boelcke of Feldfliegerabteilung 13 whom he had known at the Darmstadt air station (where Boelcke had completed his training on biplanes). Boelcke took an immediate liking to the Fokker and applied for one. Although he had learned to fly at the Halberstadt flying school, it is doubtful whether Boelcke had flown a rotary-engined aeroplane before. On November 26 a Fok. A became available at Rethel but was reserved for another officer. When Boelcke complained vigorously another Fok. A was ordered for him. It was delivered on December 9, and he flew it immediately from Rethel to

Fok. A.I of Feldfliegerabteilung 54.

Pontfaverger, and from then on it was in regular operational use for short-range missions.

Other pilots had to undergo a conversion course at Schwerin unless, like Oblt. H. Kastner and Oblt. von Hiddessen, they had previously flown similar monoplanes. Oblt. A. Muehlig-Hofmann (the first military pilot of the Fokker Spider) and B. Wentscher were among those who went to Schwerin to collect their Fok. A monoplanes. Both arrived there during December 1914. Muehlig-Hofmann left in January 1915 with Fok. A.195/14, which he flew extensively on the Eastern Front for artillery observation. He had the opportunity of comparing it with a captured Russian Morane–Saulnier Parasol, and found the Fok. A more pleasant to handle; the Morane was distinctly more prone to spin. Wentscher also flew on the Eastern Front, spotting for the artillery of the 3rd Army. His was the only Fokker in that Army; later he had one of the first Fokker M.10 biplanes for the same kind of work, but equipped with wireless for signalling to the artillery batteries.

Oblt. Kastner flew his Fok. A.202/14 with conspicuous success on the Eastern Front until he was ordered to form Feldfliegerabteilung 62, a unit whose name will appear in later pages.

Fok. A.136/14 was one of the few M.8s that were supplied to the coast-defence units of the Navy.

The official (but not necessarily comprehensive) Army records for December 1914 mention ten fully operational Fok. A of the M.8 type. By June 1915 the number had risen to fifteen, but thereafter the remaining M.8s were allocated to training unts. Their operational value had declined because they carried no wireless and their climbing performance was no longer good enough even for the Eastern Front.

As trainers the M.8s rendered sterling service up to the end of 1917, notably at Schwerin. Some were later used at units training fighter pilots, and it is probable that more M.8s were built for instructional purposes than for operational duties.

The speed with which the M.8 was produced was a considerable achievement, especially in view of the primitive and limited facilities at Schwerin. Early in 1915 photographs were published showing a batch of fourteen M.8s and one M.5L ready for delivery at Schwerin. But the pressing demands of the front and the schools were more than Fokker's works could meet. The Halberstadter Flugzeugwerke G.m.b.H. was therefore asked to build a batch of M.8s under licence. These aircraft had the factory type number Halberstadt F.14 and the service designation Halb. A.II (Halb. A.I was a Taube type supplied to air corps units before the war).

The Halb. A.II with 80-h.p. Oberursel was practically indistinguishable from the Fokker-built trainer version of the M.8. Until the large-scale production of the Fok. D.VII was initiated in 1918 the M.8 was the only Fokker design to be produced under licence. The first two Halb. A.II appeared at the front late in 1914. In the spring of the following year five were operational. All were withdrawn in August 1915 and taken over by the military flying school at Halberstadt. The Halb. A.II weighed 363 kg. empty and 645 kg. in flying trim; its load was 180 kg., and the wing weight was stated to be 95 kg. The Halberstadt concern did not seek to develop its experience with welded steel-tube fuselages but reverted to wooden construction and adhered to it until the end of the war.

A Fok. A was captured intact in the British sector early in 1915. In

The Halberstadt A.II could be distinguished from the Fok. A.I by its lack of side windscreens and the recessed step in the fuselage side. The step on the Fok. A.I was a welded-on stirrup-type component.

An M.5L and two Fok. A.Is awaiting collection at Schwerin.

the descriptions that appeared in French and British aviation journals the Fokker was dismissed as an inferior copy of the Morane–Saulnier, and it seemed that no Allied pilot had tested the machine sufficiently thoroughly to establish its full capabilities. Its performance was of course not outstanding, especially at altitude; and the Oberursel was much inferior to the rotary engines available to the Allies.

If the Fokker M.8 was popular with its crews the engineering experts at home were less enthusiastic. Reports from the front indicated an alarmingly poor serviceability rate for Fokker aircraft of all types and a high accident rate. The root of the trouble was the engine, its unreliability made the greater because of maintenance by unskilled mechanics. At the behest of the *IdFlieg* a commission of three competent civilian engineers[1] were sent to the front to make a technical appraisement of the Fokker A's of Feldfliegerabteilung 40.

The findings of the investigation were by no means unfavourable, considering that the new aircraft had been put into production and sent to the front with little time for trials. However, the commission questioned the advisability of welding vital components, for welding was still prohibited in the official technical requirements. The commission thought that the Fokker fuselage should be replaced by a wooden structure similar to that of the Pfalz monoplanes. Dorner went to Schwerin to discuss with Fokker the redesign of the Fok. A.

Fokker, always out of his depth when tackled by engineering experts, passed Dorner to Kreutzer for the discussion of the technical aspects. Kreutzer, nonplussed by the eminently qualified designer's weighty arguments against the reliability of welding in general and welded steel-tube fuselages in particular, called in Platz.

Dorner immediately recognized Platz as the welding expert who had done some exceedingly tricky jobs for him some years before. An atmosphere of friendly understanding was quickly created and Dorner was

[1] Dipl.-Ing. H. Dorner, a pioneer of aeroplane design since 1909 and later one of the leading aircraft designers of the war; Dr. Schmidt, an airscrew specialist; and Dr. Heller.

prepared to hear Platz's arguments in favour of the Fokker construction methods. Having heard them he agreed to Platz's suggestion that fuselages or other components specified by Dorner should be tested to destruction and that, if they proved to have a satisfactory margin of strength without failure on account of faulty welding, the *IdFlieg* commission would not, at least for the time being, insist upon the re-design of the monoplane.

Platz quickly conducted the required proof-loadings on specimens selected by Dorner. Dorner, of course, was present at these tests; Fokker kept out of the way. The results were exceedingly good: none of the welding proved defective; and in fact the tested structures far exceeded in strength and resilience what Kreutzer and Platz had claimed. There could be no doubt that the structural methods were entirely sound and safe.

Dorner returned to Adlershof, and nothing further was heard at Schwerin about wooden fuselages for the Fokker A. Nevertheless the technical requirements governing the acceptance of military aircraft continued to state that weldings in vital structural components were forbidden. Eighteen months later the welded steel-tube fuselage again fell under suspicion.

In March 1915 the German air corps was reorganized on lines suggested by Colonel von Eberhardt six months earlier. A *Feldflugchef* was appointed to advise the High Command and initiate measures for making the air force more effective. The post was given to Major Hermann von der Lieth-Thomsen, a fortunate choice, for he had taken an intelligent interest in air warfare. On his staff were Major Siegert as Inspector of Aviation Troops and Hauptmann Helmuth Foerster as adjutant.

Thomsen immediately introduced several new and startling changes in anticipation of the development of air combat and strategic bombing that he foresaw. Thomsen's requirements included the arming of reconnaissance and bomber aircraft so that they could defend themselves, the introduction of large bombers, the flying of protective patrols to seal off important zones of operation, the urgent training of more flying personnel, the use of wireless telegraphy for artillery-observation work, the provision of liaison officers with aviation experience between the Feldflugchef and the operational squadrons. He also sought the formation of specialized squadrons in place of the general-purpose units, the complete mobilization of the aviation industry, and the provision of armed single-seaters similar to those then being flown, somewhat tentatively, by some French pilots.

The Cabinet Order of March 11, 1915, defined the authority of the Feldflugchef and divested the *IdFlieg* of its control over the staffing and equipment of operational units. The *IdFlieg* was now subordinated to the Feldflugchef and ceased to be an incongruous part of the *General Inspektion des militärischen Verkehrswesens* (Inspectorate of Military Transport).

In accordance with this new policy aimed at gaining command of the air, the B.A.O. and B.A.M. strategic-bombing formations were transformed into fighting units and renamed *Kampfgeschwader* (Combat Wings).

The Kampfgeschwader were under the direct control of G.H.Q., and were highly mobile; each consisted of six *Kampfstaffeln* (Combat Squadrons). They were quickly re-equipped with C-type two-seaters of 150–160 h.p., each armed with a machine-gun on a movable mounting on the rear cockpit. Additionally a few twin-engine three-seat biplanes with two or three machine-gun positions were brought into service for offensive patrols beyond the lines, but these A.E.G. K.I. battleplanes were slow, rather unmanoeuvrable, and consequently ineffective.

Later on, the Kampfgeschwader were given some single-seat fighters, especially at times when German command of the air was most to be desired (e.g., during the Verdun offensive). These temporary concentrations ultimately led to the establishment of specialized single-seat fighter squadrons (*Jagdstaffeln*).

The machine-gun and armoured airscrew of the Morane–Saulnier Type N (*Photograph: Imperial War Museum*).

CHAPTER VI

THE FOKKER FIGHTER AND ITS GUN

ON APRIL 19, 1915, the Morane–Saulnier Type N monoplane flown by Lieutenant Roland Garros was hit by a shot from the rifle of an aged reservist guarding a railway near Courtrai. This chance hit was enough to cut the petrol supply to the engine, and Garros was obliged to land in enemy territory near Ingelmunster. His attempts to burn his aircraft failed, and it was captured intact.

The machine was fitted with a Hotchkiss machine-gun and the Saulnier armoured airscrew. The Germans realized that they now had in their hands one of the French aeroplanes that had shot down several German machines with an apparently magical device that enabled a fixed machine-gun to fire straight ahead through the revolving airscrew.

Now that the secret was known, the Germans decided to copy it without delay. Hauptmann Foerster was ordered to see whether similarly armoured airscrews could be made. He took Garros' propeller to Doeberitz, where Simon Brunnhuber quickly made a copy. However, when it was fitted to an engine on a test-bed and subjected to a test firing with a machine-gun, it became painfully obvious that either the steel of the deflecting wedges was not of armour-plate quality or else the German bullets had better armour-piercing capabilities—the airscrew was shattered, the test-bed disintegrated, and the bevy of high-ranking officers watching the test escaped injury by the skin of their teeth. Obviously a more thorough approach would have to be made.

Foerster next got in touch with Fokker and asked him to come to Doeberitz to study the problem. Fokker was allowed to take back to Schwerin the airscrew from Garros' monoplane and a brand-new Parabellum air-cooled machine-gun with ammunition. This was just being introduced as the observer's free-mounted weapon in the C-class armed two-seaters. It fired 100-round belts of standard infantry ammunition ("S" bullets). Quite an event, for an alien, in wartime, to be given the latest type of machine-gun with ammunition.

It will probably never be known for certain who at Schwerin actually suggested replacing the primitive armouring of the airscrew by a trigger-actuating synchronization linkage that fired the gun once during every revolution of the propeller when neither blade was in the line of fire. Fokker, of course, claimed that he and he alone invented this and told of

Installation of Parabellum gun on Fokker M.5K/MG, Factory No. 216.

the pains he took in evolving the actual mechanism. Since all claims by Fokker that he originated inventions or designs are *a priori* suspect, and can in the majority of cases be proved false, it is highly probable that in the case of the gun-synchronizing mechanism he was not the inventor—especially as he did not have even an elementary knowledge of machine-guns and their functioning, and he did not have enough engineering knowledge to devise linkages and so on.

It is highly probable that Heinrich Luebbe, Fokker's close collaborator in this development, conceived the idea[1] and executed it. Luebbe was a

---

[1] It should be noted that the basic idea of a mechanism enabling a machine-gun to fire through a revolving airscrew was not new: Franz Schneider devised one that was patented on July 15, 1913, in the name of the L.V.G. (D.R.P. No. 276,396); in France, L. Saulnier made actual firing trials with a synchronizing mechanism in June 1914; the British patent No. 23790 A.D.1914 was taken out by the Edward Bros. on their synchronizing gear; the Russian Lt. Poplavko had been working on the problem since 1913 and his gun gear was fitted to a Sikorsky S.16, while his compatriots Smyslov and Lt. Cdr. V. V. Dybovski designed and built a new synchronizing gear in November 1914. It is believed that Schneider's mechanism was tested by the German Army in 1912 but was rejected because the official view was that the aeroplane could never become a fighting machine. It is therefore possible that no great mental effort was

watchmaker by profession, but he understood guns and later became one of the leading specialists on aircraft weapons in Germany. He was certainly the designer of a later synchronizing gear also attributed to Fokker.

The advantages of a synchronizing mechanism were fairly obvious: the airscrew could retain its efficient shape; the airscrew shaft was not subjected to irregular flexural hammering by bullets striking the deflector plates; no ammunition was wasted; and the rate of fire could be high.

The synchronizing mechanism that was evolved at Schwerin, chiefly by Luebbe, Heber and Leimberger, was similar in principle to Franz Schneider's gear. It consisted of a simple linkage of cams and push-rods between the oil-pump drive of the Oberursel and the gun trigger, and was called *Stangensteuerung* (push-rod control). It was mounted on an improvised firing stand and tested till it worked; it then required only a means of starting and stopping it at will, and this was designed and embodied in the mechanism.

A full-scale installation of the gun and synchronizing mechanism was made on a Fokker M.5K (Factory No. 216) incorporating cases for the full and empty ammunition belts, and feed guides connecting these cases with the gun. The welded construction of the fuselage greatly simplified the conversion: all brackets and attachments could easily be welded on where they were wanted. To assist in the adjustment of the mechanism the airscrew was replaced by a plywood disc on which the outline of the propeller was drawn. When properly adjusted, a trial was made with an actual airscrew. The converted M.5K with its gun was flown briefly by Fokker and seemed to work well. The aircraft was then redesignated M.5K/MG.

Day and night work by his team enabled Fokker to return to Doeberitz, only a few days after his invitation to go there, complete with an armed fighter prototype. He announced with pride that he had come to demonstrate a much better fighter than the Morane–Saulnier, and proceeded to do so.

At first, none of the witnesses seemed to understand why the airscrew remained undamaged after the gun had been fired, for no armour protection of any kind could be seen on the blades. Fokker explained the *Stangensteuerung* mechanism and demonstrated it in action. Everyone present, especially Oblt. W. von Buttlar, then in charge of armament development, was considerably impressed. Staff officers from the front who had urged the immediate adoption of Saulnier's armoured propeller were highly gratified to see that something better had been found. They now pressed for an early demonstration of the aircraft at GHQ before the Feldflugchef, and for operational trials. Fokker promised full co-operation.

---

required of anyone at Schwerin to think of the idea of fitting a synchronizing mechanism in place of Garros' armoured airscrew. There is in fact reason to believe that Heinrich Luebbe and Fritz Heber knew about Schneider's invention, and told Fokker of its superiority when he showed them Garros' armoured airscrew.

Fokker M.5K/MG with Parabellum gun and head-rest.

All the firing trials and the demonstration at Doeberitz had been made with the light Parabellum machine-gun type MG.14, of D.W.M. design, developed in November 1914 for the armament of the C-type two-seaters. Its installation on the Fokker M.5K had been a rather hasty one. Some thought had been given to sighting; and an adjustable head-rest had been fitted to ensure that the pilot's head was in the correct position when aiming the whole aircraft. The gun was fired by pressing a push-button mounted between the two handles of the control grip beneath the blip-switch.

The original M.5K/MG, thus armed, had no military designation but

First installation of LMG.08 gun on Fokker M.5K/MG.

LMG.08 gun on Fokker M.5K/MG, Factory No. 258. The arrangement of the pilot's
head-rest can be clearly seen.

was later given the military order number E.1/15. It was later modified
to have the LMG.08 machine-gun in place of the Parabellum and, after
being a spare aircraft at the front, it was used for instructional purposes
at the Fokker school and was still flying in the autumn of 1917.

The military authorities adapted the slightly heavier but more reliable
air-cooled version of the MG.08 gun for operational use in aircraft; it
was a direct development of the original Maxim gun. Designated
LMG.08, the aircraft gun was a design of the Royal Rifle Factory at
Spandau (hence the all-too-often misnamed Spandau guns—there was no
such German weapon designation). Having no stock, it had a longer
barrel for equal weapon length; it could fire up to about 600 rounds per
minute; and it was easier to instal than the Parabellum.

The first installation of the LMG.08 was made in the Fokker M.5K
whose factory number was 258, and guns of this type were fitted to the
first two single-seat fighters Fok. E.2/15 and Fok. E.3/15 that Fokker
took to the Western Front a week or two later. Until April 1916 all
German single-seat fighters were armed with the LMG.08; from May
1916 all fixed guns in German aeroplanes were of the type LMG.08/15,

an improved design that was not only lighter but could fire up to 800 rounds per minute. When the gun was synchronized the rate of fire was appreciably reduced. This was particularly the case with the original form of the Stangensteuerung, in which the trigger was pulled only once during every revolution of the propeller. Later improvements to the mechanism doubled the possible rate of fire.

At the request of the Feldflugchef an order for forty or fifty Fok. E.Is was placed immediately by the *IdFlieg*. Fokker was asked to build them as quickly as possible; if he could not produce the aircraft quickly, manufacture under licence by another firm would be arranged. Fokker was also asked to go to selected aerodromes at the front to demonstrate his fighter and instruct inexperienced pilots and mechanics in the handling of the aircraft and its armament. On this tour Fokker took with him the first two Fok. E.Is of the batch under construction and probably also an unarmed M.5 or M.8 trainer.

On May 23, 1915, he gave a successful demonstration of flying and air firing before the German Crown Prince at Stenay. Among the officers who received their initiation on the Fok. E.I at Stenay was Leut. Otto Parschau. His earlier experience with the M.5 and Fokker A enabled him to master the new type quickly and naturally, and he flew it so well that he accompanied Fokker during the rest of the instructional tour, giving exhibition flights and demonstrations.

The Fok. E.I, like the M.5, could accommodate a slim passenger immediately behind the pilot, and Fokker was able to take up aspiring fighter pilots. They could thus get the feel of the aircraft and see how the engine and gun should be handled. The Feldflugchef had confirmed that only pilots with experience on rotary-powered monoplanes should be allowed to fly Fokker monoplanes right away: all others had to take the Schwerin course. As with all such rules in the German military organization, however, there were exceptions.

From Stenay Fokker was sent to Douai at the request of Major F. Stempel, Flying Corps staff officer at the H.Q. of the 6th Army, where the German position in the air fighting over the Arras sector had become precarious. Fokker and Leut. Parschau arrived there with their two E.Is early in June 1915. At and around Douai were a number of Feldflieger-abteilungen, including the recently formed but already famous Fl. Abt. 62 under Hauptmann H. Kastner; among the pilots were Leutnant Oswald Boelcke and Fähnrich (later Leut.) Max Immelmann, who had had combat experience on armed two-seaters. Also at Douai was Brieftauben-Abteilung-Metz which was being re-equipped with armed C-types and flying defensive patrols.

The primary reason for sending Fokker into the Verdun and Arras areas was in fact to familiarize the B.A.O. and B.A.M. formations with the use of the Fok. E.I as an offensive weapon, since both units were being reformed as combat wings. Indeed, the first pilots to receive the Fok. E.I were from B.A.O. and B.A.M. Single E.Is were allocated to a few Feldfliegerabteilungen in areas where Allied aircraft held command of the air to act as escorts for unarmed two-seaters. It was intended to issue Fokkers for this purpose to all similar units. Fokker left Douai on July 12, 1915. By that time, eleven German pilots were operating Fokker fighters on the Western Front; there were none on any other front at that time. Boelcke got his E.3/15 about a week before Fokker's departure.

Some comment should be made on Fokker's improbable story, related in his autobiography, of his exploits as a "German fighter pilot". His assertion that he was at any time ordered to stalk and shoot down an enemy aircraft to prove the effectiveness of his invention strains credulity to the limit. If, as he avers, he "nearly" did so, only refraining from committing murder because of "twinges of conscience", then he must have planned such an exploit entirely on his own. No German officer of any responsibility would or could have ordered a *civilian*—and a foreigner at that, from a country not much in sympathy with Germany—to go and shoot down an enemy soldier. Such a preposterous order, or even mere suggestion, would have been entirely contrary to fundamental German conceptions of discipline and traditions of honour. An officer giving such an order, or permitting such a violation of military decency and of the Geneva Convention, would have been cashiered immediately, if not committed to prison by court martial.

Fokker certainly wore German uniform at one time, thanks to Oblt. Bruno Loerzer, who lent him the attire. This was done as a measure of protection to Fokker: the Oberursel was unreliable, and so was Fokker's navigation. If he were to fall into the hands of the Feldpolizei (Field Police), these tough characters might have become highly suspicious of the pilot of a German military aircraft who was dressed in civilian clothes and by his accent might have been a Belgian of Flemish nationality. The Feldpolizei rarely had the luck or the skill to catch a spy, and it might

Fokker (in civilian clothes) at Douai, June 24, 1915, with one of the first Fok. E.Is.

have required some high-level intervention to secure Fokker's release from their grasp.

Fokker's fanciful account can impress only those who know nothing of the discipline and fanatical pride of officers of the German Flying Corps.

The production Fokker E.I differed in some ways from the Parabellum-armed M.5K/MG No. 216 that Fokker had demonstrated at Doeberitz after brief trials of the synchronizing gear. The other M.5K monoplanes that were converted into fighters were also designated M.5K/MG, but all had the LMG.08 gun in a cleaned-up installation and were to all intents and purposes Fok. E.Is.

It is not possible to determine whether the M.5 fuselage was modified for production as the E.I. No drawings or specifications are available, possibly because they never existed; the E.I never underwent a proper type test, so urgent was the demand from the front, but a few strength tests were made at Adlershof at a later date. It therefore seems reasonable to assume that such modifications as were made were confined to the armament installation.

The Fokker E.I retained the bench-type seat, so that a passenger could be squeezed in close behind the pilot. Boelcke made use of it to give joy-rides and occasionally to give pilots unaccustomed to Fokkers an introduction to the type, but it was not used in the Kampf-Einsitzer-Schulen: the extra weight of a passenger lengthened the take-off run considerably and the climb was poor. Some batches of Fokker E types (but not the naval versions) had bucket seats with fore-and-aft adjustment.

Operational use of the M.5 had shown that direct downward vision was needed. The usual wing-root apertures impaired the climb and were not too satisfactory, so it was suggested that a flap should be provided in the cockpit floor, opened by a lever. Fokker adopted the device and it was embodied in all Fokker E types.

The Fok. E.I carried 70 litres (16 gals.) petrol, sufficient for a maximum endurance of two hours, and 16 litres (3·5 gals.) of oil. This was a considerable load, for the Oberursel engine had a voracious appetite. The Service originally wanted to specify longer flight endurance because they wanted the aircraft as an escort fighter to protect the two-seaters, which could carry fuel for up to four hours. The position of the ammunition boxes precluded any enlargement of the gravity tank behind the engine: indeed, the reverse would have been desirable. A large additional tank was therefore fitted behind the cockpit. It was also some way behind the centre of gravity and, when full, made its presence felt during the take-off. Once in the air, however, it did not noticeably affect the aircraft's handling qualities.

Different petrol-feed systems were fitted to various versions of the Fokker E types. Aircraft for the Navy had a hand pump to pressurize the rear tank in order to transfer the petrol to the gravity tank; control was by means of a three-way fuel cock. This simple system was extensively used in German two-seat aircraft of the time. It was frequently augmented by a small engine-driven air pump, a relief valve being fitted to the tank to reduce excess pressure. An earlier pressurization system using cooled exhaust gas had proved unreliable because soot in the exhaust tended to clog the relief valve, with unpleasant consequences.

However, most of the Fokker E aeroplanes had an automatic petrol feed between the rear and gravity tanks. These aircraft had a small windmill-driven pump, which was mounted on the starboard front V-strut of the undercarriage within the slipstream. The pump feed was safer than pressure feed, for the engine was sensitive to variations in pressure, and an over-rich mixture would cause it to stop. This method of fuel transfer by direct pumping, without pressurization, seems to have been first employed on the French R.E.P. monoplane of the pre-war period, some specimens of which had been captured by the Germans. A similar system, designed by F. Schneider, was fitted on L.V.G. biplanes.

The original armament installation had been hastily made and was heavy. It was progressively modified and improved, the modifications being embodied as they were devised, consequently gun installations varied in detail. The more fundamental modifications were necessitated by the Fokker team's lack of experience with weapons of any kind. They underestimated the hammering effect of the recoil force, and the fact that a hot charge would produce a multiple of the gas pressure. Blast effect dictated the addition of reinforcing strips to the top of the engine cowling. The gun was mounted centrally on most Fokker monoplanes, but some pilots wanted it offset to starboard. Boelcke insisted that the gun should be aligned with its barrel axis parallel to the upper longerons of the fuselage. Immelmann, on the other hand, urged Fokker to instal guns with 15 degrees upward elevation to facilitate attacks on two-seaters from below and behind, and the guns of the Fok. E.IV were originally mounted at this angle. Boelcke found that Immelmann's idea, though good in theory, was unsatisfactory in practice. He pointed out that aiming would always be inaccurate unless fire was always opened at a fixed distance. It had not been realized that firing ranges in aerial combat were usually so short that the drop in trajectory mattered little.

Many Fokker E types, even up to the Fok. E.IV, retained the tripod head-rest that Fokker had devised for the first experimental aircraft to ensure correct alignment on the target. Most of the successful veteran fighter pilots, Boelcke and Immelmann included, never used the head-rest, but preferred the ring-and-bead sight. Other pilots preferred rectangular frame sights, but these were not fitted to later fighters and the ring-and-bead sight was standardized.

Many unofficial modifications to sights, cartridge feed, gun adjustment, and so on, were made in the field, but were neither adopted by Fokker nor approved by the technical authorities of the Flying Corps. At Schwerin much experimental work was done by Luebbe with the assistance of

Heber and Leimberger, and valuable experience and information were acquired. But complaints continually came from the front that the gun itself and its synchronizing mechanism were giving trouble in combat. Had the gun and its synchronizer been of 1918 quality the Allies would probably have suffered three times as many losses as they did.

The Fok. E.I wing structure was basically that of the M.5K. Minor modifications suggested by operational experience were embodied but the main features were unchanged. The Fok. E.I wing had ash spars. Ash was scarce and spruce was unobtainable in Germany after the end of 1914, so later E types had a front spar of Polish pine, which was plentiful. The spars were not laminated, but were spindled out on a routing machine.

The poplar ribs were similar to those of all earlier Fokker monoplanes after the M.2 and were of the characteristic Fokker aerofoil section. The steel-tube compression struts were attached to the spars by ball-and-socket fittings that permitted the wing to flex when warped. The wing warping was not unduly stiff in operation, and the Fokker monoplanes were not regarded as tiring to fly, even in gusty weather. For the internal bracing, piano wire with plain end loops and ferrules was used, and was stronger than that of the M.5K.

The wing-tip formers, which were thin enough to flex when the wing was warped, were bent from ash laths in simple jigs. The raked tips were more rounded than those of the M.5K prototype. A narrow walkway of plywood was provided on each wing close to the fuselage, and the compass was housed in the starboard wing. This was done in an attempt to keep the compass as far as possible from the steel fuselage but even so it was still erratic. German aeronautical compasses were considerably inferior to British instruments.

Recessed attachment points in the fuselage accommodated the plain end fittings of the spars, the connexions being made by bolts lying in the line of flight, thus permitting some up-and-down movement of the wings. Like all Fokker aeroplanes, the E.I could be easily assembled, dismantled and transported by road, a characteristic that was always highly valued at the front.

The front bulkhead of the fuselage carried a circular ring frame to which the engine cowling was attached. The standard cowling, shaped and welded from aluminium sheet, retained the Morane–Saulnier shape. It was held in place by a wire loop attached to lugs welded to the lower longerons. The aluminium side panels extended farther aft than those of the M.5, providing better protection against the Oberursel's fiery reaction to over-priming or after long glides without petrol adjustment.

Both tanks were, like those of the M.5, cylindrical; the gravity tank had a division for castor oil. Both tanks were of soldered brass sheet—a disadvantage, as tin was becoming scarce and the Services had rejected welded aluminium tanks, which had proved to be unreliable.

The box containing the ammunition belt was installed just above the pilot's knees; the rear-facing door served as a map case. The spent cartridges were jettisoned through a chute, the empty hemp belt being recovered by the pull of a spring-loaded drum. The latter device was a necessity, for Boelcke had had trouble with a loose belt end that had blown into the elevator. Full belts were loaded from the cockpit.

To the hand-grip on the control column was added a key lever for firing the machine-gun. It was fitted between the two handles, below the press-button of the blip-switch.

The cockpit equipment was spartan in its simplicity, and there was no dashboard for instruments, its place being filled by the ammunition box. Air-speed indicators were not regulation equipment; indeed, few pilots wanted them. By way of a revolution counter there was usually a sight glass, fitted on the starboard side near the petrol cocks; this also indicated oil flow. An altimeter and a fuel contents gauge completed the instrumentation.

In all versions of the Fok. E the pilot sat rather high. He therefore had a good field of vision but at altitude and in cold weather he was cold. In the event of overturning on landing he was tolerably well protected in spite of his high seat: he usually had time to duck down inside the cockpit before the aircraft turned over.

It was not until October 1916, eighteen months after the introduction of the Fok. E.I, that component weights and strengths were established at Adlershof. Fok. E.63/15 was subjected to a technical investigation, and proof loadings confirmed that its strength was adequate.

Details of performance are scanty, however. Until late in 1918 the

Max Immelmann on his Fok. E.I.

Germans made no serious attempt to determine the speeds of their aircraft: it was held that there was no reliable method of determining level speed at altitude: a development of photo-theodolite procedure with variometer recording was regarded as too crude. Speeds were therefore assessed relatively by racing two aeroplanes over a known course. The Fokker E.I was tested against one of the fastest aircraft of the period, a Rumpler C.I (160-h.p. Mercedes), which was a two-seat, two-bay biplane. To everyone's surprise, the Rumpler gained on the Fokker. A top speed of 130 km. per hr. (80 m.p.h.) near sea level is usually quoted for the Fok. E.I, and this was probably not far from the truth.

More attention was paid to determining climbing performance. Each individual aeroplane was required to climb to certain altitudes in stipulated times before it was accepted; its load was specified and checked; a sealed barograph (later two) had to be carried in a place inaccessible to the crew in flight, its installation and removal being performed by the Flying Corps officer who witnessed the acceptance document.

The more unscrupulous German aircraft manufacturers circumvented some of the requirements: for example, an inflated bladder inside the petrol tank enabled an aircraft to be tested with "full" tanks but much reduced weight. With great ingenuity one Johannisthal firm got rid of whole batches of inferior two seaters by replacing the officially supplied barograph paper by similar paper printed with reduced ordinates that concealed the poor climbing performance of their products.

Small wonder, then, that front-line units often complained bitterly that they were provided with aeroplanes that were quite incapable of climbing to specified altitudes with their war load. The *IdFlieg* and their Adlershof acolytes kept on pretending that their acceptance procedure was sound and that their *Bauaufsichten* (Resident Technical Officers at firms) were thoroughly competent and honest.

But there is little reason to think that such shady practices were resorted to in the acceptance tests of Fokker single-seaters. De Waal was responsible for such tests and he was not a man who would be a party to deceptions of this kind. When a Fokker's climbing performance was poor it was the fault of the Oberursel.

The Oberursel was a source of frequent complaints. A particular annoyance was the fact that the qualities of engines of the same batch differed greatly, a reflection on the inefficiency of production control at the Oberursel Works.

Oblt. Kastner was one of the first pilots to fly offensive patrols as well as escort duties with the Fok. E.I; he also induced Boelcke and, later, Immelmann to continue these operations. At Fl. Abt. 62 Fokker selected Leut. Boelcke for tuition. When Fokker departed after a stay of about two weeks he left one of his demonstration aircraft (E.3/15) with Boelcke. Apart from his successful combat use of the Fokker, Boelcke made good use of its passenger-carrying capability to give brother officers, mechanics and pretty nurses their baptism of flying in a single-seat fighter.

Immelmann did not wish to leave the front for conversion training at Schwerin, so he persuaded his Commanding Officer, Kastner, to allow him to try the Fok. E.I after instruction by Boelcke. After a few solos on an unarmed training monoplane (possibly an M.8) on July 30, 1915, Immelmann tried the E.I next day, fired 30 rounds at a ground target and landed successfully. On his next flight in this aircraft (probably E.3/15) on August 1, 1915, he attacked a British aircraft that was bombing Douai aerodrome, wounded the pilot and obliged him to land. This was the first victory in aerial combat won by a Fokker monoplane. It heralded a period of success for the German Flying Corps.

It has already been indicated that neither Immelmann nor Boelcke was the first to fly the Fok. E.I operationally: five or six pilots, all more experienced than Immelmann, had been doing so since mid-June. Until Immelmann's victory, however, the Fokkers had been used only for defensive patrols and escort work that had given no opportunity for combat. Immelmann's successful use of the Fokker more or less as an interceptor led the German authorities to believe that the new fighters would be more usefully employed as hunters. Major Stempel developed the idea by suggesting that small units of the single-seaters should be temporarily formed in areas where air superiority was urgently needed: this offered the hope of more successes than the allocation of single Fokkers to reconnaissance and artillery-observation squadrons. As a result of Stempel's suggestion the first *Kampf-Einsitzer Kommando* (K.E.K.) or Single-seat fighter Command was formed under Immelmann, and two more were formed soon afterwards from the single Fokker E.Is of various Feldfliegerabteilungen.

In the Verdun area, where Major Haehnelt was *Stabsoffizier der Flieger* (Staff Officer for Aviation, abbreviated as StoFl.), Fokker Commands were also set up soon afterwards. Unfortunately these temporary concentrations of three Fokker E.Is were still under the orders of the Feldfliegerabteilungen that provided the aircraft. Boelcke, who was given command of the K.E.K. at Sivry, urged that the fighter units should be stationed at airfields nearer the fighting lines than those of the ordinary Abteilungen. The Fokker Commands organized their own aircraft intelligence service to eliminate hunting without the certainty of meeting enemy aircraft. This was the beginning of *Jagdstaffel* development; i.e., of independent units equipped with single-seaters and having as their sole task the attacking of all kinds of enemy aircraft and observation balloons. Nevertheless, the German conception of the tactical use of fighter units was a long way behind the ideas propounded by the French Commandant de Rose, and remained so throughout the war.

Although the Fok. E.I had its imperfections it had a tonic effect at the front. The infantry in the trenches became aware that enemy aircraft were increasingly denied the air above the battlefield, and the ground troops were far more impressed by a Fokker's head-on attack than by the

107

Buddecke in flight in E.36/15.

manoeuvring, however skilful, of the C-type two-seaters to bring their observers' guns to bear.

The Allies discovered to their discomfiture that the sky over German territory had become increasingly inaccessible and that heavy losses attended their attempts to penetrate it. Few Allied aircraft that crossed the lines returned without having been attacked by aeroplanes of seemingly superior performance, fitted with menacingly efficient armament.

Such encounters with the Fokker fighters led to tales of miraculous aircraft flown by super pilots. These stories grossly exaggerated the modest qualities of the Fokker single-seaters, but some sections of the Allied press seemed to like to make its readers shudder, and sensational reports of mysterious invincible weapons sponsored by the Kaiser were splendid "news". Like all similar exaggerations, these stories were gleefully welcomed on the German side, for it was obvious that they undermined Allied morale.

During October–November 1915 a maximum of 26 Fokker fighters were in operational use in the west; about four were sent to the Eastern Front to be flown by selected officers. The pilots who flew them were anything but wonder-men. With few exceptions they had been selected

Buddecke about to take off in E.36/15.

108

because they knew how to handle rotary engines and had flown light monoplanes. Very few of them had previous experience in air combat, such as Boelcke had; none had any training at all in air-fighting or in firing a machine-gun in the air. They had all flown two-seaters on reconnaissance or artillery-spotting duties; a few had experience in bombing; most of them had never flown an armed aeroplane before. And this was the material from which the successful Fokker pilots were formed: these were the men who tried to discover the rules of air-combat by—literally— hit-and-miss methods.

Parschau, the first to get a Fok. E.I for service at the front, and Kastner, W. von Buttlar, B. Wentscher, Walz and others, had flown the Fokker M.5 before the war and had flown the Fok. A operationally. Boelcke trained himself to fly the Fok. A and used it in the field. Buddecke had taught himself to fly on a Nieuport monoplane with a Gnôme engine in the U.S.A. before the outbreak of war. Hoehndorf had had flying tuition in the Morane–Saulnier school at Villacoublay in France. Immelmann had been initiated by Boelcke on a Fokker two-seater; as he was an exceptionally gifted pilot, this rather sketchy tuition had been sufficient. Others, like Mulzer, Wintgens and B. Loerzer had been through a conversion course at Schwerin. Kurt Student had a day or two's conversion flying at Mannheim. Ernst Udet had been taught to fly rotary-engined aircraft at a base aviation park, but had smashed a Fok. E on his first flight, and it was only by some previous air-combat experience that he was saved from being grounded. Manfred von Richthofen had been sent back to fly two-seaters after crashing a Fokker monoplane.

The successes of Immelmann, Boelcke, Parschau, Buddecke, von Althaus, Hoehndorf, Berthold, Walz, Wintgens, Leffers, Notzke, Franke, Mulzer, Kissenberth, Udet and others, provided ample proof of the quality

Buddecke's Fok. E.I, E.36/15, ready for road transport.
109

of the little monoplanes in the hands of skilled pilots. By the end of 1915 British losses of aircraft, pilots and observers had become heavy. During the whole month of July 1915, the R.F.C. recorded a total of forty-six air combats: in December 1915 the same number was reported during a single day of aerial operations. On January 12, 1916, four aircraft were lost with eight officers; others returned damaged and with injured crews.

On January 14, 1916, an order was issued from Flying Corps headquarters:

> "Until the Royal Flying Corps are in possession of a machine as good as or better than the German Fokker it seems that a change in the tactics employed becomes necessary. It is hoped very shortly to obtain a machine which will be able to successfully engage the Fokkers at present in use by the Germans. In the meantime, it must be laid down as a hard and fast rule that a machine proceeding on reconnaissance must be escorted by at least three other fighting machines. These machines must fly in close formation and a reconnaissance should not be continued if any of the machines becomes detached. This should apply to both short and distant reconnaissances. Aeroplanes proceeding on photographic duty any considerable distance east of the line should be similarly escorted. From recent experience it seems that the Germans are now employing their aeroplanes in groups of three or four, and these numbers are frequently encountered by our aeroplanes. Flying in close formation must be practised by all pilots."

This order may have been inspired by the success of No. 3 Squadron R.F.C. in December 1915. On the 15th, Immelmann shot down near Valenciennes the Morane–Saulnier LA parasol monoplane No. 5087 flown by Lts. Hobbs and Johnston of No. 3 Squadron. Four days later the squadron sent three Moranes on the Valenciennes reconnaissance, two of them acting as escorts to the third. The formation was attacked, unsuccessfully, by Immelmann and by two other German aircraft.

Immelmann concluded that two or more Fokkers were required for attacks on formations, to break them up and permit attacks on the individual aircraft. Boelcke had come to the same conclusion somewhat earlier when flying in the Verdun sector, where 200 German aeroplanes, including B.A.M. and B.A.O., had been massed for an all-out offensive against the cream of the French Army.

The opportunity to test the idea was soon provided, for it was at about that time that the Fokker K.E.K. were established. As already noted Boelcke's was at Sivry, only six miles behind the fighting lines.

British losses continued, and during March 1916 the R.F.C. lost fourteen aircraft in fights with Fokkers. In Parliament pointed questions were asked, notably by Mr. Joynson-Hicks and Mr. Pemberton-Billing, about the depredations of the Fokkers; the Press contained dark hints about "treason in high places". In the *Daily Chronicle* of January 21, 1916, Mr. Philip Gibbs wrote cautiously that the Fokkers were a grave menace indeed; they were deadly fighters, faster than any British aircraft —"the idea that we have nothing equal appears . . . to be supported by the number of casualties. . . ." The censor let this report from the front pass.

In June 1916 the critics of the British air effort succeeded in forcing a public enquiry. This did nothing to help shoo the Fokkers away—they had meantime become quite outdated anyway—but it helped to clear the air and eliminate some of the dead wood in the British organization.

The French, like their British allies, soon found themselves hounded from the sky as soon as they approached the front: their Maurice Farman and Caudron biplanes were virtually defenceless against the Fokkers. On August 2, 1915, a French bombing attack on Saarbrücken proved a disastrous failure: nine aircraft were shot down by the Fokkers, and as a

Oberleutnant Kurt Student with his Fok. E.I, winter 1915–16.

consequence the French bombing squadron formed at Malzeville for strategic attacks on German industrial centres was disbanded.

Like the R.F.C., the French resorted to formation flying, but with the difference that their formations were of single-seat fighting scouts. They went much further, in fact, for they re-equipped and amalgamated fifteen *escadrilles* to form the first fighter wing of single-seaters, under Commandant de Rose. De Rose introduced formation offensive patrols of three or four aircraft. The wing was equipped with the new Nieuport Bébé sesquiplane which was inferior to the Fok. E in its armament but had a far better performance and unequalled manoeuvrability. This more formidable opposition was yet another reason why the Fokkers had to operate in small formations. They had to take their French adversaries more seriously from that time onward.

In the R.F.C. the D.H.2 helped to restore the balance, more by virtue of superior performance than any other quality, for its armament, like the Nieuport's, was inferior to that of the Fokker.

The Germans helped to ease the lot of British and French aviators,

111

The Fok. E.I was used in small numbers by Austria.

early in 1916, by their mistaken belief that the air over an area of intense ground operations or preparation for an offensive could be denied to an enemy. Before and during their Verdun offensive of February 21, 1916, the Germans maintained standing patrols of armed two-seaters and single-seat fighters in given sectors. Thus, nearly half as many machine-guns were airborne in German aircraft as were used on the ground. Maintaining the air barricade meant that the 72 armed two-seaters employed on it were not available for other duties: thus the only French supply line to the Verdun fortress escaped bombing, a single road between Bar-le-Duc and Verdun that carried 8,000 lorries daily. This omission frustrated the German offensive: the idea of an aerial blockade had caused the miscarriage of a serious thrust. Nevertheless, the mistake was repeated on the Somme.

The Allies made much of the fact that Fokker pilots seldom crossed the fighting lines. It was not want of courage that prompted this caution: they had been ordered not to fly over enemy-held territory. The German command did not wish the Fokker synchronizing gear to fall into Allied hands, and the unreliability of the Oberursel was well known. Immelmann, Boelcke and a few others often disobeyed the order; as long as all went well, their superiors turned a blind eye. Success in daring attacks was always an acceptable excuse for disobedience in the German Army; failure might have resulted in a court martial.

For tactical reasons, too, the Fokkers stayed on their own side of the lines. It was the official German view that it was more important to deny the enemy access to the air over German territory than to try to shoot down great numbers of enemy aircraft. German fighter pilots were therefore instructed to attack enemy two-seaters and bombers and to ignore single-seat fighters as far as possible. In a memorandum written in the summer of 1916, Boelcke laid down that a fighter pilot should not visualize himself as an individual nor seek personal success: his first duty was to act strictly in accordance with military thought and exclusively in the interests of the tactical situation or of the needs of the ground troops.

112

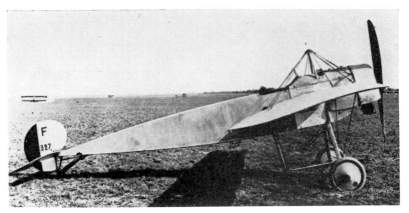
This Fok. E.I, believed to be E.327/15, fell into French hands intact. This photograph was taken at Pau.

The "lack of offensive spirit" displayed by Fokker pilots in combat engagements was often misrepresented. It is explained by a study of combat reports, which reveal that the guns malfunctioned more often than they fired properly. The LMG.08 had been developed by gun specialists who knew nothing of conditions of air combat and were too arrogant to accept the advice and co-operation offered by the *IdFlieg*. The hemp belt would freeze above 9,000 ft., or in winter after absorbing moisture. The lubricating grease in the gun mechanism froze. Hang-fire rounds were a not-infrequent hazard. The early push-rod synchronizing gear was unreliable: the gun could be fired only at normal engine speeds; at slow speeds the gear linkage worked erratically. The impulse-transmission push-rod contracted in cold weather; the effect could be quite pronounced, for the trigger movement was small.

This explains why Fokker pilots were frequently obliged to break off engagements quickly. When his gun jammed, the Fokker pilot needed both hands to clear it and reload. While thus occupied he could not control the aircraft: he had to hold the stick between his knees, or, in later Fokker monoplanes, he applied the elevator locking device for the same purpose; in either case he had to turn away from the enemy and break off the engagement.

The somewhat makeshift Fok. E.I was rather heavy: a comparison with the Pfalz E.I proved this. From the front came urgent appeals for an aeroplane of better performance that could match the Nieuport single-seater in speed and climb. Greater reliability of armament and engine was also sorely needed: too many combats had to be broken off because the gun jammed, and the Oberursel's erratic behaviour did nothing to inspire confidence. The authorities had urged the Oberursel works to hasten the production of a 100-h.p. nine-cylinder engine, which was to be supplied to Fokker for use in an improved fighter.

113

To redesign was essential. Kreutzer did this without making major changes in the basic design. The new aircraft was designed for the 100-h.p. Oberursel. This necessitated little modification of the engine mounting, but the undercarriage wheels had to be moved forward a few inches to reduce the tendency to nose over. This in turn required some modification of the forward cable attachment to keep the cables clear of the wheels. Despite the heavier engine the seat did not have to be moved, for the supplementary fuel tank placed the centre of gravity rather far aft on the Fok. E.I, even with the heavy gun. The tank had now to be made even larger. The top decking was slightly reduced in height; this permitted an improved gun installation and made sighting easier.

A small triangular fin was added under the stern of the fuselage to counteract swing at take-off. On operational aircraft, however, the fin was often removed, probably because it collected mud and stones while taxying. For the same reason some Fokker E monoplanes had the bottom of the rudder cut off close to the tailskid. To reduce drag the upper wing-bracing pylon was reduced in height, but it was made of heavier steel tubing to give more protection if the aircraft turned over. The height of the undercarriage was slightly increased to accommodate airscrews of larger diameter which would, it was hoped, improve the climb. A clamping device was fitted to the control column: this could lock the elevators to allow the pilot to clear gun stoppages more easily.

The new design was given the Fokker type number M.14, and the first version of it had the military designation Fok. E.II. It was the first German aeroplane to be designed as a single-seat fighter: that is to say, it was not an adaptation of an existing unarmed type.

Deliveries of the new nine-cylinder Oberursel were so delayed that the

The original Fokker M.14 had a Parabellum machine-gun.
114

Fok. E.II No. 69/15 with 100-h.p. Oberursel.

first production aircraft stood for weeks on Goerries aerodrome awaiting engines. The prototype and some production machines destined for training purposes were fitted with the 80-h.p. Oberursel.

Fokker had urged Platz to cut down the M.14's wing area to that of the Pfalz, which had proved to be appreciably faster than the Fok. E.I. The consequent reduction in the span of the E.II made it more difficult to fly. There was some reduction in the all-up weight, but by how much is not known, for available Service records confuse the E.II with the Fokker Einsitzer II—which was simply a designation used at the front for the few operational M.5K scouts.

Fokker and Kreutzer had worked quickly to respond to the wishes of the operational units. The first Fok. E.II reached the front in July 1915; eight were operational by October. Fifteen months later, in December 1916, the last operational survivor of the type was still in service in a quiet sector of the Eastern Front.

Contrary to expectations the climb was only a little better than that of the E.I. Fokker therefore decided to revert to wings of larger span, and the result was the most famous of the early Fokker fighters, the Fok.

Fok. E.II No. 69/15.

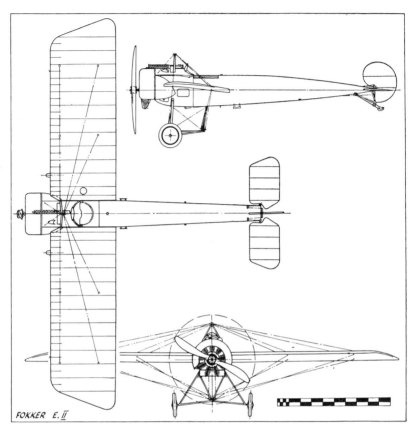

FOKKER E. II

E.III. It had the same type number, M.14, as the E.II. The new wings spanned 9·52 m. (31 ft. 2·7 in.) against the 8·95 m. (29 ft. 4½ in.) of the E.I.

The Fok. E.III reached the Western Front in August 1915. With its increased wing span and area it was an immediate success. All fighter pilots were eager to have one as quickly as possible, their appetites whetted after the first three aircraft had displayed their qualities.

Substantial orders, the largest he had had up to that time, were placed with Fokker by the Army. The Navy, too, pressed for several for use in their coastal defence formations. Production was of course limited by the output of the Oberursel Motor Works. To increase engine output, other firms were encouraged to produce similar, if not better, rotary engines.

The Goebel Gandenberger Machine Factory at Frankfurt produced in a remarkably short time a modified Gnôme with nine cylinders. Designated Goe.I and rated at 100 h.p., the engine performed well when test-flown in a Fok. E.III at Schwerin, but it arrived too late to alleviate the engine shortage. It was fitted to the E.III with Works No. 520, which

116

The Fok. E.II flown by Vizefeldwebel Eduard Böhme of the Bavarian Fliegerabteilung 9.

was accepted by the Army on April 8, 1916. Allert, one of Fokker's Works pilots, flew it for nearly three hours, climbing to 13,200 ft. in ninety minutes. The *IdFlieg* decided not to adopt the Goe. I, but encouraged the firm to develop an engine of twice the power.

A similar fate befell the new Siemens Sh.I bi-rotary engine of 90 h.p., later 115 h.p. This had taken longer to develop, and when ready for production it was too late to be effective. Its unconventional nature and its late arrival prevented its use on an appreciable scale: it was experimentally installed in a few fighter aircraft. The Siemens company, well aware of Fokker's jealousy of his competitors, had tried to have their new engine tested in a Hanuschke monoplane, possibly because they did not fancy having the tests made at Schwerin under Fokker's direction. An experimental installation of the Sh. I was in fact made in a Fok. E.III, but it is uncertain whether it was done at Schwerin or independently by the Services at Adlershof. The results of this installation are not known.

The prototype Fok. E.III had also been tried with an 80-h.p. Le Rhône from a captured Nieuport. Thus powered, the Fok. E.III had a better rate of climb than the standard version with the 100-h.p. Oberursel and a markedly increased ceiling. The German authorities urged the Oberursel firm to consider copying the Le Rhône with its controlled inlet and exhaust

Fok. E.III No. 419/15, Factory No. 401.

Front view of 419/15.

valves that reduced the loss of power at altitude. Performance at heights of 4,000 m. (13,000 ft.) had begun to become important.

On the M.14 type the *Stangensteuerung* synchronizing gear was improved and the gun's rate of fire speeded up by a modification introduced on October 20, 1915. This increased the rate of fire from 400 rounds per minute to 450–600 r.p.m. Unfortunately it also increased the risk of malfunctioning and consequent damage. Boelcke had already found out what could happen when the gear failed. On October 1, 1915, he shot his propeller away; part of the engine and mounting broke up, but he was able to force-land without harm; it took more than a week to repair the damage. Others were less fortunate. There is little doubt that not a few of the Fokkers claimed by Allied pilots in fact shot themselves down because of the failure of the *Stangensteuerung*. The standard Fok. E.III carried only one LMG.08. Two guns were occasionally fitted, but it was found that the additional armament reduced the rate of climb too much. Nevertheless, a number of Fok. E.IIIs, notably those used in the east, had the twin-gun installation, but carried less ammunition.

At the end of May 1916, the Central Flying School in Britain tested a Fok. E.III that had been captured intact in April. This seems to have been E.215/15, accepted at Schwerin on March 28, 1916; its factory number

Fok. E.III No. 210/15, apparently after having come down in British territory. (*Photo: Imperial War Museum*).

118

Fokker poses in front of an E.III.

may have been 480 or 512, both having been E.IIIs accepted on that date. The C.F.S. test report stated that the engine was not running full out and gave no more than 1,210 r.p.m. at most. The top speed near the ground was between 86 and 88 m.p.h.; at 11,000 ft. it was 78 m.p.h. The rate of climb at 1,000 ft. was 700 ft./min.; at 11,000 ft. it dropped to 80 ft./min. This Fok. E.III may have been the aircraft now exhibited in London's Science Museum; this seems to be the only example of the famous Fokker fighting monoplane that survives fairly intact.

The twin-gun installation was developed after Boelcke told Fokker that

The starboard wing of a Fok. E.III. Note the compass housing and the narrow plywood walkway at the root.

119

Austrian Fok.E.III, 03.43, armed with a Schwarzlose machine-gun.
(*Photo: Peter M. Bowers*).

it would be welcomed, not only because it would double the fire-power but also because it would reduce the effects of the frequent gun troubles. The grip on the control column was modified: it had two key levers, side by side, to fire the guns; and the handles of the grip proper were smaller and parallel to each other. Better climbing performance and greater speed at altitude were needed. Oberursel were now building a two-row engine of some 160 h.p. that might effect the necessary improvements.

Immelmann had even more ambitious ideas. He proposed a battery of three guns for maximum fire power during the few seconds in which the enemy aeroplane could be held in the sights. His experience convinced him that the first attack was all important, and that surprise attacks from below and behind were likely to be most effective: an observer could neither spot the attacker nor use a defending gun if he had one. For such attacks Immelmann thought the guns should be mounted at an upward angle. He also required the cocking levers to be conveniently placed in the cockpit, better protection against draught, a climb to 3,000 m. in no more than 15 minutes, and a speed of 160 km./hr. (100 m.p.h.). Immelmann stressed the importance of good performance at altitude.

But three guns with their ammunition were a heavy load, and a new variant of the *Stangensteuerung* would have to be devised for such a battery. Fokker was not perturbed by such technical problems, so Immelmann's scheme was tried. Immelmann requested that the new fighter be powered by a 160-h.p. two-row Le Rhône engine taken from a special Morane that had landed intact in the German lines. Although a modification of the aircraft built to incorporate Boelcke's suggestions, Immelmann's machine might itself have served as a basis for further development. Boelcke was to have the first production machine of the new type, with the two-row Oberursel and twin guns; Immelmann's was to go direct to the front for operational evaluation.

Apart from the increased armament, the new type had a number of modifications to the airframe and was designated M.15. The two-row Oberursel U.III needed a fore-and-aft mounting, to which end Platz devised a spider type of mounting similar in principle to that of the

120

Avro 504. This engine mounting provided attachment points for strong external drag bracing, which Kreutzer still considered essential. The cowling had to be completely redesigned, not only because of the new mounting but also to provide better cooling, especially of the rear row of cylinders. The upper bracing pylon was strengthened, and a turtle-back fairing was fitted behind the cockpit to reduce draught. The passenger space had been abandoned in the M.14.

The M.15 prototype (probably E.125/15, factory No. 374) was ready early in November 1915. It had the first 160-h.p. Oberursel, and was assessed by Parschau at Schwerin. His report, dated November 13, 1915, is as follows:

"The following climbing performance was achieved with fuel for 1½ hours, two machine guns and 950 rounds of ammunition on board—
1·0 km. in 2·75 minutes
2·0 km. in 7·0 minutes
3·0 km. in 15 minutes
4·0 km. in 28·5 minutes
During offensive patrols, practical climbs are—
3·0 km. in 20 minutes
4·0 km. in 40 minutes
In level flight at 1·0 km. altitude the indicated maximum speed is 195 km/hr (121 m.p.h.). Maximum speed determined by flying over known distances seems to be about 165–170 km/hr (103–106 m.p.h.).

Oswald Boelcke in a Fok. E.IV.
121

"Considerable force has to be used in warping the wings in steep turns; this can be eased by blipping the engine. The aircraft's high speed may make it approach a target too quickly when attacking from the rear, and it may be advisable to cut the engine or to approach from below and astern.

"Ammunition belts of hemp are better than metal belts. The belt feed guide no longer has the right-angle bend, and the ammunition containers have been reduced in width so that cartridges no longer come loose in the belt; the containers are less susceptible to vibration because they have a forward support. These modifications should make ammunition-feed trouble less likely.

"During longer flights oil fumes can be troublesome. The latest modification therefore provides for the sealing of the fuselage from the engine. The fuel consumption is reasonable. At high altitude the engine loses much power owing to the low temperature. A suggestion made by Morell for a shielding device should be tried."

Leutnant Frhr. von Thuena, an experienced pre-war pilot then in charge of aircraft development at the *IdFlieg*, added a postscript recommending a variable cowling for the engine: this should operate in accordance with the dynamic air pressure, to reduce the loss of power at altitude. He suggested also that an atomizing cone should be fitted in the carburettor jet to achieve a more uniform mixture.

Lt. Parschau's rather optimistic report convinced the Feldflugchef that the Fok. E.IV was indeed a very advanced aeroplane. It did not greatly

Max Immelmann's special Fok. E.IV with three machine-guns.

A standard two-gun Fok. E.IV, No. 174/16.

matter that Parschau had overestimated the speed, but it soon became obvious that he had failed to assess the aircraft's lack of manoeuvrability. Immelmann's special E.IV (E.189/16, Factory No. 385) with its triple gun installation was ready in December 1915. The special Le Rhône and its airscrew were not immediately available, so a 100-h.p. Oberursel was temporarily installed to enable Fokker to test the machine. After the Le Rhône had been fitted, Fokker saw a welcome opportunity of demonstrating the new aircraft when a rumour of an air attack on the Krupp works had produced a concentration of noted fighter pilots at Essen. But the synchronizer malfunctioned, sixteen bullets struck the propeller and nearly shot the blades away. A thoroughly frightened Fokker had to make a hasty landing.

The aircraft was sent back to Schwerin for repair, and Immelmann finally took it over on January 16, 1916. Various troubles prevented him from using it in action before February 6, 1916. In March he shot both propeller blades away but managed to land without further damage. He seems to have destroyed two Allied aircraft while flying this special Fok. E.IV, but he came to dislike it. Lack of spares for the big Le Rhône led to its replacement by a 160-h.p. Oberursel. Boelcke, who was interested in the multi-gun installation, tried the aircraft but reported adversely on the tilted guns.

Boelcke had received his standard E.IV on December 13, 1915. He too had the experience of shooting off his own airscrew: the resulting unbalance caused failure of the engine mounting, but he managed to land safely. On May 31, 1916, Immelmann had another incident of the same nature when he was flying a standard twin-gun Fok. E.IV. Fokker blamed the failure of a rocker arm in the engine for cutting through all but two of the engine-mounting struts. This was by no means impossible, but it is equally probable that the synchronizer had failed again—as Immelmann himself apparently believed.

Production of the 160-h.p. Oberursel was slow—all its cylinders were machined out of solid steel blocks to the closest tolerances—and regulated production of the Fok. E.IV. Moreover, its lubricating castor oil was

123

scarce. It was therefore decided that the Fok. E.IVs were to be reserved for top-ranking fighter pilots. Less distinguished pilots were to stick to the Fok. E.III, which was in quantity production.

On the whole, the E.IV was a disappointment. Its performance fell short of expectations, partly because the authorities had specified much too great a load for the little monoplane, partly because the engine's low compression ratio led to loss of power at altitude. This last defect was aggravated by the poor feeding allowed by the automatic inlet valves.

Boelcke, then in command of the Fokker detachment at Sivry, reported on March 24, 1916, that the E.IV's speed, although appreciably less than the promised 100 m.p.h., was adequate for operational purposes. In climbing, however, much speed was lost, and several Nieuport biplanes had escaped Boelcke because of this deficiency in the Fokker. Above an altitude of 3·0 km. the rate of climb was inadequate.

The 160-h.p. Oberursel was tolerably good when new, but lost 40 to 50 r.p.m. at altitude; after some use it deteriorated quickly and would lose 100 or more r.p.m. at operational height.

But the chief drawback was that the Fok. E.IV was less manoeuvrable than its predecessors, owing to the big rotating mass of the engine. Quick turns could only be made by blipping the engine: this entailed loss of height, a hazardous matter when fighting an enemy flying at the same altitude or higher.

It was in his report of March 24, 1916, that Boelcke condemned the upward-firing guns originally advocated by Immelmann. On the strength of Boelcke's report the Feldflugchef decided that fixed guns should be aligned with the direction of flight as before. On March 29 Boelcke was sent to Schwerin to discuss with Fokker the design of a better fighter, preferably a biplane.

By that time the Fokker monoplane's supremacy was on the wane, and

Another standard Fok. E.IV, No. 189/16.

124

The Fokker M.5L flown by Ernst Ditzuleit to Kiel-Kopperpahl in 3½ hours.

by the summer of 1916 it was painfully obvious that the Fokker had been kept operational too long on the Western Front and its replacement by aircraft with more reliable engines and better performance was overdue. In the east, Fokker monoplanes went unchallenged until late in 1916; and coast-defence units of the Navy, which had only Russian naval aircraft to deal with, were able to use them even longer. Austria seems to have made some little operational use of the small number of Fokker monoplanes supplied to her *Luftfahrttruppen*, for they were seen in action by the Italians. They seemed to score no confirmed victories, however, and none of them fell into Italian hands.

In the west, defeats and losses of Fokker monoplanes became progressively more numerous from April 1916 onwards. Most of the Fokker pilots paid dearly for their early successes: of the first fifteen none lived to see 1917. On April 30, 1916, Graf von Holck was shot down in flames in his Fokker E.III over Verdun during a combat with three Caudrons. In June, Hauptmann von Gersdorff, leader of No. 1 Combat Squadron, was shot down in flames. Boelcke, too, had a close shave when a French Nieuport shot him down with its unsynchronized gun. On June 18 Immelmann crashed to his death, and the fate of the Fokker E was sealed. All Fokker fighter monoplanes were either relegated to training duties or sent to the Eastern Front.

The cause of Immelmann's death has been, and will probably continue to be, the subject of controversy. All accounts[1] agree that his twin-gun Fokker E.III broke up in the air, but it is uncertain whether its disintegration followed structural failure after malfunctioning of the interrupter gear caused in airscrew breakage, or by damage resulting from the attack of Lt. G. R. McCubbin and Cpl. Waller in an F.E.2b of No. 25 Squadron R.F.C.

On his last flight Immelmann was flying a standard Fok. E.III with

[1] Except a fanciful and totally inaccurate version that appeared in the August 1930 issue of the American journal *Popular Aviation*.

Ditzuleit's M.5L at Kiel-Kopperpahl, 1915. Ditzuleit is second from the right; at extreme left, Oppermann; third from left, Truckenbrodt.

twin guns and a single-row 100-h.p. Oberursel. Although the significant portion of the aircraft was very badly damaged, the Germans claimed that it contained clear indications that Immelmann's synchronizing gear had failed, one airscrew blade had been shot away, the resulting unbalance had torn the engine from its bearers and caused severe damage, and complete structural failure had been accelerated by the pilot's attempts to regain control of his aircraft.

Not unnaturally, it was thought that parts of the forward fuselage might have failed because of faulty welding. Sand-loading tests carried out by the *Prüfanstalt und Werft*[1] of the *IdFlieg* at Adlershof vindicated the Fokker construction methods: the fuselages that were tested to destruction were not only faultless but were substantially stronger and more resilient than they were required to be.

A word must be said about the fighter component of the *Marine-Flieger-Abteilung*, the coastal defence unit of the German Navy that flew landplanes. The unit had maintained an interest in Fokker aircraft after Ernst Ditzuleit had proved to the Navy's satisfaction that these aeroplanes could be used for longer flights. In the summer of 1915 he flew the Fokker M.5L "S.27 Kiel" to Kiel-Kopperpahl, the flight lasting $3\frac{1}{2}$ hours. Although the cylinders of his 80-h.p. Oberursel had turned blue by the time he landed, the flight was accepted as evidence of the Fokker's capabilities. The Navy therefore sent a detachment of seven

---

[1] Known as P.u.W., later restyled *Flugzeugmeisterei* or *Flz.*

126

pilots, including Ditzuleit, to the Kampfeinsitzer-Schule at Mannheim, and a number of Fokker E.IIIs and E.IVs were ordered. These aircraft were used operationally, mainly in the east. Of the seven naval fighter pilots, only two survived the war.

Apart from the various experimental engine installations that have already been described, a number of experimental modifications of Fokker monoplanes were devised and tried at Adlershof. It is doubtful whether records of most of these experiments will ever be found. They included attempts simultaneously to reduce drag and improve cooling, to protect

Boedecker (in naval uniform) with Fok. E.I, No. E.15/15 of the Kampfeinsitzer-Schule, Mannheim-Sandhofen.

127

the pilot from oil and exhaust fumes, to improve the altitude performance of the engine by exploiting the ram effect of the airstream, to make the engine more accessible, and so on.

An interesting but fruitless experiment into which Fokker was talked was the "invisible" Fok. E.I.

The idea of making aeroplanes less visible by covering them with transparent material (in those days, cellulose plastics) was not new. One of the earliest proponents of the idea was Roesner, who originally worked as the designer for Rumpler and later became famous as the designer of the Gotha bombers and seaplanes. In 1911 he constructed an aeroplane with a covering of fine wire mesh made airtight by a cellulose solution. A year later the Austrians conducted similar experiments with an Etrich Taube. In 1913 a Russian, W. A. Lebedieff, covered a Henry Farman biplane with cellulose-plastic sheet in place of the rubberized fabric, but the covering was heavy and would not stay taut enough. Later in 1913 a Moreau parasol monoplane was exhibited at the Paris Aero-Salon with a semi-transparent covering of fine silk sandwiched between two cellulose-acetate films.

During 1914 experiments with a Deperdussin monoplane proved that transparent coverings might make aircraft more rather than less conspicuous, owing to light reflecting from shining surfaces. Nevertheless the French tried the idea again during 1915 on a Voisin biplane, but soon gave it up.

From 1913 onwards the German pilot and inventor A. Knubel had tried to raise interest in his scheme for a covering of highly inflammable cellulose-nitrate. He built an aeroplane of his own design and covered it with this transparent material, but a wing failure in September 1915 caused his death.

Rumpler, too, had devised an "invisible" aeroplane, which he offered to the Army. On test, however, the cellulose sheets contracted and split with loud and alarming reports at the lower temperature experienced when airborne, and the pilot (Professor Dr. Kurt Wegener) was relieved to reach the ground safely. Similar transparent coverings were proposed by Neuber and J. Krauss but were rejected, after laboratory checks, by the Adlershof experts. They were right.

Fokker, knowing the practice of stalking enemy planes adopted by Boelcke and Immelmann, thought it would greatly increase their chances of making surprise attacks if their Fokkers were "invisible". People at the front, ignorant of the technical problems involved, thought so too. An experimental Fok. E.I was therefore covered with cellulose sheeting. It was complete with machine-gun and ready to go to the front after a quick test by Fokker. Fokker flew it—it was seen over Schwerin—but it never reached the front. It was quietly put aside for conversion to a normal E.I.

A very experienced fighter pilot of this period, now a retired Colonel-General, was recently asked what specific troubles characterized the

The Fok. E.I that was experimentally covered with cellulose sheet.

armament of the Fokker monoplanes. He replied emphatically that, although there were annoying troubles in combat, no-one minded it at the time: the main thing was that pilots had a synchronized machine-gun in a manoeuvrable aircraft: that was all that mattered.

The aircraft's principal shortcomings were five: the undercarriage was weak; the rate of climb and performance at altitude were poor; all versions of the Fok. E were considerably inferior to the fast little Nieuport sesquiplane; the gun or guns jammed at awkward moments, especially when the weather was too cold or moist for the hemp belts; and worst of all was the malfunctioning of the synchronizing mechanism with its attendant dangers.

Production at Schwerin expanded satisfactorily. By the end of 1915 the works had a labour force of 430 and a staff of fifty. About 230 complete aeroplanes had been produced, apart from purely experimental machines and repairs; most of them had been monoplanes of the M.5, M.8 and M.14 types; small numbers of M.7 and M.10 biplanes had also been built. Fifty hectares of land had been rented on Goerries aerodrome for assembly and flight-acceptance purposes.

A new arrangement brought a permanent Bauaufsicht (resident technical

An experimental Fok. E.III with a full-circular engine cowling.

officer), who was empowered to accept for the Service each individual aeroplane on the spot instead of waiting for a military acceptance team to turn up to take over a whole batch of completed aircraft. The Bauaufsicht had authority to verify the results of acceptance flight tests by works pilots: these had to be checked at random by military test-pilots at the request of the Bauaufsicht. Thus the supply of aeroplanes was speeded up, and an accumulation of aircraft at the factory was prevented.

The Fokker factory's output for 1915 is perhaps best presented in tabular form:

Month of 1915	Aircraft accepted	Aircraft supplied	Remarks
March	11	18	
June	18	18	
July	26	32	Most were biplanes
August	36	31	Figures include 25 monoplane fighters (E.I & E.II)
October	29	23	All were E.I or E.II
November	32	25	Included 22 Fok. E.III and prototype E.IV
December	18	30	Included 29 Fok. E.III

Deliveries of Fokker E types up to July 1915 totalled seventeen Fok. E and two Fok. E.II with 80-h.p. engines for training purposes. Between May 1915 and July 1916, the Fokker works constructed at least fifty-six aircraft of the Fok. E.I type, including machines for the German Navy and for Austro-Hungary.

Such supply documents as are available, but not necessarily complete, indicate that at least 258 aircraft of the Fok. E.III type were constructed at Schwerin between September 1915 and August 1916.

Whatever else the Fokker monoplane fighters did, they made Fokker's name famous: he was regarded everywhere as a master-mind. He did nothing to reflect some of this undeserved glory upon those of his collaborators to whom it was due: on the contrary, he was most anxious to leave no doubt that his was the genius that invented, designed and perfected his deadly weapons of air combat.

In this Fokker succeeded, as far as the pilots and staff officers at the front were concerned: there was no doubt that they fully believed in his engineering mastery. During his demonstration tour at the front he had made most useful connexions and could count on getting first-hand information from the front in the shape of hints and tips; this would enable him to keep ahead of all other German aircraft manufacturers. There was, of course, nothing sinister or underhand about this: in fact, the Feldflugchef Thomsen himself encouraged direct contact and consultation with leading fighter pilots such as Boelcke, Parschau and Immelmann; a number of useful conferences took place at Schwerin and elsewhere. Fokker was liked, because he provided the weapon; he was willing to experiment and try out all hints for improvement.

CHAPTER VII

THE FOKKER–KREUTZER BIPLANES, 1915–16

WHILE THE Fokker monoplanes were making the name of Fokker world-famous, the firm's financial position was improving out of all recognition. Military orders had brought profits; credits were now easily obtained against government guarantees; financiers approached Fokker with attractive offers. Ample funds became available to Fokker and all other German aircraft manufacturers for the expansion of production facilities and the purchase of equipment and materials.

Fokker was able to repay the loans made to him by his father, his uncle, and the Cremers, and did so without delay. He also repaid Hans Haller, his first financial helper at Johannisthal. In consequence of these settlements the Fokker Aviatik G.m.b.H. was dissolved on January 13, 1915, by decision of the shareholders. This body had been merely a holding firm for the shares of the foreign partners of the Fokker Aeroplanbau G.m.b.H., as a legal means of giving the Fokker Works the status of a German-owned enterprise: the military authorities were not normally permitted to place orders with foreign-owned firms. Now a holding company was no longer needed; moreover, Fokker intended to adopt German nationality if such a course were suggested to him.

When the dissolution of the Fokker Aviatik G.m.b.H. was announced, it was widely assumed in Allied countries that the Fokker works at Schwerin had either gone bankrupt or had closed because of Fokker's return to Holland. The British journal *Flight* praised young Fokker's high patriotic sense, but the only change was that Fokker was now the sole owner of his firm. Hans Haller was retained as business manager for the time being, but in December 1915 he relinquished his executive position and severed all connexions with Fokker. The Fokker Aeroplanbau now changed its name to Fokker Flugzeugwerke G.m.b.H. with "technician" A. H. G. Fokker as sole director.

The works at Schwerin grew substantially. But whereas all other German aircraft firms invested at least a part of their profits and government-backed credits in new equipment, enlarged workshops, comprehensive material-testing laboratories, up-to-date drawing offices and so on, Fokker was a stingy as ever. He resisted all suggestions that better working facilities should be provided: every addition or expansion had to be makeshift and dirt cheap. His ignorance of engineering production was partly to blame for this parsimony; it certainly could not be attributed to lack of funds. The main reason was his firm resolve to invest as little as possible in anything that could not immediately be converted into cash. Fokker always had an eye to the possible need for making a quick getaway from Germany: he has recorded how he bought up foreign currency and valuables with a view to leaving nothing of value behind him.

As a result of this policy the Fokker works were never anything better than a shoddy collection of shacks and sheds, while Fokker's profits grew and were stored away for his own benefit. It is strange that the German authorities apparently thought nothing of the marked contrast between the Fokker works and those of comparable German firms.

The staff, too, increased; and more instructors and works pilots were engaged. Among the latter were Alexander von Bismarck, unfit for active service on account of poor eyesight, and M. Scherff, airman hero of the Balkan war. Kuntner and Ditzuleit volunteered for active service. The former became an Austrian pilot and was soon decorated for gallantry, but died in a crash in 1916. Ditzuleit survived an exciting career as a naval pilot of fighters and seaplanes. He did much to promote Fokker aircraft in the Navy. However, when he wanted to rejoin the firm immediately after the armistice, Fokker's business manager Horter claimed never to have heard of him. Haller tried to rectify the injustice thus done to one of Fokker's oldest associates, but failed. Fokker himself had probably forgotten that his first mechanic ever existed.

It has already been noted that work on the seven Fokker M.7 two-seat biplanes ordered by the Admiralty before the outbreak of war had been suspended in face of *IdFlieg* pressure for the M.8 monoplane. Development of the M.7 was resumed late in 1914, by which time the Admiralty

The prototype Fokker M.7. This aircraft was photographed in January 1915.

132

had more than tripled their original order. The prototype was ready in January 1915; as usual, Fokker tried it first. After three days of test flying he declared himself satisfied with it and pronounced it safe and serviceable. De Waal and Weidner found it pleasant to handle and with better load-carrying ability than the M.8 monoplanes. To permit the completion of the stipulated sand-loading tests on the prototype, it was arranged that military acceptance trials were to be deferred until the first production aircraft began to come out in February.

The M.7 was a sesquiplane. The great overhang of the upper mainplane was emphasized by the inward inclination of the interplane struts; the extensions were braced from above by cables from inverted-vee king-posts; they warped to provide lateral control, the warp-return cables running over king-posts.

The fuselage, engine installation and undercarriage resembled those of the M.8. In the M.7 the cockpits were separated, and the observer had more room; the pilot occupied the rear seat, as in the later biplane type M.10. Dual control was provided. The upper wing was made in one piece, the lower in two panels attached to fittings welded to the lower longerons. The upper wing was connected to the fuselage by two inverted-V struts of steel tubing braced fore-and-aft and diagonally by steel cables. This structure was not very rigid, which may have contributed to the wing flutter mentioned below.

Judged against the standards of its day, the M.7's performance was creditable. A total load of 230 kg. (506 lb.), including fuel for $1\frac{1}{2}$ hours,

This photograph of a Fokker M.7 shows the low king-posts on the upper wing, and the warp-return cable running spanwise over them.

could be carried. With this load the M.7 climbed to 800 m. (2,600 ft.) in six minutes and to 2,000 m. (7,560 ft.) in 22 minutes.

The prototype underwent the prescribed sand-loading test at Schwerin early in February 1915. With engine removed, the aircraft was slung inverted from the roof of the hangar, the fuselage being supported by trestles. A uniform load of sand was then distributed carefully over the wings. No account was taken of the stress relief provided by the taut wing covering of doped fabric. A photograph of this sand-loading test was published in *Flugsport*. The military officials were satisfied that the machine was safe enough for operational service; but in fact it was not.

During February, von Bismarck made an acceptance flight with one of the first production M.7s, accompanied by Sergeant Opel. While making steep turns at low altitude, von Bismarck felt severe wing flutter, the control column rocking in his hands. The amplitude of the torsional flexing in the extensions of the upper wing grew; von Bismarck tried to reach the ground quickly in a steep spiral glide, but the wing failed and the M.7 crashed. Von Bismarck and Opel were seriously injured.

About this accident von Bismarck says: "I crashed on this biplane because of wing failure close to the ground, following a steepish spiral glide from about 200 metres. The strain was too much for the wing structure. This aircraft had warping of the extensions of the upper wing, similar to the Morane–Saulnier. The upper pylons had, however, been made too low; this gave a rather shallow wing bracing. The irregular and high stress during the glide induced flutter in the wing extensions. The oscillations suddenly increased noticeably, until the wing failed. Scherff must have suffered the same fate, although in his biplane the height of the bracing pylons had been doubled as in all subsequent biplanes. It was lucky for me that the wing failed at a very low altitude, otherwise we would most certainly not have survived."

On his recovery, von Bismarck found that his services were no longer required by Fokker. He joined the Halberstadt Aircraft Works as a test pilot. He was destined always to suffer from the injuries he sustained in the M.7 crash.

Blame for the accident was laid upon the unfavourable angles of bracing and warp-return cables provided by the king-posts above the upper wing. The height of these pylons was therefore increased on all M.7s.

But this did not cure the trouble. On April 17, 1915, Scherff took off in the second of the Austrian M.7s on an acceptance test; his passenger Hoengen was a foreman mechanic. Scherff handled the aircraft with caution, for he was not certain that the structure was as safe as Fokker had claimed it to be. After completing the prescribed one hour's flight at 2,000 m. he came down in a shallow glide. At low altitude the upper wing extensions began to flutter violently. This time a warping cable broke before the wing itself failed. Scherff managed to steer the almost uncontrollable aircraft to shallow water near the shore of the Ostorf Lake, where it finally crashed. Scherff was thrown out into the water; he suffered serious internal injuries and nearly drowned. Hoengen seemed less badly hurt, but died a year later.

Scherff spent well over a year in the Schwerin hospital gravely ill; more than once his life was in danger. In all this time Fokker never paid him a visit. Indeed, he dismissed Scherff a few days after the accident. Later, he even forbade him to enter the factory or aerodrome.

After a partial recovery, Scherff was able to work for other aircraft firms as a test and acceptance pilot. He always had a high reputation for his reliability, skill and integrity in his dangerous profession.

Scherff's accident was ascribed to defective material. Fokker maintained that design changes were not called for, but the authorities thought

Fokker M.7 of the naval defence squadron, Kiel.

differently: all M.7s were grounded until the structure was reinforced. An investigation by Adlershof experts revealed that the wing-attachment bolts of the production M.7s were less well secured than those of the prototype. Although this could not have been the direct cause of the two wing failures Fokker was bluntly warned to pay more attention to his standards of production. The warning had no lasting effect, however.

A strengthened version of the M.7 was proof-loaded at Schwerin, and the ban on the type was lifted on April 24, 1915. The empty weight was now 394 kg. (870 lb.), or 30·5% of the total. Loaded, the aircraft weighed 676 kg. (1,490 lb.), a figure much larger than the original estimate. The rate of climb of the strengthened M.7 was consequently poor.

The Fokker M.7, or Fok. B, equipped both landplane coastal defence squadrons of the German Navy for a time; these units were at Kiel and Wilhelmshaven.

Some M.7s were used for training purposes at Johannisthal, and a few went into the Fokker school and gave good service. One of the Fokker

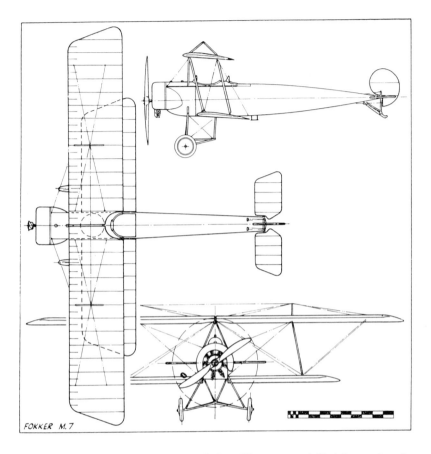

FOKKER M.7

school machines crashed: the pupil, Lt. Gloege, was killed instantly; the instructor, Franz Krebe, was injured. This crash, like von Bismarck's and Scherff's, occurred during a gliding turn.

Three M.7s had been ordered by the Army Flying Corps. Perhaps because of the type's reputation they never went into service, although they were accepted and paid for. They may have been transferred to the Fokker school. The *IdFlieg* suggested that a more substantial biplane, fitted with wireless telegraphy for artillery spotting, should be developed. The result of this suggestion was the M.10. On the whole, the M.7 had been a failure.

Fokker was still keen to build seaplanes. The Admiralty paid well, and their officials were much less fussy than those of the Army, in which the growing influence of engineering specialists was creating difficulties for Fokker. He had an advantage in the shape of the Schwerin; lake of his competitors, only the Flugzeugbau Friedrichshafen (a Zeppelin subsidiary) had facilities for trying out new seaplanes close to the factory.

Fokker W.3.

The conversion of the M.7 into a twin-float seaplane seemed feasible. The wing loading would be too high for good take-off performance, however, and a re-design was needed.

With the permission of the *Reichsmarineamt*, one of the rejected M.7s was converted and modified. It was fitted with two-bay wings of greatly increased span; the interplane struts were inclined inwards at such an angle as to provide internal wing bracing bays of equal length. The upper wing had long extensions, the landing wires and warp-return cables being supported by the usual inverted-vee king-posts.

The floats were those of the unsuccessful W.2; they were of wooden construction, plywood-covered, and had obviously been designed by somebody connected with naval aviation. These floats, more than a year old, were connected to the M.7-type fuselage by a strut system that was more robust than that of the W.2. The new seaplane floated tail-high, but a small tail-float was retained as a precaution.

The completed aircraft was given the type number W.3. It proved to be unsatisfactory. A few trials by Fokker indicated its reluctance to leave the water, although it carried virtually no load. It is uncertain whether the naval authorities discouraged development or Fokker still lacked the patience to make modifications and develop systematically. At any rate

Fokker W.3.

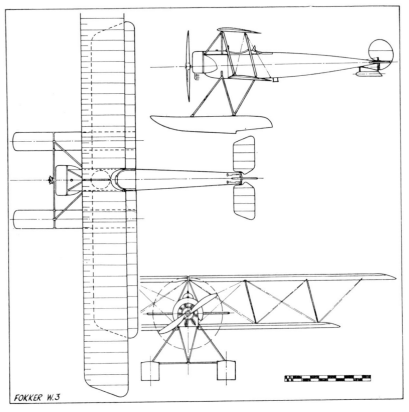

FOKKER W.3

the prototype was dismantled, reconverted into a standard M.7 landplane, and supplied for training purposes to the Marine-Landflieger
Abteilung at Johannisthal.

While the M.7 was giving so much trouble, Fokker was doing some
thinking about fighting in the air. Firms were encouraged to fit a machine-
gun to the observer's cockpit of their two-seat types. Such armament was
purely defensive; what was needed was an offensive fighter aircraft.

Fokker decided to build such an aircraft without official guidance or
advice. He confidently expected to achieve quick results by using components of existing types.

Two M.7 fuselage structures, engineless but each with its individual
standard tail group, were joined by a biplane structure. Between these
fuselages a nacelle was mounted centrally on the lower wing. In this the
pilot sat, sandwiched between two 80-h.p. Oberursel rotaries, one driving
a tractor airscrew, the other a pusher. Outboard of the fuselages the
equal-span wings had two-bay bracing. Two gunners were to be carried,
one in the front of each fuselage; no armament was ever fitted, however,
and there was no provision for rearward defence.

Fokker M.9.

Fokker M.9. (*Photo: Imperial War Museum*).

By the standards of its time the basic idea of the Fokker M.9 was reasonably promising, and the aircraft might have proved better than the A.E.G. K.I, apart from its lack of rear defence. But the execution of this interesting experiment was utterly unsatisfactory. It was a makeshift, hastily assembled without any attempt at engineering; and its tests by Fokker were correspondingly slapdash.

For towing, a transverse bar was attached to both fuselages of the M.9.

For the first take-off, six men were posted along the intended run armed with fire extinguishers; others sat in two motor-cars and on motor-cycles with engines running, ready to rescue the pilot in the event of mishap. The take-off run was rather long. On landing, Fokker complained that the fuselages moved when the wings were warped. He made another flight alone, and finally took up two passengers (military mechanics) in the gunners' positions in an attempt to correct the M.9's tail-heaviness.

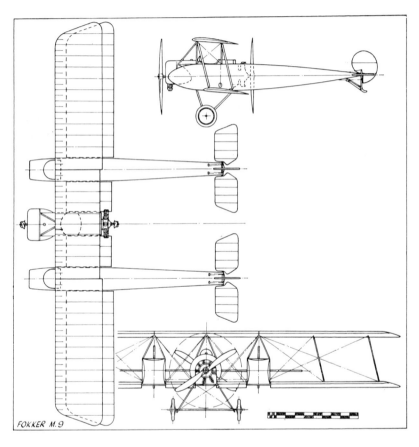

FOKKER M.9

Henze recalls that all these flights took place within the space of a few days and were quite short.

After this perfunctory testing of a radical new design Fokker gave up. The M.9 was put aside for dismantling, and its development was completely abandoned. Any aeronautical engineer could have foreseen that the lack of any rear connexion between the fuselages would permit flexing and lead to unsatisfactory control. If Fokker had had more patience he might have made something of the M.9. However, his attention was then fully taken

Fokker M.10E, Factory No. 172. This aircraft had the additional front cabane struts, but its king-posts were short and were faired over with fabric.

up by the work on the M.5K/MG single-seat fighter, which began when the M.9 was abandoned.

The M.10 was a development of the M.7, which it closely resembled; but its wing structure was more substantial and it was improved in some details. Like its predecessor it was an unarmed two-seat artillery spotter, in which the pilot occupied the rear seat.

The M.10 prototype retained the not very rigid cabane structure of the M.7. This aircraft was Factory No. 169. It was later modified to have the 100-h.p. Mercedes engine in place of the standard 80-h.p. or 100-h.p. rotary. The Mercedes-powered version was soon abandoned as being too heavy.

The production M.10s had two additional struts to the forward cabane struts; these were standardized. The wing-warping levers were moved

Production M.10E of Flieger-Abteilung 9b. Note the tall king-posts.

Fokker M.10E in Austrian service. (*Photo: Wolfgang B. Klemperer*).

farther aft, leaving more room in the observer's cockpit, where a wireless transmitter was installed.

Most production M.10s had the 100-h.p. Oberursel U.1 engine. However, those used as trainers and some of those supplied to Austria had the 80-h.p. Oberursel, which was more easily obtained from existing stocks or from obsolete aeroplanes.

The prototype Fokker M.10, Factory No. 169, in its modified form with 100-h.p. Mercedes engine.

The M.10 was produced in two forms. The original single-bay form of the design was named M.10E ("E" signifying *einstielig*, or single-bay). It differed from the earlier M.7 in having its lower wing slightly farther aft, greater wing chord, and heightened upper-wing king-posts.

First of the type to be accepted by the Army Flying Corps was Factory No. 171, which was taken over at Schwerin on June 7, 1915. Modifications were demanded, however, and the acceptance did not become effective until the following month. This M.10E and its immediate successors had the 80-h.p. Oberursel. The type was also delivered to Austria.

The military load of the M.10 affected its climbing performance adversely, so new, two-bay wings were designed. The first machine to have them was Factory No. 199. This version of the design was designated M.10Z, the "Z" signifying *zweistielig*, or two-bay.

The prototype was accepted for the Army Flying Corps at Schwerin on November 17, 1915, and was sent to Adlershof for further trials during December. The wings of the M.10Z were of equal span, and the entire

143

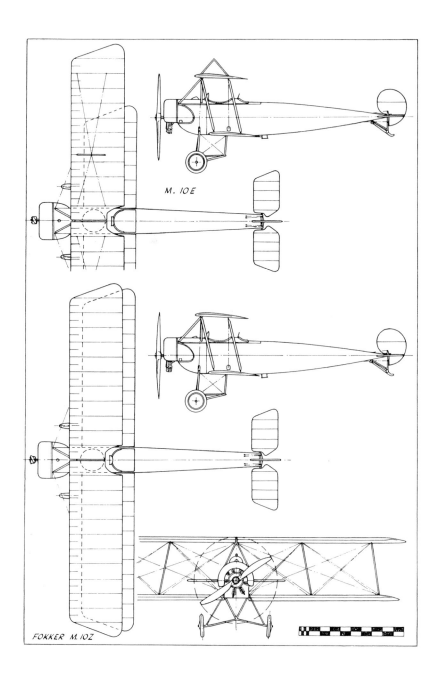

M. 10 E

FOKKER M. 10 Z

144

This Fokker M.10Z, Factory No. 199, made its acceptance flights on November 17, 1915, and was delivered on December 13, 1915.

Reinhold Platz is second from the left in this group, standing before an M.10Z at Schwerin. Third from the left is Kreutzer; at extreme right, Vorberg.

wing cell warped to provide lateral control, whereas on the M.10E only the upper-wing extensions warped. The new arrangement was more practical and safer, because the danger of torsional flutter was much reduced.

A small batch of M.10Z biplanes, known in the Service as Fok.B.II, gave good service on some sectors of the Eastern Front. The type was also supplied to the Navy and Austria. Various M.10 biplanes were still flying on training duties until late in 1917.

During the first half of 1915 the Fokker works had developed and constructed no fewer than six different aircraft types: the M.7, M.9, M.10, M.14, M.15 and W.3. These included monoplanes, biplanes and float-planes, and development embraced several variants and trial engine installations. One cannot but admire Fokker's energy in undertaking so many projects: even in those days of uncomplicated aeroplanes and simple equipment his output would have been a remarkable achievement for a much larger aircraft works.

For all this work Fokker had only a couple of draughtsmen and no trained designer. Admittedly, the "design work" for prototypes, and modifications, were done on the job by the try-and-fit method. No stressing was attempted. All the prototypes were built within the busy production organization; there was no separate experimental shop. Fokker thought this was the way to carry on development: he paid no heed to Dr. Lissauer's advice to separate production from development.

The Fokker M.16E, nicknamed *Karausche.*

CHAPTER VIII

BIPLANE FIGHTERS

FROM THE first weeks of 1916 it had become increasingly clear that the era of the monoplane fighter was over. The French Nieuports quickly proved their superiority; and in the British sectors the D.H.2 and F.E.2b pushers challenged the Fokkers' supremacy. All German aircraft manufacturers were asked urgently to submit new single-seat fighter biplanes for evaluation.

Fokker learnt that the Albatros and Halberstadt concerns were busy developing biplane fighters with water-cooled engines. He had been given the views of the operational pilots by Boelcke and other experienced fighter pilots who had visited his works. The Feldflugchef and other high-ranking officers had let Fokker understand that they expected him to produce a superior fighter as quickly as he had done in the past. It was suggested that he, like Euler, Siemens-Schuckert, Pfalz, and Albatros, might try to produce a copy of the Nieuport scout. It is not known whether Fokker was given the opportunity of trying a captured specimen.

Fokker felt that the existing M.7 and M.10 designs could not provide the basis of a new fighter design, and that a new line of development must be initiated. Choosing a suitable engine presented a problem. The rotary was not very popular, yet it was light and conferred high manoevrability and a good rate of climb at low altitudes. The six-cylinder water-cooled engines were reliable, easy to service, and had a better performance at altitude; but they were heavy, more complicated, and demanded a larger airframe. It therefore seemed wise to have parallel lines of development, using both water-cooled and rotary engines: Fokker initiated this

The first form of the M.16Z, with the 160-h.p. Mercedes engine.

policy and kept to it up to the end of the war. It proved sound, and was welcomed by the *IdFlieg*; moreover, the flexibility it permitted enabled the firm to find a market more easily.

Fokker and Kreutzer were aware that three qualities were of primary importance in a fighter aeroplane: climb, manoeuvrability, and speed at altitude. Immelmann had stressed these necessities, plus high fire-power to decide combats quickly.

For a good rate of climb and high operational ceiling, weight had to be kept down. This placed the water-cooled engine at a disadvantage, even when allowance was made for its lower fuel consumption. On the other hand, the water-cooled engine gave more power at altitude and more powerful models were becoming available.

The single-row rotary conferred the best manoeuvrability on the aircraft to which it was fitted. But the most powerful Oberursel of this kind was the U.1, which gave only 100 nominal h.p.; more powerful types by Goebel and Siemens were still experimental. As the Fok. E.IV had proved, manoeuvrability was impaired when a two-row rotary was used. The balance of favour therefore appeared to lie with the water-

The Fokker M.16ZK built for Austria with the 185/200-h.p. Austro-Daimler engine.

Fokker in the pilot's cockpit of the M.16ZK.

cooled engine of higher horse-power, especially the 160-h.p. Mercedes. The difference in drag between the two types of power unit was not great, owing to the unavoidable drag of the water-cooled engine's radiator. The side radiators favoured by Fokker counterbalanced the smaller fuselage cross-section and cleaner cowling permitted by an in-line engine.

In the airframe proper, Fokker had found that a short wing span generally gave best manoeuvrability, and that wing warping was more powerful than ailerons besides being simpler and cheaper. These views

The Factory number (435) of the M.16ZK is visible in this photograph. This has led to the erroneous belief that the aircraft had the Austrian number 04.35.

149

were shared by operational pilots, but the engineers at Adlershof preferred ailerons because the wing structure would not collapse immediately in the event of a bracing cable being severed by a hit.

All these factors pointed towards biplanes with equal-span wings, the choice of wing-warping or ailerons to be made by the customer.

The size of the new fighter was governed by weight and wing loading. To exceed a loading of 35 kg./m.^{2} (7·2 lb./sq. ft.) was asking for trouble: aerodromes at the front were small and rough, the pilots were not accustomed to high stalling speeds, and stringent restrictions of the BLV limited the length of take-off and landing runs. On the other hand, to keep the wing loading below, say, 25 kg./m.^{2} (5·1 lb./sq. ft.) would have necessitated oversize wings and added structure weight. Hence the dimensions of the new fighter biplane were limited.

The aerofoil section used in the M.5 wing had proved efficient, so Fokker decided to retain it. Aerodynamic progress did not matter to him; wind-tunnel tests and related experiments seemed to him and to Kreutzer a mere waste of time.

Fokker considered that a two-seat fighter ought to beat all competition in the field. The *IdFlieg*, however, did not like the idea: they thought that, with the engines then available, the additional weight of a gunner and his armament would reduce the rate of climb too greatly.

Fokker discussed his idea with the Austrians' representative at Schwerin. They were interested in his proposal, and made available to him one of their new 185/200-h.p. Austro-Daimler engines. This heavy but reliable six-cylinder water-cooled power unit was the most powerful aero-engine that Fokker could get at that time.

In an ambitious attempt to develop several ideas quickly and with a view to winning early orders, Fokker and Kreutzer pursued parallel lines of development simultaneously. This policy resulted in the construction of the types M.16 and M.18 powered by stationary water-cooled engines, and the M.17 and M.19 with rotary engines. Each of these types appeared in single-bay and two-bay versions, the greater wing area of the latter being selected for two-seaters or when a single-seater with improved climbing performance was wanted. The wing arrangement was indicated by adding to the type number the suffix letter E (einstielig) or Z (zweistielig). Each type could have either wing-warping or ailerons for lateral control.

First to appear was the M.16E, a single-bay biplane with a 100-h.p. Mercedes engine. In an attempt to provide the pilot with a wide field of vision its fuselage completely filled the gap between the mainplanes. Upper and lower wings were attached directly to the longerons of the deep, slab-sided fuselage. All four wing panels were of equal size and shape; there was no stagger; the gap, which was made as small as possible, was slightly less than the chord. A simple V-type undercarriage was fitted. The deep fuselage earned the aircraft the nickname *Karausche*, a kind of carp.

The M.16 was flown during the winter of 1915–16 but, handicapped by its low-powered engine, it had a poor performance and was unsuitable for military use. A single LMG.08/15 gun was fitted on the port side of the cockpit, but the M.16E was never flown with its full load.

The M.16E was followed by the larger and more powerful M.16Z, a two-bay, two-seat biplane powered by a 160-h.p. Mercedes engine. As on the M.16E, the deep, ugly fuselage occupied the gap between the main-planes, and lateral control was by wing warping. The engine was carefully cowled, even the cylinders being enclosed. This was an unusual feature on a German aeroplane; the Daimler company did not like it, but it improved the efficiency of the tail. Flat radiators were fitted on the sides of the fuselage.

The cockpits of the M.16ZK.

The fuselage tapered to a point at the tail. This resulted in a weak and unsatisfactory mounting for the rudder. Aerodynamically the rudder was not efficient: the large vertical area of fuselage ahead of the centre of gravity led to directional instability, and the rudder was partially blanketed by the big, badly shaped fuselage.

When the promised Austro-Daimler engine arrived it was fitted to a modified M.16Z airframe. The engine was again fully enclosed, but only the upper part of the cowling was of metal: the lower nose contours were

151

formed by light steel tubing that were covered with fabric. This arrangement seriously impaired the accessibility of the engine. The original side radiators of the Mercedes-powered version were replaced by block-type radiators, known as *Ohrenkühler* (ear-shape radiators).

The pilot's seat was mounted directly on top of the main tank. The cockpit accommodation was cramped, the two seats being close together. The gunner enjoyed the small advantage of being able to fold his seat and stand up to stretch his legs; but so limited were the dimensions of the pilot's cockpit that the rudder bar was situated under the rear of the engine crankcase.

Petrol was fed under air pressure to a small gravity tank situated above the ammunition box for the pilot's gun. This tank held enough petrol for fifteen minutes' flight at full throttle. The fixed forward gun was a Schwarzlose, synchronized by a Fokker gear. The observer's gun was a sub-machine-gun of Mannlicher type on a simple flexible mounting.

The Austrians preferred aileron control, so large surfaces with overhanging horn balances were fitted to the upper wing. This feature earned the aircraft its designation M.16ZK, in which K signified *Klappenverwindung* (flap control). A new balanced rudder, somewhat like that of the M.4, was fitted a short way forward of the end of the fuselage.

Despite its obvious shortcomings the M.16ZK was accepted by the Austrians, largely on the strength of its ability to climb. On April 1, 1916,

The armament of the M.16ZK.

The M.17E in its original form.

Otto Ahlert, a works pilot, with one Henze as passenger and full load aboard, reached an altitude of 6·0 km. (19,700 ft.). This was an excellent performance for the time. Subsequently a batch of these Fokker biplanes were constructed in Austria, all with aileron control and the Austro-Daimler engine. Series production began in May 1916 under the supervision of Fokker's assistant, F. W. Seekatz.

The rotary-powered counterpart of the M.16 was the M.17; the development of the two types ran parallel. The first version of the M.17E had the 80-h.p. Oberursel engine and was generally similar to the M.16E. The M.17E was smaller and had a crash pylon above the fuselage. A triangular aperture in each side of the fuselage improved the pilot's field of view.

This was particularly necessary because the broad engine cowling obstructed the pilot's view when landing. Lateral control was by wing warping, and a rudder of the M.4 type was fitted. The armament consisted of a single LMG.08/15, mounted centrally.

The M.17E is believed to have been tested at Adlershof but did not meet with approval. Its climbing performance was mediocre, and the limited view from the cockpit was criticized by both the Germans and the Austrians. The poor climb could be attributed to the low power of the engine, the narrow gap, and the unsatisfactory airflow over the top of the upper wing.

Fokker liked the M.17E, however. He used it for a time as his personal aircraft, and it seems that he contrived to have it sent to Holland before the war ended. In 1919 it was overhauled for him by the Spijker Works in Amsterdam.

The original form of fuselage was fitted with two-bay warping wings of greater span and narrower chord. This modification made no significant improvement in the performance.

Fokker and Kreutzer now believed that greater success might be achieved with a fuselage of more conventional form. A much-modified M.17E was therefore built. This aircraft had a fuselage similar in pro-

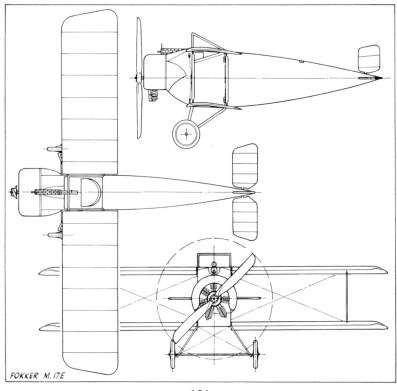

FOKKER M.17E

154

Fokker in the cockpit of the M.17E. In this photograph the aircraft has a modified undercarriage with double forward legs.

portions to that of the monoplanes; the upper wings were attached to a centre section that was supported on short vertical struts. The upper wing was level with the pilot's head, and the wings were staggered. The stagger made a welcome improvement in the downward field of view. Wing warping was retained.

A cut-out in the trailing edge of the centre section gave access to the cockpit. To improve the forward view the LMG.08/15 was now installed to starboard. The fuselage had a pointed stern, and the rudder, somewhat similar to that of the M.4, looked small and insecurely mounted. A short top-decking was fitted behind the cockpit.

This modified M.17E bore the Fokker Factory No. 499. So quickly was its development undertaken that it was tested before the end of the winter of 1915–16. The type was accepted by the Austrians, who were then in urgent need of a manoeuvrable fighter. Factory No. 499 was sent from Schwerin to Wiener Neustadt on April 13, 1916.

The production aircraft used by the Austrians resembled No. 499, but their fuselages terminated in horizontal knife-edges, and they had standard comma-shaped rudders. The limited endurance of the M.17E obliged the Austrians to use it as a defence aircraft only; a few were later used in fighter training units.

An M.17E of the modified type was tested with two machine-guns in an arrangement basically similar to that of the British S.E.5. A fixed, synchronized Schwarzlose gun was mounted in the fuselage, and a movable Mannlicher was carried on a somewhat elaborate mounting above the centre section; the latter gun could be pulled down for upward firing.

155

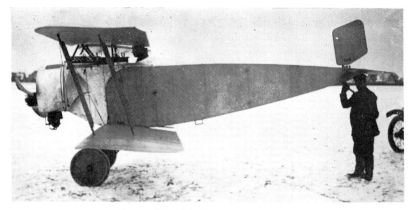
The modified M.17E, Factory No. 499.

One source implies that this aircraft, or one identically armed, was used by the Austrians, but absolute confirmation is lacking.

The two-gun M.17E had a strengthened undercarriage, of which each forward leg consisted of two steel tubes. In an attempt to improve performance and find more favour in the *IdFlieg*'s eyes, the type was also tested with the 100-h.p. Oberursel U.1. The climb was still not good enough, however, and Fokker was told to come back with something better.

The German Army experts looked more favourably on the M.17Z. In this variant, improved climb was sought by fitting longer wings of higher aspect ratio and greater area.

The first M.17Z was powered by a captured 80-h.p. Le Rhône engine. This gave the aircraft a better altitude performance and helped to convince the *IdFlieg* experts that Oberursel should copy the Le Rhône type instead of struggling on with their obsolete Gnôme developments.

As originally built, the M.17Z prototype had the same fuselage as the M.17E, with pointed stern and small, forward-mounted rudder. The strengthened undercarriage with double forward legs was used, and was retained for all subsequent biplanes in the M series.

Test flights showed that the fuselage was too short. It was therefore lengthened by about two feet; at the same time the Morane–Saulnier stern arrangement was re-introduced, giving the familiar horizontal knife-edge to the fuselage and the inverted tripod that carried the tailskid and provided a second hinge point for the comma-shaped rudder.

At the same time, the wing span was reduced by about a foot. Wing warping control was retained. The cut-out in the upper-wing trailing edge was enlarged; the wing itself was at eye level. In an endeavour to improve the pilot's forward view the centre section did not have the aerofoil section of the wings proper: in front of the forward spar the under surface of the centre section was taken forward instead of following

156

Modified Fokker M.17E with experimental armament, apparently for Austria.

the dipping contour of the wing section. This gave the centre-section leading edge an arched appearance; contrary to popular belief, the centre-section itself was not arched.

After the 80-h.p. Le Rhône had been replaced by a 100-h.p. Oberursel, a prototype was subjected to a type test at Adlershof on April 17, 1916 (i.e., three days after the Austrian acceptance of the M.17E). The Type-

The same, or a similar, Fokker M.17E, believed to be in Austrian service.

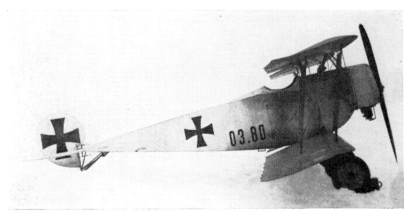

Fokker M.17E wearing Austrian serial number 03.80.

Test Committee stated in its report that the aircraft was distinctly better than the Fok. E.III and could well replace that type. Before the Committee would recommend more than the placing of a small experimental order, it required the M.17Z to be cleared for structural strength. A minor criticism of the type was that the ground clearance of the airscrew was only 11 cm. (4½ in.). The BLV requirements stipulated a minimum of 30 cm. (12 in.), but it seems that neither Fokker nor Kreutzer was aware of this.

Proof-loading tests at Adlershof revealed the need for certain structural modifications, but the M.17Z was ultimately recommended for adoption as an operational type. The structural tests covered the three types

Although this M.17E is here represented as the 500th Fokker aeroplane, this is doubtful. Some records indicate that the Factory No. 500 belonged to a Fok. E.II accepted on March 20, 1916. In the group of men, Kreutzer is to the left of the engine, Platz to the right. Next to Platz is de Waal. This M.17E had a 100-h.p. Oberursel.

The Fokker M.17Z.

Fok. D.I, D.II and D.III; this was possible because all stressed components and field lengths were practically identical. The tests are described in Appendix III.

In point of time the acceptance of the M.17Z occurred shortly after the acceptance of the M.18Z; consequently the M.17Z, although the senior of the two designs, was officially designated Fok. D.II. Austria bought a few M.17Z biplanes but seemed to prefer the M.17E as being faster and more manoeuvrable.

The German order was for 132 aircraft, all with the 100-h.p. Oberursel. The standard armament was one LMG.08, later LMG.08/15. The earliest production machines (M.17ZF) still had wing warping, but Fokker had to undertake to fit ailerons to the remainder (M.17ZK).

The first Fok. D.IIs did not reach the front until better aeroplanes were already available. Part of the delay was caused by structural modifications necessitated by the strength tests, but some production hold-up must have occurred, possibly because Fokker's ramshackle workshop facilities were

An early production Fok. D.II with warping wings (Fokker M.17ZF).

159

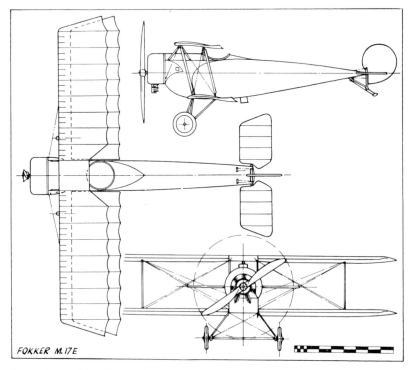

FOKKER M.17E

clogged up with other orders. A number of the Fok. Es were still building at the time; Fokker was beginning to pay for his parsimonious attitude to his factory and its production facilities.

Not until July 27, 1916, did the first production Fok. D.II (Factory No. 687) go into service; it was followed by a few more early in August. One of these first few D.IIs landed intact in Swiss territory, the pilot having lost his way in poor visibility. Allied experts studied this new Fokker with great interest, and the Swiss police had a hard job preventing the aircraft from being spirited away piece-meal by Allied agents. This Fok. D.II seems to have survived in the Swiss Flying Corps.

The later production D.IIs had the required aileron controls. They also had a small refinement in the form of a light stringer along each side of the fuselage; this improved the support for the fabric covering, which was apt to flutter unpleasantly after losing its original tautness. This modification was introduced after September 1916.

On the whole, the Fok. D.II was a disappointment in operational service. It was obsolete when it reached the front, and its performance at altitude was inadequate compared with the contemporary fighters flown by the Allies. Fokker admits in his autobiography that it was inferior to the Albatros D.I and D.II. The type was therefore quickly withdrawn from the Western Front. Small numbers were used in quiet sectors in the east, in Macedonia, and in Turkey. They were useful where either cold weather or high ground temperatures gave an advantage to rotary engines. But most of the Fok. D.IIs were used at home establishments.

Sixteen of the type had been supplied by September 1, 1916; forty-nine were in operational use on November 1, 1916, sixty-eight on January 1, 1917. By September 1, 1917, only ten remained in service.

Running parallel with the development of the M.17 was that of another single-seat fighter, designated M.18 and powered by the 100-h.p. Mercedes. This engine was chosen because other operational aircraft were no longer able to use the 100-h.p. and 120-h.p. Mercedes, and quantities of both were readily available. The 100-h.p. engine was well liked by front-line pilots; so its availability and popularity were regarded as justification for an attempt to develop a Mercedes-powered single-seat fighter.

In its original form the M.18E differed little from the *Karausche*. The flank radiators were similar to those of the original M.16E; the engine installation was also generally similar but had a cleaner cowling. The vertical tail assembly incorporated a fixed fin and was a complete change from the tail design that Fokker had favoured until then. A single LMG.08/15 was installed in the same position as that of the M.16E.

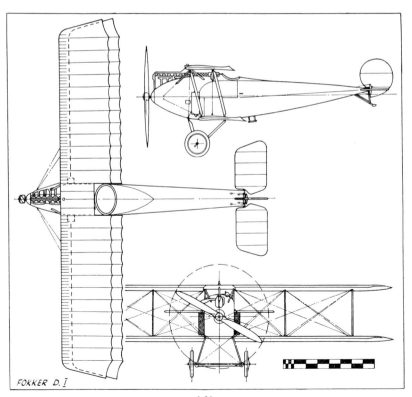

FOKKER D. I

The M.18E remained experimental and was not developed. Like the other single-bay machines, its climbing performance was inadequate: a larger wing was needed.

While developing his single-seat biplanes, Fokker learned that the new Halberstadt single-seater had found favour with pilots at the front. It was a two-bay biplane, not very different from the general Fokker concept, with fuselage stern and tail design fairly similar. The Halberstadt had a shallower fuselage and cabane struts, however; the upper wing was level with the eyes of the pilot, who sat with his head in the trailing-edge cut-out.

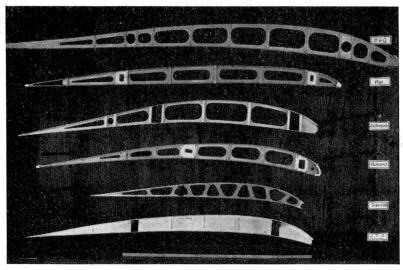

Typical German wing ribs. From top to bottom: A.E.G., Ago, L.T.G., L.F.G., Fok. D.II, and L.V.G.

Two examples of the Halb. D.I had gone to the front as early as February 1916 for operational evaluation. This type, which had the 100-h.p. Mercedes, was withdrawn for modification, but according to general opinion it was far better than the Fok. E.III. In June 1916 eight Halb. D.IIs, with the 120-h.p. Mercedes engine, appeared in the Somme sector and acquitted themselves very well.

The historical facts about the Halberstadts incidentally make nonsense of Fokker's statement that his Fok. D.I could claim to have been the first German single-seat fighter biplane with a water-cooled engine.

A two-bay version of the M.18 was built. Like the M.17Z, it followed the example of the Halberstadts in having a shallower fuselage and conventional centre-section bracing. In fact, most components of the new M.18Z were identical with those of the M.17Z, but the mainplanes were of greater chord.

162

The Fokker M.18E.

The first M.18Z still had the 100-h.p. Mercedes engine. Like the M.17Z, its fuselage had a pointed stern and the precariously mounted parallelogram rudder. In fact, the fuselage was the same width (820 mm.) at the

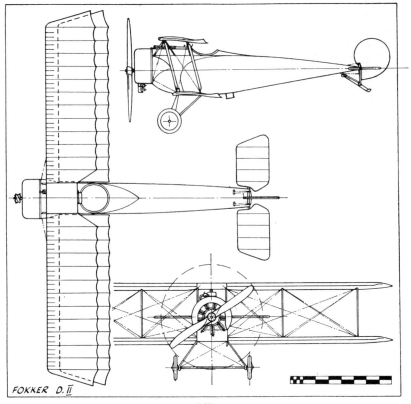

FOKKER D.II

163

The Fokker M.18Z.

cabane as that of the M.17Z. The M.18Z had balanced ailerons on the upper wings, and the radiators were two compact blocks, similar to those of the second version of the M.16Z.

An improved and cleaned-up prototype, but still with the 100-h.p. Mercedes, was submitted for an official type test at Adlershof on April 15, 1916; i.e., before the M.17Z. This aircraft, Fok. D.I, No. 140/16, Factory No. 670, reverted to wing warping: Fokker had found that this conferred better manoeuvrability. The fuselage stern and tail design had reverted to that of the monoplanes, with comma rudder and tripod support for tailskid and rudder. The LMG.08 machine-gun was mounted to starboard, and the radiator blocks had a more elongated form.

Fokker claimed in his autobiography that "in its official tests the D.I proved to be the fastest and most efficient fighter available". However,

Fokker with the M.18Z.

164

The first Fok. D.I, No. 140/16.

this statement is not supported by any Service records; it is doubtful if any official trial of any kind could have led to such a supposition. In fact, the performance of the Fok. D.I, even when fitted with the 120-h.p Mercedes, was inferior to that of the Fok. E.IV, which was then operational.

So far from being the fastest and most efficient fighter available the D.I was adversely criticized. The Type-Test Record of April 15, 1916, signed by Professor Dr.-Ing. Bendemann (Director of the D.V.L.) and by Dipl.-Ing. G. Madelung, both officers of the German Flying Corps and eminent aeronautical engineers, contained this rather devastating passage:

"When seen from a distance of twenty yards the Fok. D.I makes an excellent impression. However, Herr Direktor Fokker is advised to imitate the technological progress embodied in the construction of the Albatros D.I, of which he has taken photographs. This suggestion relates as much to the difference in workmanship between the two aircraft as to all the technical details of the Fok. D.I. Apart from these considerations, the wing warping needs the use of far too much force."

Front view of No. 140/16.

Martin Kreutzer with the first Fok. D.I, No. 140/16.

The inadequate ground clearance of the airscrew was also criticized, as in the case of the M.17Z.

Fokker was present when the Type Test Committee of engineering and Service experts made their pronouncement. He was furious when he learnt that the only order he was to get was one for three aircraft with the 120-h.p. Mercedes. These three were to be evaluated to see whether a better rate of climb could be obtained from the Fok. D.I. In any case, further orders would not be forthcoming unless the aircraft's structural strength was proved in tests to destruction at Adlershof.

Thus was Fokker disabused of the idea that by good salesmanship he could palm off any hastily and shoddily constructed aeroplane on to the German Flying Corps because fighter biplanes were needed for the

Fok. D.I in Austrian markings. This aircraft has a fin and warping wings. (*Photo: Wolfgang B. Klemperer*).

166

Western Front. He had thought that his contacts with high-ranking officers and leading fighter pilots would be sufficient to overcome the technical doubts raised by the engineering experts. Now he found that the engineering experts could not be swayed by any pressure.

The Type Test Committee's tart reference to Fokker's photographic activities followed repeated warnings that he must refrain from photographing other firms' prototypes and experimental ideas in the top-secret *Prüfanstalt und Werft* at Adlershof. Civilians and cameras were strictly prohibited there, and ordinary mortals who offended against this rule were liable to be instantly arrested and charged with a grave offence against military secrecy and state security. Fokker therefore had good cause to be grateful for the lenient treatment of his photographic indiscretions.

After a comprehensive structural test programme, including many repeats and requests for modifications, the Fok. D.I was accepted structurally, but the margin of reserve strength was small.

An Austrian Fok. D.I with horn-balanced ailerons.

The airframe supplied for the structural tests had been styled—possibly by Fokker himself—"Captain Boelcke's aircraft". This may have been done in an attempt to emphasize the urgency of the tests and to assure an easy passage. However, there is no record that Boelcke ever wanted this particular aircraft or took any steps to accelerate its acceptance. The test results for the Fok. D.I are included in Appendix III.

The modified Fok. D.I No. 140/16 was again submitted to Adlershof on July 12, 1916, and was passed for service.

The structural tests cost Fokker nothing. As requested, he was present throughout the week of testing, glared at the experiments, and complained to all non-technical officers he knew that these confounded engineering scientists were biased against him. To his mind it was unforgivable that

167

Austrian Fok. D.I with ailerons. (*Photo: Peter M. Bowers*).

the Fok. D.I had not been sent immediately to the front, where they were so sorely needed.

Fokker was given an order for twenty-five Fok. D.Is with 120-h.p. Mercedes engines but, as with the D.II, he was requested to ensure that all later machines had aileron control. The first production aircraft had the Fokker designation M.18ZF; the later machines with ailerons were M.18ZK. Some of the later production D.Is had a small fin in front of the rudder; others had modified undercarriages.

The Austrians were also interested in the Fok. D.I Some examples were bought direct from Fokker; others were built under licence apparently by the *Ungarische allgemeine Maschinenfabrik A.G. (M.A.G.)* of Budapest. Some at least of the Austrian machines had a fully-cowled engine, doubtless an Austro-Daimler, and a large fin.

To the orders of the *IdFlieg*, about eighty Fok. D.Is were delivered. They were useless on the Western Front. Up to September 1, 1916, ten aircraft had been supplied for operational evaluation. On September 22, 1916, Captain Albert Ball first sighted a Fok. D.I when it was climbing away from Jasta 2's aerodrome at Vélu. Ball, flying a Nieuport, attacked it and shot it down. On September 29, 1916, an officer of Jasta 2, flying one of the first Fok. D.Is to be delivered, was shot down by a Nieuport biplane in the Somme sector.

Boelcke rejected the Fok. D.I as being insufficiently manoeuvrable, preferring the modified Halberstadt fighter. The correctness of his judgment is borne out by the reports of British fighter pilots, who regarded the Halberstadt and Alb. D.I as superior in speed and capability to all contemporary Allied fighters. Boelcke went on to favour the Alb. D.I and D.II. So the bulk of the Fok. D.Is went to quiet sectors of the front and to home-establishment units. Up to November 1916 seventy-four Fok. D.Is were in service at the front. Their number then dropped to four.

A few of these aircraft gave good service in Turkey and Mesopotamia,

168

however. With them, Buddecke, Schuez and their gallant fellow pilots scored victories over obsolete British aircraft under primitive and trying conditions.

The Fokker D.I brought loss to the Fokker organization. On the evening of June 27, 1916, Martin Kreutzer, chief designer of the Fokker aircraft company (though never acknowledged as such), took off in a production Fok. D.I on an acceptance flight. Shortly after take-off he crashed close to the aerodrome. When being taken from the wreckage he was conscious enough to explain that the rudder had jammed during the first turn. Fokker hurried to the scene and shouted reproaches at the mortally injured man. Platz witnessed this exhibition with disgust. Kreutzer died next day in the Garrison Hospital at Schwerin.

An Austrian Fok. D.I, possibly a MAG-built aircraft. It had an Austro-Daimler engine and a large fin.

CHAPTER IX

AFTER KREUTZER

AT THE time of Kreutzer's death further prototypes of his design were under test; other experimental variants were building, supervised by Reinhold Platz; and various modifications were in hand.

Closely following the M.17 and M.18 came the M.19, virtually a modified Fok. D.II with a 160-h.p. Oberursel U.3 twin-row rotary and a wing area as large as that of the Fok. D.I. The M.19 had a much better performance than its two predecessors; it was more formidable as a fighter, having two guns. Its armament thus made it a counterpart of the Fok. E.IV. The M.19 had the same "spider" engine mounting and an identical cowling. There were other similarities of fuselage details in the M.15 and M.19, and the fuel system was the same.

In its wing design and arrangement the M.19 differed little from the M.17 and M.18, having identical spar sections, bracings and bay lengths. Since this was so, the official structural tests also covered the airworthiness of the Fok. D.III, as the M.19 was officially designated (see Appendix III). The characteristic shape of centre section was retained. Although this improved the pilot's forward view it was aerodynamically harmful, as it had an adverse effect upon the lift distribution over the span. Its detrimental effect on the climb was made worse by the large cut-out in the trailing edge. But the importance of lift grading and induced drag was little understood at that time by aircraft designers, least of all by Fokker.

A D.III had been offered to Boelcke. On September 1, 1916, he took over Fok. D.III No. 352/16, which was the first operational aircraft of the type. It was sent to him for evaluation before the D.III had passed its Type Test at Adlershof; this was permissible because the type had been cleared structurally. Although other and better single-seat biplanes had reached the front by the time Boelcke received D. 352/16, he achieved some immediate successes with it and at first liked the type. On the day after he received his D.III, September 2, 1916, Boelcke shot down his twentieth victim, a D.H.2 flown by Captain R. Wilson. During the following two weeks Boelcke added five more victories to his score while flying this Fok. D.III, this during a period of hard air fighting when German air power was beginning to re-assert itself after the eclipse of the Battle of the Somme.

But Boelcke found that the D.III was no faster than the Sopwith

1½-Strutter and considerably slower than the Nieuport scout. He therefore changed over to the Alb. D.I, which had arrived a few days before the Fok. D.III. This was much faster, especially when diving. The Alb. D.I was soon followed by the Alb. D.II, which was a further improvement and gave its pilot a better view from the cockpit.

On Boelcke's advice the Fok. D.III was withdrawn from the active sectors on the Western Front. During the next few months it was used in areas where air-combat activities were less intense. But while production of the D.III was proceeding at Schwerin, it was decided to relegate all Fok. D.IIIs to the equipment of Home Defence interceptor units. A

Boelcke's Fok. D.III, No. 352/16.

contributory factor to this decision may have been the unreliability of the two-row U.3 engine with the front-line squadrons. The air defence of parts of Germany had by this time become so important that special single-seat fighter units, known as *Kampf-Einsitzer-Staffeln* (KEST), had been formed.

The Fok. D.III served as a home-defence fighter until late in 1917. It was not popular with pilots. The engine was mainly to blame; and apart from this the aircraft's stability was not good.

In common with the Fok. D.I and D.II, the D.III was first built with wing warping. Boelcke, like Fokker, preferred warping to ailerons: it provided a more powerful control and gave the best manoeuvrability. The late-production D.IIIs (e.g., D.379/16) had the aileron control preferred by the engineering experts. The two variants had the Fokker type numbers M.19F and M.19K, respectively.

171

Boelcke with a Fok. D.III.

In November 1916 Fok. D.III D.369/16 was tested to destruction. Apparently it was then felt that the results of the tests carried out on the M.18 might no longer be valid for the production aircraft. There was reason to suspect the reliability of Fokker products, but surviving test documents give no specific reasons for the tests.

Although the wing structure as a whole proved satisfactory, the tests of other vital components were less re-assuring. The fuselage proved to have only 90% of the required strength. The rudder and elevators failed to come up to their specified strength; the control circuits to both surfaces displayed excessive friction (43% against the maximum permitted 20%); and the control cables stretched far too much.

Modifications to the wing included the addition of a plywood strip along the leading edge to give better handling strength; this strip ran back as far as the front spar. It was probably one of the first modifications of the wing introduced by Platz. Finally, three riblets were fitted between the full-chord ribs: the Fokker E.III wing, with ribs at the same pitch of 350 mm., had only single riblets.

During 1917, a Fok. D.III was used at Adlershof in a series of tests designed to determine the mass moment of inertia. The specimen aircraft had balanced ailerons, a gap of 1,300 mm. and a stagger of 300 mm.; its centre of gravity was found to be 540 mm. above and 200 mm. behind the leading edge of the lower wing. The weight of the detachable wing panels was 78 kg. (173 lb.), or 17·3% of the weight empty. This was

172

Fok. D.III, No. 365/16.

heavier than the wings of the Spad S.VII, which according to German structural tests had more than satisfied all BLV requirements, and which in its wing design was considered exemplary by the engineers of the German Flying Corps.

With full load the Fok. D.III had moments of inertia of 154 mkg./sec² about the axis of yaw, and 76 mkg./sec² about the axis of pitch. These values were substantially greater than those for the Spad S.VII, a fighter with a stationary engine of comparable horse-power. The tests disproved the assumption that rotary-powered aeroplanes must always be more manoeuvrable because of smaller inertia.

Deliveries of Fok. D.IIIs to the Army Flying Corps between September 1916 and the spring of 1917 totalled 159. Seven were in operational use in September 1916, thirty-four on January 1, 1917; by February 1917, however, only seven remained operational. A few examples were supplied to Austria. It is uncertain whether the type was built there under licence, but one source states that "Fokker D.Is" powered by the 160-h.p. Oberursel

A late production Fok. D.III with ailerons. Apparently this aircraft was interned in Holland after a forced landing and was used by the Dutch Army.

173

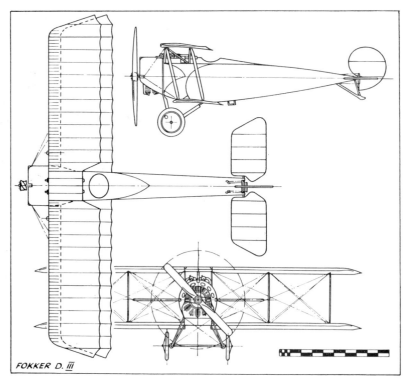

FOKKER D. III

were built by the M.A.G. concern at Budapest. This statement may be wrong in one or more respects, but it may indicate that M.A.G. produced a version of the D.III.

Fokker had counted on a larger order for the D.III. He felt certain that it was superior to the Alb. D.I, and blamed the Albatros Works for robbing him of the fruit of his labours. The pilots at the front had let him down by choosing the Albatros, and the Adlershof engineers had in his view used shameful subterfuges to prevent his superior aircraft from reaching the front before the Albatros. The fact that aircraft had to be completely airworthy for operational purposes was not quite clear to him.

In fact, the Alb. D.I and Alb. D.II were unquestionably better fighters than any of the Fokkers; their superiority was not attributable solely to their 160-h.p. Mercedes with its better performance at altitude. It had been the unbiased judgment of operational fighter pilots that had led to the large orders for the Albatros types. Robert Thelen and R. Schubert, both qualified engineers, had triumphed over Fokker with a well-designed aircraft.

Fokker's next product, the M.20, was an attempt to better the Albatros types by using the same engine, the 160-h.p. Mercedes. Fokker had already tried to instal one such engine in the M.18, but the structural tests were so discouraging that the development was not pursued. Now it was essential to revive the idea, especially as the 160-h.p. Oberursel gave neither speed nor altitude performance and was not liked by pilots.

The M.20 was little more than a rehashed Fok. D.I, modified to accommodate the larger and heavier engine and two machine-guns with their double supply of ammunition. To compensate for the increased side area forward of the centre of gravity a triangular fin with an area of 0·35 sq. m. was fitted. The prototype was provided with ailerons when it was presented for its type test early in October 1916. However, Fokker had not bothered to increase the structural strength of the airframe: wing spars, etc., were all identical with those of the Fok. D.I. This was asking for trouble.

The new type was subjected to structural tests at Adlershof from October 2 to October 7, 1916. This was an uncommonly long time for any new type, particularly for an aircraft that was little more than a modification of three tested and approved designs.

Fokker was again asked to attend the tests—he had complained about prejudice against his products—and he was there, morose and bitter. The tests did nothing to cheer him up: the wings collapsed in the Case A test (see Appendix III) when the sand loading reached 4·32 times the scheduled load. The acceptable minimum factor was 5. Failure occurred when a bolt that held the turnbuckle of a main bracing cable tore out. Closer examination revealed that both the cable and turnbuckle had been under strength. On top of this, Fokker was unable to deny that the turnbuckle did not even fit the cable; this, he explained, as if it were a valid excuse, was attributable to a "mistake" in the assembling of the aircraft.

New components were obtained from Schwerin and the loading was repeated. This time another turnbuckle broke, in a cable attached to the fuselage.

The engineers conducting the tests now urged that all major cables in the wing bracing be replaced by cables of 65% higher strength. Even this

The prototype Fok. D.IV.
175

could not produce a load factor better than 4·77, and further strengthening of the wing bracing was needed.

Detail tests in the Adlershof laboratories proved beyond any doubt that the material of the bracing cables was so inferior that it should never have been used in any aircraft. Fokker had bought it, probably very cheaply, apparently from scrap.

Until this shocking discovery was made, all cables, turnbuckles and bolts had been supplied by Schwerin. This was the accepted procedure during official strength tests. Now, however, the testing engineers replaced such Fokker-supplied components with material from government store. This was an unprecedented action. Braced with this good-quality cable and components, the M.20 wing cables could be loaded to a factor of 5·03 without undue deformation. The loading was then discontinued in order to preserve the aircraft for the other loading cases as required by the BLV. To achieve this minimum result, the Adlershof technicians had had to perform five major sand loadings and two subsidiary loadings, apart from many laboratory investigations.

The report on this first stage of the M.20 testing contained a stern warning to Fokker that he ought to arrange for more efficient supervision of his production, and that the utmost care ought to be taken to ensure that no defective materials were embodied in any vital structure. Valuable lives might have been saved if Fokker had heeded this admonition. As it was, he departed fuming that those slide-rule wielders had again got the better of him.

Structural tests for Cases B and D were resumed after the damaged wing had been replaced by a new one from Schwerin. This was actually a concession, because the minor damage to the wing ought to have been repaired and the subsequent tests conducted on the same set of wings.

The required load factor of 3·5 in Case B was not attained: the rear spar buckled in one of the inboard bays of the new wing when the sand load corresponded to a load factor of 3·31. Again, Fokker was present.

The *IdFlieg* now insisted on a stronger rear spar. When the wings were accordingly modified, a load of 3·58 was achieved in Case B and 3·00 in Case D without undue deformation or failure of any vital member.

Structural tests of the tail unit revealed the need for further modifications. The elevator collapsed under only 72% of the specified minimum loading, while the rudder stood up to 98% of its load. All the tests had to be repeated after the components had been strengthened.

By this time a number of production aircraft had already been completed. Fokker had again hoped that they would be rushed to the front without waiting for structural testing. In all of these prematurely constructed aircraft, the centre-section bracing had to be reinforced by the addition of a diagonal strut on each side. The resultant N-struts became a characteristic of succeeding biplane types.

Towards the end of 1916 the fuselage of the Fok. M.20 was tested, complete with a new fin. The structure collapsed at only 68% of the

176

specified minimum tail load; what was worse, it collapsed through buckling of the lower longerons. This was not a local failure in an easily replaced member: it pointed to serious underdimensioning or shoddy material or negligent workmanship—not, as Fokker liked to explain apologetically, "merely a slip during assembly". The *IdFlieg* demanded the use of stronger steel tubing in the fuselage structure and the immediate modification of all the aircraft of the type already built at Schwerin. A considerable part of Fokker's big profits was going down the drain, but he had only himself to blame.

This Fok. D.IV, No. 1640/16, had an improved engine installation with a large spinner.

The structural investigation established beyond doubt that the Fokker works relied on guesswork when designing new aeroplanes, that they did no experimental stressing, and that their products could not be trusted. All this was brought home to Fokker by the responsible officers of the *IdFlieg* who studied the reports.

Fokker went back to Schwerin. He felt defeated, thanks to his weak spot—engineering. However, he had already entrusted Platz with the organization and running of a laboratory for the conduct of strength-testing materials, components and entire aircraft structures—at minimum cost, of course. Fortunately, Platz was good at this sort of thing: he was not only exceptionally skilled and interested, but could be relied upon to spend not a penny more than was absolutely necessary.

What was equally essential was a new and better design. After Kreutzer's death, Fokker tried two new designers, one after the other. Where these "aeronautical experts" had come from and where they went to, nobody knew. They were newcomers to aircraft design and lacked experience. Neither was able to satisfy Fokker; neither completed a single experimental aircraft before being sacked.

Fokker was given an initial order for twenty Fok. D.IV aircraft; this was later increased to thirty. This was disappointing to him, of course, but he later admitted that the flying qualities of the Fok. D.IV had not been so good as those of the Fok. D.III. Nevertheless luck had not completely deserted him: the Albatros D.III fell into disrepute just when the first Fok. D.IV reached the Western Front. This allowed the D.IV to have some initial success in January and February 1917, notably with Jasta 2 (now named the Boelcke Squadron). But by April 1917 the Fok. D.IV had become useless for the Western Front. Very few went to the front, anyway, and of those only four were left by October 1917 to serve somewhere in Russia or Mesopotamia. Altogether thirty-three D.IVs were supplied, the additional three being special versions with wings of longer span and greater area.

The D.IV was the last Fokker type to have side radiators. These were forbidden on new types after November 10, 1916. Wing-mounted radiators were to replace them.

After the Fok. D.IV had been discarded from service on the Western Front, priority for deliveries of the 160-h.p. Mercedes D.IIIa engine was given to the Albatros works and later to the Pfalz concern. This was so, not to discriminate against Fokker, but simply because the Albatros and Pfalz fighters were in great demand for the hard-pressed Western Front, especially in the Somme, Aisne and Flanders areas. Fokker's complaint about delays in the supply of engines was understandable, but was hardly justified from the Service point of view.

To add to Fokker's displeasure, he was directed to build, under licence, 400 A.E.G. C.IV two-seaters that were required for instructional purposes. This happened just at the time when he had no-one to design new types for him, but the contract at least had the virtue of keeping the Schwerin factory occupied. Production of the A.E.G. two-seaters was

One of the three special Fok. D.IVs with long-span wings.

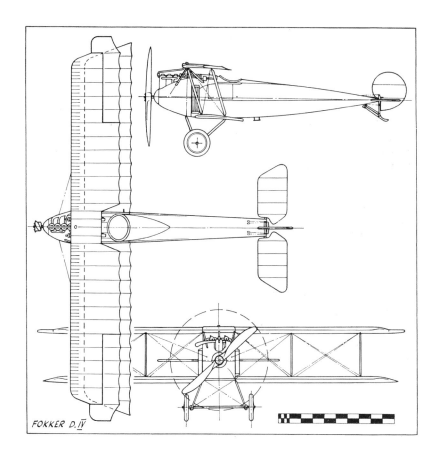

FOKKER D.IV

thought to be particularly appropriate to the Fokker works, for the aircraft had welded steel-tube fuselages; the wings had tubular steel spars but wooden ribs. Moreover, it was hoped that Fokker's organization would profit from the experience of producing a carefully designed aircraft.

Fokker complained bitterly that the A.E.G. C.IV was so immensely complicated that he could not make a penny of profit from the order, large though it was. Hauptmann Dr. Hoff, whom he approached in the matter, advised him to study the soundness of the A.E.G.'s design.

The licence-production at Schwerin was supervised by Dr. Koner, the new expert on production control and materials. The first Fokker-built A.E.G. C.IV (Fok) No. 255/17, was accepted after a flight test at Schwerin on August 1, 1917, and was submitted for a type test on August 25, 1917.

In the autumn of 1916 the Nieuport scout was still one of the most formidable fighters on the Western Front. Forced to accept the fact that he was unable to beat the Albatros by using the same water-cooled engine, Fokker decided to try again with a small, light, rotary-powered

One of the Fokker-built A.E.G. C.IV two-seaters.

fighter more like the Nieuport. The Fok. D.II might serve as some sort of basis for a new type. The Service version of the D.II had grown too big and too slow, and had lost in manoeuvrability. Fokker thought that the original M.17E version was more promising, so the low-fuselage version that had been tried during March 1916 was subjected to a thorough re-design by Platz.

The new design bore the Fokker type number M.21. Its fuselage and engine installation were virtually identical with those of the M.17E, but the width of the fuselage was reduced to 720 mm. The tail design was similar to that of the monoplanes and the Austrian M.17Es. The under-carriage had the double forward legs of the previous Service types, but in the M.21 they were faired together.

In order to improve the pilot's view the upper wing was appreciably further forward than that of the M.17E. To compensate for the change, the upper wing was swept back by 6 degrees. The inverted shovel-blade

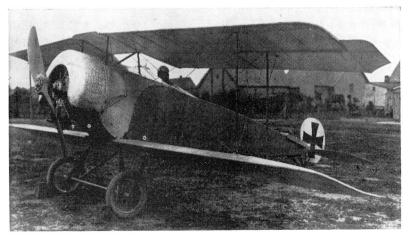
The Fokker M.21.
180

centre-section was retained, and the diagonal member in the centre-section struts connected the lower end of the forward strut and the upper end of the rear strut on each side. Large horn-balanced ailerons were fitted to the upper mainplane only; wing warping had been abandoned for good. The lower wing of the M.21 retained practically the same shape and position as that of the M.17E.

Fokker found the new aircraft highly manoeuvrable, and faster than the D.II with the same engine. He was at this time in the process of acquiring the major holding of the shares of the Oberursel concern and was therefore doubly anxious to make his new venture a commercial

The Fokker M.22, prototype of the Fok. D.V.

success. So much did he like the M.21 that, years later, he praised its ultimate development as the most manoeuvrable biplane he had ever flown. But the speed would have to be improved for Service use.

Platz was therefore given the task of cleaning up the design to make it more presentable for the *IdFlieg*. He focused his attention primarily on the fuselage and engine installation. A close-fitting, full-circular cowling replaced the original horse-shoe cowling, and a large spinner was fitted to the airscrew. This installation reduced drag considerably but left only a narrow annular gap for cooling air; consequently the engine overheated when the aircraft was climbing in hot weather.

The circular engine cowling was carefully faired into the fuselage sides by light formers and stringers that ran to a point just behind the cockpit. The basic fuselage structure remained that of the M.21. The M.22, as the improved design was named, appeared without the fairing over the front legs of its undercarriage, but production aircraft (Fok. D.V) had it.

In fighters of less than 140 h.p. one machine-gun (LMG. 08/15) was regulation equipment. In the M.22, as in its predecessors, the cartridge box was placed inconveniently close to the pilot's knees. It was directly behind the 85-litre (18·7-gal.) gravity tank. This tank now fitted the shape of the fuselage; the earlier cylindrical tanks had been abandoned because of the need to carry more fuel. The M.22 had only this one gravity tank, thus doing away with the need for petrol pumps or pressure feed.

The wings retained the shape, ailerons and aerofoil section of the M.21, but the gap was slightly reduced. The characteristic centre-section was retained, but its diagonal strut ran the opposite way from that of the M.21. In structural details the wings resembled those of preceding Fokker

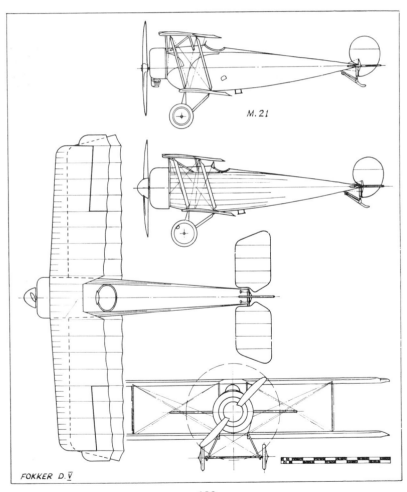

M.21

FOKKER D.V̄

biplanes, having three riblets between each pair of ribs, and wire trailing edges. The spars were spindled out from planks of Polish pine; originally they were much lighter than earlier Fokker spars, but they had to be strengthened. Ailerons, rudder and elevator were welded steel-tube frames.

Late in October 1916 Fokker sent Fok. D.V No. 2710/16 (Factory No. 1068) to Adlershof for official strength tests. Like its predecessors, the D.V failed to pass: the wings collapsed under a sand load equivalent to a factor of 4·0 in Case A; both spars of the starboard upper wing failed in the inner bay. Fokker was frantic but again could blame no-one but himself: Platz had pleaded to be allowed to test the wings to destruction in their new experimental workshop before sending the aircraft to Adlershof, but Fokker would not hear of such waste.

A Fok. D.V airframe.

The Flugzeugmeisterei requested that the wings be strengthened before any further structural tests were carried out. A new pair of upper-wing panels were built quickly and arrived within a week. These wings had modified spars and proved satisfactory under test. Finally, a lighter and more easily made spar was proposed by Platz and was accepted by Adlershof. From this time onwards, tests in Platz's new experimental department at Schwerin greatly reduced the time and resources that the Adlershof laboratories had to spend on Fokker products.

The controls and control surfaces of the Fok. D.V were found to be reasonably satisfactory in strength, although the ribs of the rudder needed stiffening by the insertion of wooden webs. However, the unduly high resilience and friction in both control circuits were again criticized. The Fokker works apparently did not practise the pre-stretching of cables. Large control forces did not matter to Fokker, who flew only short test hops. He did not realize that fighter pilots often made four or more flights per day, each lasting more than an hour and probably entailing combat.

In such conditions, large control forces mattered. The Fokker works were therefore asked to improve their control circuits in future designs. Fokker referred this to Platz.

On October 11, 1916, the Type Test Committee of the *IdFlieg* decided to recommend the Fok. D.V for production as a promising type with very good flying qualities. It was indeed the best Fokker fighter that had been built up to that time. Admittedly, its performance was not spectacular, but nothing better could be expected of the 100-h.p. Oberursel rotary.

E. Ditzuleit states that he never flew an aircraft with better flying qualities; he personally much preferred the Fok. D.V to the later Fok. D.VII and to the captured rotary-powered Sopwith types that he tried out.

A production Fok. D.V.

On Ditzuleit's recommendation the Navy acquired a number of Fok. D.Vs for operational use, but the type proved too sensitive for most naval pilots and there were many crashes. The Fok. D.V had a sharp stall, following which the port wing dropped quickly. It had a very short take-off run, lifted itself off the ground without any movement of the controls, and climbed by itself, without any change in the elevator angle, to settle at a height of 2 km. (6,600 ft.).

The Fok. D.V did not find favour with Army pilots on the Western Front. Manfred von Richthofen rejected it in favour of the new Albatros D.III, which had a better climb and higher ceiling. But the Albatros was much less manoeuvrable than the Fok. D.V. The Fokker might have had a warmer reception if its Oberursel engine had not acquired so much notoriety.

The type saw most of its service with fighter training units, where it became a valuable instructional aircraft; as such it remained in service until the end of the war. All those who could handle it were fit to fly any other sensitive fighter; they also retained pleasant memories of its qualities.

As an instance of the nature of the Fok. D.V, the Richthofen Fighter Wing received two Fok. D.Vs when the Fok. Dr.I triplane was introduced. Flying the D.V, pilots had to prove their ability to handle rotary-powered fighters before they were allowed to fly the triplane.

Deliveries of D.V fighters to the Army appear to have totalled 216, beginning with an order for twenty, placed after completion of the structural tests. The first three were delivered in January 1917; by the end of the following month, twenty-five were operational.

As usual, Fokker had begun to produce the type before it was approved for production; consequently all completed components had to be modified, with considerable waste of time and effort.

A standard Fok. D.V dismantled for transit.

After the second of the two short-lived successors to Kreutzer had hurriedly departed from Schwerin, even Platz could not help being aware of the vacuum that existed within the firm. Somewhat diffidently he suggested to Fokker that he be allowed to try his hand at designing a new aeroplane according to his own ideas. At this time Platz had just completed the basic redesign of the M.17E as the M.21. Fokker jumped at the idea. From then on, for an uninterrupted period of eighteen years, a succession of original and successful designs earned the name of Fokker a world-wide reputation in aeronautical engineering.

Not that life was going to be easy for Platz, for he had had another sample of Fokker's ideas on equipment in the new experimental department for which Fokker had made him responsible. His team consisted of twenty of the best workers, a good foreman, and one draughtsman.

The experimental department's equipment was typically Fokker: that is to say, improvised from scrap, odds and ends, all at minimum expense. Any trained engineer would have insisted on having standard testing machines and the usual facilities found in such laboratories. At Schwerin there were none.

Platz recalls that the principal device for testing anything was an eleven-foot-long steel beam of T-section; this was hinged to a wall of the shed. With this lever device (an invention of Platz's) a load of several tons could be imposed upon experimental components in tension, compression and bending. There were also a couple of gas-welding plants, two drawing boards (one for Platz, one for the draughtsman), and some small tools—drills, vices, clamps and the like. The only equipment actually bought new was purchased on the express order of Fokker—a Yale lock for the door.

While production of the Fok. D.II and D.III was under way, several experimental developments of the M.22 were built by Platz with the object of producing a really useful Service type.

As the illustration shows, the single-bay variant had "D.VI" painted on the fuselage. This may have been done in anticipation of an order that did not materialize; there is no official record of a Fok. D.VI of that design and date (the true Fok. D.VI did not come into being until twelve months later, and looked quite different). It cannot even have been a government-ordered prototype.

In external appearance this so-called D.VI resembled the production Fok. D.V, but the diagonal member in the centre-section struts ran the opposite way from that of the Fok. D.V, and the disposition of the bracing cables was different. These modifications were not requested by the Flugzeugmeisterei, and Platz cannot now recall why they were made.

The development of the Fokker M.22 that had "D.VI" stencilled on the fuselage. This aeroplane was in no way connected with the Fok. D.VI.

186

The experimental machine had no fairings over the front legs of the undercarriage.

At least one other aircraft, virtually identical with the so-called D.VI, existed. This aircraft differed visibly from the other by having more stringers in the fuselage side fairings, differently arranged bracing cables, and faired front legs in its undercarriage.

A two-bay, long-span variant was built, and was variously known as the M.22ZF, streamlined M.17Z, or streamlined Fok. D.II. In effect it was a marriage of a Fok. D.V fuselage and a set of Fok. D.II warping wings. The arrangement of its centre-section struts resembled that of the D.II.

A somewhat similar aircraft had a Siemens bi-rotary engine, in which the cylinders and airscrew revolved in opposite directions. The engine was probably the nine-cylinder Sh. II of 110 h.p. It needed a front bearing, and a spider mounting like that for the 160-h.p. Oberursel was produced.

The cylinders of this engine rotated at only 800 to 900 r.p.m., consequently the cowling arrangements of the Fok. D.V were no longer adequate. As the illustrations show, a smaller airscrew spinner was fitted and the cowling had a number of slots which, with internal guide vanes, provided satisfactory cooling. The slots were so placed that ejected oil could not spray into the cockpit. The slow-running Siemens engine required a large-diameter airscrew; this in turn necessitated a rather tall undercarriage, which consisted of two simple steel-tube vees with single-tube front legs. The structure of the mainplanes differed from that of the M.22ZF in minor details, and the interplane struts were slightly farther inboard.

The Siemens-powered Fokker was armed with two LMG.08/15 guns

This M.22 variant was very similar to the so-called D.VI.

and must therefore have been developed far enough for firing trials to be conducted. A test of a 110-h.p. Siemens aircraft at the Fokker Works is mentioned in official records. The type remained experimental, however, and never had a Service designation or order number. It is unlikely that the aircraft was built as a flying test-bed for the Siemens engine.

The year 1916 had not been an easy one for Fokker. None of his various aircraft experiments had produced a success like that of his first single-seat fighter. He seemed out of the game as far as producing original new aircraft types was concerned; instead he was obliged to build A.E.G. two-seaters for training purposes. This was an unpleasant demotion for Fokker.

In other respects he had less cause for displeasure. He had bigger orders than ever before and had expanded his interests by the end of 1916. He was no longer the owner of only the shabby Schwerin factory and the sheds on Goerries aerodrome, for he had acquired two piano factories (the Perzina Pianoforte Fabrik and the Pianoforte Fabrik Nuetzmann) in which Fokker aircraft components were made; he had also acquired the majority holding of shares in the Oberursel Motoren-Werke and had become a director of the Ungarische Allgemeine Maschinenfabrik A.G. of Budapest, which had a licence for the manufacture of Fokker aircraft.

In addition to becoming an industrialist, Fokker had also become a German national. In his autobiography he claims that he was compulsorily naturalized and registered as a reserve in the German Army. It is unlikely that this was true: Franz Schneider, a Swiss citizen, was in precisely the same position as Fokker, and he stated before witnesses that the German authorities did no more than politely remind aliens in leading positions in the German aircraft industry that applications for naturalization would be favourably considered and the procedure (normally tedious) would be made easy for them. Moreover, such a change in their status would be officially welcomed. Similar invitations are conventional in all countries.

There was never any threat of military service, as Fokker alleges. In his "poetic licence" he overlooked the fact that the Germans had enough to worry about without becoming involved with a neutral and not-too-germanophile Dutch government over a fellow who was most willing to assist the German war effort for cash.

Fokker apparently became a good patriotic German, praising in public the German war effort and the German aircraft industry in particular. German papers quoted him widely when, in a speech, he deprecated Allied attempts to achieve air superiority. He mocked reports supposedly stating that captured Fokker aeroplanes would be copied by the Allies, saying: "We already have better types at the front, and they will not fall into enemy hands so easily." This does not sound like a forcibly naturalized Dutchman trying to escape from the clutches of German militarism.

The shareholders of the Oberursel Motoren-Werke were also treated to a stirring patriotic address by Fokker. They were impressed by Fokker's sincerity and idealistic motives, and this greatly helped Fokker in acquiring the majority holding of Oberursel shares.

Meanwhile, aircraft armament had progressed. Aerial combat was now a daily occurrence, and combat techniques had been developed to the point where uniform training could be given to fighter pilots. Several types of single-seat fighters were in service, but it was obvious that their equipment at least had to be standardized. Two-seaters were now also being armed with a fixed, synchronized machine-gun. All new aero-engines had to be made with a standard drive for synchronizing gears.

The Fokker M.22ZF, streamlined M.17Z, or streamlined Fok. D.II.

The original cam-and-push-rod control, which had proved to be somewhat temperamental, had been replaced by a new and ingenious development evolved by Luebbe. This *Zentralsteuerung* (central control), as it was called, had flexible drive shafts in place of the push-rods of the *Stangensteuerung*. The new device became regulation equipment. Post-war attempts in the U.S.A. to copy this simple and reliable synchronizing gear failed.

The higher-powered single-seaters that were coming into service had two-gun armament, all with the LMG.08/15 gun and the *Zentralsteuerung*. From 1917, optical sights were added. Many German pilots seized their opportunity, when it presented itself, of replacing the regulation optical sights with captured British Aldis sights, which gave a wide-angle view.

In general, individual installations or adaptations to suit the personal tastes of pilots were discouraged. But when a fighter pilot attained the stature of Manfred von Richthofen he could indulge his personal fancies. Von Richthofen did not think the press-button on the control column was the best or most natural device for firing an aircraft's guns. He was a

The M.22ZF variant that had the 110-h.p. Siemens–Halske Sh.II engine.

keen game hunter, and wanted a trigger as similar as possible to a rifle's trigger. Fokker agreed with alacrity to provide such a device.

The trigger itself was designed, with great attention to detail, by an engineer of No. 13 Bauaufsicht. Fokker was able to cash in on the magic of the name of von Richthofen, for he supplied firing grips of the special type in large quantities: all aircraft, even those that Manfred von Richthofen was unlikely to fly, were modified to have the new gadget.

The standard weights of fighter armament were now:

Two LMG.08/15	22·0 kg. (48·5 lb.)
Synchronizing gear complete	5·5 kg. (12·0 lb.)
Ammunition boxes complete	4·0 kg. (9·0 lb.)
Optical sight with mounting	2·5 kg. (5·5 lb.)
Two veeder counters for rounds fired	1·0 kg. (2·2 lb.)
Total belts with 500 rounds each	25·0 kg. (55·0 lb.)
Total armament	60·0 kg. (132·2 lb.)

Until the early months of 1916, Fokker had an absolute monopoly in the supply of armament for fixed-gun installations. The Fokker works alone modified standard guns for aircraft installations and supplied the various adaptors for fitting to aero-engines. Other aircraft manufacturers were obliged to buy these things from Fokker, and Fokker mechanics went to all aircraft factories to supervise armament installations.

The appearance of the Albatros D.I and D.II was the more disagreeable for Fokker because they were fitted with another proprietary type of synchronizing gear, the Albatros–Hetzke design. Other synchronizing mechanisms were in the offing, among them two electric ones; even the Siemens firm made an attempt to break Fokker's monopoly in this field. Fokker's own production of armament at Schwerin was slow and deliveries erratic. He may have thought it was a good thing to delay the fighter output of his competitors.

But the authorities thought otherwise. They could brook no delays in the deliveries of aircraft, and a serious attempt was made to break the Fokker monopoly: arrangements were openly made by the Army to convert a gramophone factory near Berlin for the quantity production of synchronizing gears. Fokker was officially informed, and had to give in.

The authorities now demanded that Fokker should make his armament manufacture completely separate from his aircraft production, and that it should cease to be under his own direct control. He must establish a new and independent firm near Berlin. Credits would be granted and Fokker could remain the sole owner; but the new firm, the Flugzeug-Waffen-Fabrik G.m.b.H. at Reinickendorf near Berlin, must guarantee through Fokker that all armament ordered from them would be produced without delay and for all aircraft firms without preference or distinction. There must be no further rationing of aircraft armament. Fokker promised to comply with these stipulations. In his autobiography he relates this as his "great victory" over the corruption and machinations of the Army.

H. Luebbe, in whom the military authorities had complete confidence, was installed as the responsible head of the weapons firm, untrammelled by any interference from Fokker. The new factory produced monthly 300 complete synchronizing gears of the improved *Zentralsteuerung* type. With supplies of this size assured there was no need for a Government-run factory. The Flugzeug-Waffen-Fabrik started work in December 1916—just in time to cope with the enlarged programme of the *Kogenluft*.

This was one of those cases in which Fokker discovered that two could play at the same game, and that the Army meant business. Nevertheless, by giving in he had saved a profitable monopoly: apart from the fixed licence fee of 1,000 marks (£50) for each aircraft fitted with the Fokker synchronizing gear, the profits from the production of the gear itself and from all adaptation work were enormous. Fokker retained his monopoly until the war ended. And further weapon developments by Leimberger and Luebbe were still to come.

CHAPTER X

THE BEGINNING OF THE PLATZ ERA

REINHOLD PLATZ, the welder, was born on January 16, 1886, at Cottbus, in the province of Brandenburg, not far from Berlin. He possessed the quiet, matter-of-fact mentality of the Berliner, with a sense of reality and an awareness of his own limitations. Yet he could not have known the weight of odds against him when he assumed responsibility for the design and development of modern fighter aeroplanes at a time when the amateur designer had virtually ceased to exist and the academically trained specialist in aeronautical engineering had taken his place.

If Platz had known the scope of the design offices and experimental departments of Fokker's competitors—such as, for instance, those of the Albatros works—and had met the experts working in them, he might well have abandoned any thought of playing David against these Goliaths. But Platz could not know, for he had spent all his time since 1913 with Fokker at Schwerin. And yet, had he known, he might not have cared much; he had the Berliner's reaction towards things put up to make one afraid: "Bange mache, gilt nicht!"

At this time Platz had little grounding in aircraft design, although he had gained some experience in his work with Kreutzer and in the development of the Fok. D.V from the basis of Kreutzer designs. Platz was an expert craftsman and had learned to be a production engineer; he had acquired the ability economically to organize batch production under adverse conditions. But he had no training in design engineering. The elements of statics were beyond his ken. He had no knowledge of design stressing: as he has pointed out, even the basic Euler formulae for struts remained unknown to him years after he had designed the most advanced aeroplanes. Of aerodynamics his knowledge was at best elementary, even for those days: he had never heard of Eiffel's work. Goettingen was, for him, a pleasant little town near the Harz; the investigations of the aerodynamics school there were mysteries to him until long after the war. He knew nothing about wind tunnels. Fokker believed only in free-flight testing, not in the "nonsense" of scientists, whom he disliked and distrusted as much as qualified engineers. Text-books counted for nothing with Fokker: they did not fly.

However, Platz had two valuable qualities often conspicuously lacking in qualified engineers: vision, and a flair for design. Moreover, he paid attention to details, and had an insatiable curiosity for learning more about the problems he was dealing with and for finding the answers to these problems by experiment. Like Fokker, he firmly believed in simplifying the flying machine as much as possible. But whereas Fokker's belief arose from technical ignorance and the fact that simple aeroplanes were more likely to pay greater profits, Platz preferred simplicity because his experience had taught him that the simplest mechanism was always the safest and often enough the most efficient.

Platz proved to be a born engineering designer, something rather different from a trained one: he was creative by instinct, not by methods taught at a college. He possessed an extraordinary "feel" for the stresses in a structure, which was born of careful observation and ample workshop experience. It was a natural asset in design stressing, which he had to develop on his own because of his engineering ignorance. He had to develop his own methods for dimensioning vital structural members in airframes. These methods were based on systematic strength experiments; though primitive, they were effective.

The methods evolved and used by Platz were not only original but—as flying experience and later investigations by expert stress analysts showed —highly reliable. At a later period, remarkable proof of the accuracy of Platz's methods came to light. He had beaten the stressmen without knowing any basic theory and without knowledge of the relevant mathematics. It was as if a man of exceptional eyesight and a logical mind had discovered the life of microbes, without a microscope.

When Platz took over design work at the Fokker Works, he had new ideas. Kreutzer's Morane-cum-Halberstadt configuration had obviously come to the end of its usefulness, and Platz gathered from Fokker that something considerably better was wanted. To him, this was a challenge to develop a really simple aeroplane. All that he had seen and done before seemed far too complicated, with so many struts and bracings, requiring much rigging and adjustment. Platz was convinced that it should be possible to make more rigid components of integral construction. Experiments had shown that it could be done without undue weight.

There was one extraordinary aspect of the conditions under which Platz had to work at Schwerin; it obliged him to grope his way towards better designs single-handed. For some incomprehensible reason, Fokker never passed on to his designer any of the engineering documents or technical information that should have reached him. Platz was never allowed to see any official design guides, specifications, test reports, type-test memoranda, or any vital information of that kind that was specifically intended for designers. Fokker would never allow him to be present at any official type test, although the *IdFlieg* desired designers to attend the discussions on their products. Fokker did not even tell Platz the results of type tests or strength examinations. There can be no doubt that Fokker wanted to shine as the designer of the aircraft bearing his name, and was afraid that the man who did the actual work might learn too much and might himself become known.

This attitude of Fokker's made Platz bitter when he learned later that he had been denied so much that was essential for his work. Various engineering departments of the German Flying Corps were continually issuing secret technical information for the guidance of designers of Army aircraft, making known the requirements and views of the Army Flying Corps and passing on experience. The *Technische Berichte* of the Flugzeug-meisterei was a valuable secret periodical. The *Technische Mappe* contained detailed information on German and Allied Service aircraft, with engineering details, weapon installations, undercarriage development, details of new engines, type-test records, and so on. Another series of volumes contained comprehensive instructions for stress analysis of airframes; this was compiled by the foremost German authorities on aircraft statics, and was finally issued in the condensed form of reference sheets for easy use without recourse to advanced mathematics. All this was kept from Platz; nor was it read or digested by Fokker himself, who never liked literature, aeronautical or otherwise.

Apart from these, there was the *Bau und Liefer-Vorschriften für Heeresflugzeuge*, or BLV, the German designer's bible. Platz was unaware of its existence, and remained so throughout the war. He was amazed to come across the various editions in mint condition when he cleared out the safe of the Fokker firm's commercial manager Burgsdorf after the war. He had designed all Fokker aircraft since 1916 without being aware of the basic requirements governing their design.

It could be argued, of course, that Burgsdorf might have thought it his patriotic duty to withhold these secret documents even from Fokker: after all, Fokker was, or had been, an alien, and the documents contained a warning of the penalties awaiting anyone who disclosed their contents to unreliable people such as aliens. Platz is convinced, however—and former engineering officers of the German Flying Corps concur—that the commercial manager withheld the documents at Fokker's express behest.

That Fokker was allowed to get away with this till the end of the war is the fault not least of the Bauaufsicht at Schwerin and possibly of the engineering departments at Adlershof. Roland Betsch, the permanent technical officer of the Bauaufsicht, for instance, knew Platz well and knew that he designed the Fokker aircraft. He must have deduced from Platz's various queries that Platz was completely in the dark about basic technical information and the contents of test reports on his aircraft, all of which ought to have reached him. One would have thought it Betsch's duty, as the officer responsible for technical liaison between the *IdFlieg* and the firm, to report Fokker's odd practices to his superiors and to propose appropriate action for dealing with a situation that was detrimental to the war effort and must have hampered him in effectively discharging his duties. But he appears not to have done so.

The engineering specialists seem to have suspected at an early stage that Fokker's engineering knowledge could not be extensive; it would have been logical for them to wonder who was designing his aeroplanes. One would have thought that it was their duty to track down this mysterious designer and contact him, instead of listening to Fokker's silly replies to technical questions. Although they were, as G. Madelung assures us, much annoyed by the flippant and evasive answers that they got from Fokker, none of them demanded that the designer of the aeroplanes should be present during the type tests and sand-loading experiments.[1]

Yet there was one occasion when the Adlershof engineers met the Fokker designer in the flesh. A few questions might have established his identity, but all that these enlightened people did was to take no notice of his presence and to misspell his name. This was late in the war, when Fokker was threatened with criminal proceedings and needed a scapegoat; he then saw fit to take Platz along. It was Platz's only visit to Adlershof during the entire war. (See p. 331.)

Platz himself hungered for technical information: there could be no doubt about that, and Fokker must have known. Platz would have been glad to see, for instance, any specimen stressing for an aeroplane. He would also have liked to know precisely what those Army authorities wanted. The officers of the Bauaufsicht whom he approached could give him only scanty information; they do not seem to have been very interested. All he could wheedle out of Roland Betsch were the load factors that airframe structures were expected to have. Platz was also anxious to know how his designs fared during their structural testing and in the official type tests, but Fokker evaded all these matters and merely exhorted Platz to carry on and do better.

In spite of all this, the collaboration between Platz and Fokker was otherwise good. Platz had never flown, and he had a great respect for those who not only flew but assessed the qualities of aeroplanes by throwing them about in the air as Fokker did; consequently Platz approached his work with humility and an awareness of his own limitations. The more he progressed in aircraft design, the more modest he became. He never claimed to know best, never thumped the table, rarely objected or contradicted. Fokker's suggestions were always carefully considered and put into effect even when Platz did not agree with them. It was better to let the boss come a cropper with absurd ideas than to tell him he was wrong.

---

[1] A typical example of the apparent elusiveness of the designer of Fokker aircraft is the official account of the Type Test of the Fok. Dr. I triplane on November 10, 1917, a copy of which is in the author's possession. This report names Dr. Ing. Koner as the representative of the Fokker works attending the discussions.

Koner was not an aeronautical engineer and had no part in the design or development of any aircraft type; in particular he had nothing at all to do with the Fok. Dr. I. He was employed as a specialist on materials and production control, and as such had no obvious place at a Type Test conference, where the discussion was about the good and bad points of a prototype aeroplane design, not the materials used to build it. During such discussions, Service experts argued design modifications with the firm's representative, further lines of development were suggested, and so on; the presence of the designer was clearly important.

Fokker liked Platz's humility and compliant nature and exploited them; the circumstances suited him perfectly. So Platz the self-taught designer and Fokker the first-rate experimental pilot complemented each other surprisingly well.

Experimental and developmental flying demands two main qualities of the pilot: first, he must know how to handle aircraft and have well-developed senses to note his experiences and interpret them correctly; secondly, his interpretations should suggest and facilitate remedial conclusions or improvements in the engineering domain. The latter quality is a matter of patience as well as of adequate engineering knowledge; it implies trying and trying again, making modifications until the optimum handling qualities for the aircraft in question are attained.

Fokker unquestionably satisfied the first of these requirements. He was able to fly any aeroplane safely, even when its flying qualities were poor; and he had an exceptionally fine feeling for the behaviour of an aircraft. He could also interpret his sensations correctly. But until his closer co-operation with Platz he completely lacked the patience and engineering knowledge to report his findings constructively and to undertake methodical development. In many cases when he found that a new type was "bad" he simply abandoned it. This is not the way of an experimental pilot or of an aircraft designer. Most aircraft had deficiencies of one kind or another when they were first flown; they had to be developed by patient test flying and modification. This is what Fokker now came to appreciate more and more from observing the tidy and methodical way in which Platz approached the task of designing advanced aeroplanes embodying completely new features.

From this collaboration arose Fokker the superb experimental pilot. Several examples of his achievements in this sphere occur in the pages that follow; but they were many, and most of his feats in developing new types are forgotten today. A typical example was his quick conversion of a potentially dangerous aeroplane into the Fok. D.VII, making it one of the most satisfactory aeroplanes ever flown; so much so that systematic investigation and experiments conducted at a later stage and by other pilots failed to reveal the need for further modifications.

It is a matter for reflection what the consequences for aeronautics might have been if Platz had received all the technical information that the other German designers got, and had had the advantage of the advice and suggestions given verbally to technicians in the industry when they attended the Adlershof centre. Platz himself feels it would have eased his work considerably: he would have produced his new types more quickly and more efficiently. This might have been so, but it could equally well be argued that the technical isolation in which he worked drove him to original solutions that might not have occurred to him if he had had a store of technical information available to him.

It is important to note how little thought the technical departments of the *IdFlieg* must have given to the question of maintaining direct personal contact with the design engineers of major aircraft firms. If they had had an effective liaison it could not have happened that the man who directed the technical design and development of an important aircraft firm remained unknown to them.

The new aircraft designed by Platz was to be *verspannungslos*; that is to say, it had no external bracing system of struts and cables. Hence it was named the V type; and, as the first such design, its full designation was V.1. During the war and the year or so that followed the Armistice, Platz designed forty-five V aircraft. Not all of them were *verspannungslos*, however, and the V came to signify *Versuchsflugzeug*—experimental aeroplane. Not all of the forty-five designs reached the flying stage: some were abandoned during construction or at the drawing-board stage, having been superseded by more promising ideas.

A number of the V series participated in the official comparative trials (*Vergleichsfliegen*) at Adlershof, but only a few went into production as Service types.

All the V types designed during the war were intended for use by the Army, and most of them were single-seat fighters. None was expressly designed for the Navy or for Austria.

The V.1 biplane was completed for flight five weeks after Platz had become chief designer. This was quick work. Fokker liked quick results; Platz liked to work fast, and he and his men had worked like demons. Fokker claims to have done "everything", but it seems that he spent less time in Schwerin than in Berlin, bewailing the A.E.G. contract and trying to get more profitable orders.

Platz had been told that previous Fokker fighters had not been fast enough. He was convinced that performance depended greatly on clean design, and that a good aeroplane should, and could, be clean as well as simple. He was also convinced of the feasibility of making cantilever wings, and Fokker favoured the idea. Platz had been told that only biplanes were wanted, so the V.1 embodied his ideas as well as any biplane could.

Fokker V.1.

197

The V.1 had full-cantilever wings: it had no interplane struts. Each wing was an integral structure consisting of wooden box spars and wooden ribs, covered entirely with plywood. To obtain the necessary strength, Platz used an aerofoil section of unusual thickness: it was 20% of the chord at a time when the customary thickness was about 5% or 6%. A wing of such thickness was a revolutionary development at Schwerin. Platz was not aware, at that time, that aircraft with similar wings had already been flown elsewhere. Fokker knew, but seems not to have told him.

The Fokker V.1. Two LMG.08/15 machine-guns were fitted at this stage, but were later removed.

The box spars of the wings were unusual features. They were, of course, deep and fairly wide, to resist bending and shear loads. The top and bottom members (flanges) of each spar were laminated from several laths of pine, each 0·4 in. thick; this arrangement made it simple to vary the thickness of the flanges along the span in proportion to the local stress. The upper and lower flanges of each spar were joined by webs of plywood. These webs had the outer grain of the three-ply running normal to the spar axis.

These features were new for the Fokker firm. Previously, wing spars had always been spindled out of rectangular lengths of wood and planed down to fit the slots in the wing ribs. The skinning of the V.1 wings with plywood instead of the more conventional fabric had previously been unheard of at the Fokker works.

Little use had been made of plywood in the past. Platz introduced it to an ever-increasing extent, although he came from the metal-working side and had originally had little to do with the production of wooden

198

wings before he came to be Kreutzer's right-hand man in the design department. Platz found in plywood a highly suitable and adaptable material that was available in fair quantities in Germany during the war. Thin birch three-ply was at times much easier to get than good linen and dope for conventional covering. Towards the end of the war, all fabric and dopes became poor-quality ersatz, and scarce at that.

Ply-covered wings had the further advantage of requiring no internal drag bracing between the spars. Such wings had good torsional strength and rigidity, as Platz's strength tests proved conclusively. All struts, wires, turnbuckles and fittings could be dispensed with; inside the wings, the only necessary fittings were at the wing-attachment pick-up points; in the upper wing, those for the aileron bearings and controls had to be added.

In the lower wing, the spars converged to meet at the wing tip, forming a triangular structure. There was a reason for this. Fokker had got wind

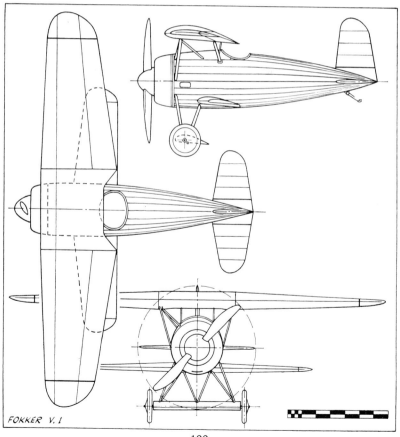

FOKKER V. 1

of the L.V.G. D.10 project, designed by W. Rethel and P. G. Ehrhardt: this was a biplane with a retractable undercarriage in which a triangular disposition of the lower-wing spars was adopted in order to provide a convenient housing for the retracted wheels. Fokker suggested that the V.1 should also have a retractable undercarriage, consequently its wing spars were disposed in similar fashion to those of the L.V.G. D.10. The retractable undercarriage was not developed, however, and Platz dropped the complication of triangulated spars as soon as he could. In the V.1 upper wing, as in those of all subsequent Platz designs, the spars were parallel.

The design of the control surfaces was unorthodox. Instead of the conventional trailing-edge ailerons, the tip portions of the upper wing rotated. Blériot had employed this method on his *Libellule* nine years earlier. In 1926, G. T. R. Hill was to demonstrate, with his Pterodactyl aircraft, that rotating wing tips provided better control at high angles of attack than conventional ailerons.

The rudder and elevators of the Fokker V.1 were similarly designed as movable extensions of the fin and tailplane. All control surfaces were aerodynamically balanced.

The unusual control surfaces seem to have proved satisfactory in flight. Fokker found no reason for changing them, though representatives of the Air Corps may have been less convinced. Service pilots in general were never enthusiastic about radical innovations, and it is still doubtful whether anyone but Fokker (and perhaps de Waal) ever tried the V.1 or the V.2. Fokker's account is silent upon this point; Platz does not know; and no officer still living can remember seeing more than photographs of the two aircraft.

However, the new control arrangement not only led to greater simplicity in the design, but also ensured that the control surfaces were unaffected by the airflow over wing, tailplane or fin. They should therefore have been effective even at the stall.

The experimental Junkers J.7 single-seat fighter of October 1917 had lateral controls similar to those of the Fokker V.1. The suggestion may have come from Fokker.

Another feature of the V.1 that was unusual for that period was the burying of all control-actuating members inside the wing or fuselage. No control horns or cables protruded into the airflow: Platz had achieved his clean aeroplane.

The upper wing, about 10·7 sq. m. (116 sq. ft.) in area, had slight taper without effective sweep-back. An odd problem arose for Platz, who had devised a new type of aerofoil section: what should its correct angle of incidence be? As he had no wind-tunnel facilities he lacked guidance in this problem. On Fokker's advice, it was decided to find out by experiment with the V.1 itself. For this purpose the incidence of the upper wing was made adjustable in flight: a crank in the cockpit actuated a lever that raised or lowered the attachment of the main spar.

Fokker made the test in his accomplished manner. He found that the aircraft flew best when the angle between the flat undersurface and the direction of flight was zero. This meant that the geometric incidence of the mean camber line was 3° 50′. The subsequent V types were designed in the light of the knowledge thus gained.

The lower wing, about 3 sq. m. (32 sq. ft.) in area, had more pronounced taper, with a swept-back leading edge and a straight trailing edge; its convergent spars have already been described. Platz disliked taper: constant-chord wings were much simpler to build. He asserted his views more firmly in the V.3 and in all subsequent biplanes and triplanes; sweep, taper and dihedral were avoided, with a few exceptions expressly demanded by Fokker. In monoplanes taper could not be avoided without incurring a heavy structure-weight penalty.

The basic fuselage structure differed little from that of earlier Fokker aeroplanes. This was understandable: Platz had contributed substantially to the development of Fokker fuselages and there was no need for a drastic change. The basic structure was faired out to a good streamline shape by means of wooden hoops and stringers, much as on the Fok. D.V; the whole was covered with fabric.

The pilot sat rather low in the fuselage. His field of vision was not particularly good: the downward view was restricted by the fairing of the fuselage and the lower wing; upwards and forwards the great thickness of the upper wing obscured a considerable area.

The engine installation and fuel system were also reminiscent of the Fok. D.V. The engine—chosen by Fokker, as the new owner of the Oberursel concern—was the 100-h.p. Oberursel. Platz cannot recall why this rather inefficient engine was chosen; he thinks it may simply be that it happened to be available. Whatever the reason, the choice was not a wise one: it prejudiced any chance of the V.1 being adopted for the Service. The engine was closely cowled and a large spinner was fitted to the airscrew. The V.1 was flown with various spinners, and with none at all, in attempts to achieve optimum performance and engine cooling.

The Fokker V.1 being flown without a spinner.

201

The undercarriage axle and spreader bars were faired over by a wing-like structure, which had the same aerofoil section as the mainplanes.

Air-speed indicators were not usually fitted to German aircraft at the time when the V.1 appeared. Fokker had one installed on the experimental machine; doubtless his primary object was to check the V.1's performance, but he may have felt it to be a necessity in view of the absence of the whistling of the airstream through the rigging of a wire-braced aircraft. The V.1 originally had a cup-type anemometer mounted above the lower starboard wing but this was subsequently replaced by a more suitable pressure-tube instrument. The pressure head was carried on a light pylon above the upper wing, to port and clear of the slipstream.

Tony Fokker was very pleased with the V.1. Unfortunately, however, it failed to meet the official requirements for fighter aircraft and was apparently turned down without even a type test or a structural test. There is no record of the V.1 nor its successor, the V.2, in the official files. No former member of the *IdFlieg* now alive can recall these two aircraft, nor can anyone remember anything about the mysterious "commission" which, according to Fokker's book, appeared at Schwerin to admire the aircraft but turned it down flatly. Platz knows nothing more than that the first two aircraft of his design were not accepted. But neither the official records nor anyone of the *IdFlieg* circle can tell us anything about such a visit, and one wonders whether the official visitors of whom Fokker wrote so bitterly may not have been from the *IdFlieg* at all: they may have been merely officers from operational units whom Fokker wished to impress before submitting the V.1 to Adlershof. That this may be the explanation is suggested by the events during the introduction of the Fokker triplane.

Fokker implies that the V.1 was too far advanced for those whom he had asked to come and inspect it, that it was too unconventional for the military, and that the technical experts were biased against him.

These accusations sound hollow. Those levelled against the engineering specialists of the *IdFlieg* are particularly unreal. These men had seen many novel designs from other firms and had already shown deep interest in the possibilities of cantilever wings and similar advanced ideas. Had they been present at Fokker's demonstration of the V.1 they would not have rejected it out of hand merely because it was unconventional: they would have investigated it thoroughly and determined its strength by structural testing.

All this makes it the more likely that the visitors were officers from the front, and that they realized the new aeroplane would be of no use for operational purposes, and told Fokker so.

Platz was left to guess why and by whom the V.1 and V.2 were rejected. He was not inquisitive about such things, and he knew that Fokker would not tell even when pressed. For Platz it was enough to know that something better had to be created.

One is consequently left to surmise why such a progressive aircraft was rejected. Two obvious deficiencies have already been mentioned: the unfortunate choice of engine and the limited field of view. It is likely that the V.1 had proved to be rather heavy, and that its rate of climb was consequently poor. Platz had taken great care to ensure adequate structural strength; such safety in his first cantilever venture entailed additional weight. The plywood-skinned wings were heavier than fabric-covered surfaces; the formers and stringers of the fuselage added weight.

The fuselage at least survived until the summer of 1918, when Fokker used it to demonstrate the safety of his undercarriage fuel tank when leaking or set on fire in combat. Even these incendiary efforts of Fokker's did not put an end to Platz's revolutionary effort, however.

The Fokker V.2 in its original form, with low-set upper wing and rudder like that of the V.1.

The Fokker V.2

Fokker had pursued the policy of parallel development of experimental prototypes, one with a rotary engine, the other with a water-cooled engine. This may account for the construction of the V.2, which had a 120-h.p. Mercedes engine.

It is not clear why Fokker chose an engine that was operationally obsolete. Platz believes that availability alone decided Fokker's choice of engines for experimental aircraft. (But surely Fokker would not have hesitated to "borrow" one of the 160-h.p. Mercedes allotted for Fok. D.IVs for a period long enough to cover the testing and demonstration of the new prototype?)

The modified V.2 with raised upper wing and revised fin and rudder.

In general appearance and design features, the V.2 resembled the V.1. It was slightly larger: the total wing area was about 19 sq. m. (205 sq. ft.), or some 4 sq. m. more than that of the V.1. The additional wing area was provided because the Mercedes was heavier than the Oberursel, and Platz believed in having the same wing loading in his parallel prototypes.

The V.2 underwent more extensive modification than its predecessor. At first the upper wing was fairly close to the fuselage, and the field of view forward cannot have been good. The wing was later raised higher above the fuselage; a clumsy radiator was let into the leading edge, where it interfered with the airflow over the wing. The view from the cockpit was still poor, and on the whole the V.2 was less impressive than the V.1.

These two cantilever biplanes had one feature that was to characterize all later biplanes and parasol monoplanes designed by Platz: the structure supporting the upper wing incorporated two splayed-out tripods of steel tubing that were attached to the front spar.

In later Platz designs, maximum weight-saving and simplification were aimed at. The fairing of the fuselage was abandoned; conventional hinged control surfaces were used; wings were covered with fabric, except on monoplanes where the need for torsional stiffness required a plywood skin.

Although the V.1 and V.2 did not go into production they represented a great step forward in general design. It is therefore worthwhile to examine the origins of the new ideas at Schwerin, and to discuss whether they were derived from information about contemporary work of other designers that might have come into the possession of Fokker or Platz.

The idea of the cantilever wing was not new. In its essence, it had existed since 1911, when Léon Levavasseur had built his Monobloc

Antoinette monoplane. Nor was plywood construction an innovation: apart from the early efforts of Béchereau, Koolhoven and Santoni of the Deperdussin firm, and of the Royal Aircraft Factory at Farnborough, the use of plywood had been thoroughly developed in Germany by Grohmann, Heinkel and Hirth, all of the Albatros firm at that time. Fokker may have known all this, but it is doubtful whether Platz knew anything about these classic developments.

Another possible source of influence on Platz might have been the work of Professor Junkers and his staff at Dessau. The first Junkers monoplane was the Ju. J.1, designed by Reuter and Mader. It was a cantilever mid-wing monoplane, and flew for the first time on December 12, 1915—one

The Junkers J.I, a cantilever monoplane of 1915.

year before the Fokker V.1 flew. The J.I wing had a steel-tube structure over which a skin of welded iron sheet was placed. With its 120-h.p. Mercedes it weighed no less than 1,100 kg. (2,200 lb.) empty. Its operational use was therefore out of the question, though with its speed of 170 km./hr. (105 m.p.h.) it was faster than contemporary German aircraft.

Fokker, sensing something to be gained, managed to wangle a flight on this "Tin Donkey". He was impressed, and judged it to be at least 20 km./hr. (12 m.p.h.) faster than any existing aeroplane. Platz is emphatic that Fokker told him nothing about the Junkers design. Platz himself had no contact with the Junkers designers; he did not see a Junkers aeroplane until July 1918, when he made his only wartime visit to Adlershof; he then probably saw the Ju. D.I low-wing monoplane. There is therefore no doubt that Junkers designs did not influence Platz in the evolution of his cantilever aeroplanes. This is confirmed by comparison of the basic aerofoil sections adopted by Platz and Junkers, apart from the differing features of their respective aircraft.

Platz is also certain that Fokker never showed him any photographs of Junkers aircraft or any others of the kind—and Fokker must have acquired plenty of them. But it can be safely assumed that Fokker would want his designer to incorporate features that he had seen in the products of other firms.

However, even if it is assumed that Fokker suggested the idea of canti-lever wings, Platz still had to evolve his own structure because he had no knowledge of Junkers research. Fokker was certainly not enough of an engineer to understand the laboratory research work at Dessau, even if he had seen it. Moreover, the construction of the Junkers wing was more complicated than Platz or Fokker would have tolerated.

Apart from the basic differences between the Junkers J.I and the Fokker V.1 and V.2, there was an amusing difference between the end products of the two approaches to design. Junkers' scientific methods and painstaking attention to details resulted in a wing covered with wrinkles across the airflow: Platz, self-taught and lacking all scientific research facilities, achieved a wing with a smooth surface in which the aerofoil section was carefully preserved throughout the span.

Example of Junkers construction.

A more sensible example that Platz and Fokker might have followed was the National Flugzeug-Werke (N.F.W.) monoplane designed by F. D. Hergt in collaboration with Professor Oesterlen of the Technical University of Hanover. The National Flugzeug-Werke were formerly the Jeannin aircraft works, mentioned in an earlier chapter. Under the management of H. Heinrichs they began to develop a monoplane with a cantilever wing. The first experimental machine, powered by a rotary engine, flew on April 15, 1916, at Adlershof. The wing had a plywood skin and two spars, which were carried through the fuselage. This avoided the principal fault of the Junkers design, in which the wing bending and torsion loads were diffused into the fuselage structure without regard to

The N.F.W. cantilever monoplane of 1916.

transfer. At a later stage a second N.F.W. monoplane flew with a 120-h.p. water-cooled engine.

The gallant attempt of the N.F.W. came to nothing. Nevertheless, the design might have been of great interest to Platz. However, he had never heard of these experimental monoplanes until recently, when he was shown the author's file.

Both the Junkers and the N.F.W. monoplanes had aroused the keen interest of the *IdFlieg*. The technicians at Adlershof did their best to help the development of these progressive designs towards the stage of operational usefuless. This is an adequate commentary on Fokker's lamentations that the V.1 had been rejected merely because it was so advanced and because cantilever wings were neither wanted nor trusted.

Platz would be the last to deny that, at that time, he had no more than a vague idea of the behaviour of an airflow over wings and fuselages. He had seen no wind-tunnel experiments and was unaware of how they could help in design; he knew nothing of Kutta, Eiffel, Prandtl, Betz, or any other aerodynamicist or hydrodynamicist. Not till long after the war did the Fokker Works authorize a single experiment at Goettingen: all wartime tests of Fokker aerofoils were made at the behest of the *IdFlieg*; Fokker would never have "wasted" a penny on any kind of scientific investigation.

Platz had no strong views on the shape of aerofoils, but was convinced that their drag must be kept acceptably low. This meant something approximating to a streamline form. He knew that a pure streamline section would not do: it had to be slightly altered: it was as simple as that.

He therefore reasoned that what he had to do was to develop a form of beam that was light, of small depth, yet strong enough for use as a spar in a cantilever wing. A two-spar system was practical and simple. The wing area was determined by dividing the estimated all-up weight by the desired wing loading; the chord was found by dividing the wing area by the span permitted by the structure. Having determined the chord and the depth of the spars, all that remained to be done was to enclose the spars in an aerofoil of modified streamline contour.

This contour was drawn by eye. For ease of production—always in the front of Platz's mind—the undersurface between the spars was kept straight. Converting the straight centre-line of a true streamline into a parabolic curve gave the mean camber line. Platz felt that such an aerofoil should cause little drag even when its depth was as great as 20% of its chord. For later designs the nose form of the aerofoil was slightly modified and, still working by eye, the shape was improved to give a more gradual transition to the flat undersurface. Thinner wings with a thickness/chord ratio of less than 20% were made for biplanes and triplanes, but the basic shape remained unaltered.

For Platz a cantilever wing was simply a compromise between the weight of the structure that was required to resist given bending loads, and acceptable wing thickness. Aerodynamic considerations did not come into his design philosophy. By this plain, practical approach, Platz arrived at an efficient, thick wing section without the painstaking researches of Junkers, Mader, von Doepp and their staff, and unaware of the wrangling of all other aerodynamicists in Germany, Britain and France, over the qualities of thick aerofoils.

All subsequent Fokker aeroplanes, large or small, had wings with aerofoil sections of this standard shape. Even fifteen years later, aerodynamicists could find no reason to modify the Platz sections; in fact they were widely copied and embodied in many successful aircraft all over the world.

Platz did not learn until much later that independent research had proved that thick aerofoils with a large nose radius gave higher lift and a less abrupt stall than the contemporary sections with heavy camber and a 4% to 6% thickness/chord ratio. Such aircraft as the Nieuport, Spad, Albatros, Pfalz and Roland biplane fighters had such wings: thin, heavily cambered, and with pointed noses, they frequently produced abrupt stalls and a proneness to spin.

Platz's aerofoil not only fortuitously avoided this drawback, but also gave all Fokker aeroplanes remarkable flying qualities, for as a rule they were easy and pleasant to fly. The Fok. D.VII was admired by its pilots and opponents alike for its tractability. Ten years later, when Fokker demonstrated Platz's transport monoplane in England and proved that it did not spin even when stalled, the experts were baffled.[1]

In the U.S.A., Bill Stout's men and other rival manufacturers took great pains to "lift" the wing sections from Fokker's demonstration monoplane during nocturnal examinations of the aircraft, by sliding copper-wire loops over the wing to obtain a profile. Thus Fokker was treated to a dose of his own medicine.

Platz and Fokker also learned that taper, although aerodynamically

[1] *See*, e.g., Reports & Memoranda No. 1096 of April 1927.

desirable in a wing, could impair the flying qualities if it were too pronounced. The phenomenon of tip stall had not yet been discovered. In
Platz's monoplane designs, only moderate taper was used. He regarded
spanwise changes in aerofoil section or incidence as sources of structural
complications, and avoided them too.

Fokker's designer knew no more about structures than he did about
aerodynamics. St. Venant's theory of beam bending was unknown to him;
so were Euler's formulae for the compression of axially loaded struts.
Bending diagrams, section moments of inertia, section moduli—all meant
nothing to him. Had he known of the mathematics required in engineering
stress analysis, he might have been deterred from his direct, unprejudiced,
empirical approach. One needs only to think of the precise stressing of a
composite tapering box beam of asymmetrical cross-section, composed of
two materials (e.g., pine timber and birch plywood): the problem of
calculating the minimum weight or maximum rigidity of such a beam
might have been a headache for a trained engineer of that period. It
was not even known which way the grain of the plywood in such a beam
should lie.

Platz started his development by loading cantilever beams of box cross-
section and noting how and when they failed in bending. From the test
results for a series of such box beams, Platz concluded that, using two box
spars, a cantilever span of eighteen to twenty times the height of the beam
could be made without being unreasonably heavy. Wood was the natural
choice of material for such spars; indeed the sparse facilities and labour
resources at Schwerin left no other choice. The tests proved that the
lightest box spars were those that had laminated wooden flanges and
plywood webs.

These webs were of birch three-ply with the outside grain normal to the
spar axis. Platz knew that the best arrangement was with the grain
diagonal, but that would mean waste and more splices, so he avoided it.
The shear loads on the webs were calculated at spanwise stations that
conveniently coincided with the lengths of the plywood sheets that were
available.

The spars could not fill the full depth of the wing section because Platz
required the capping strips of the ribs to run unbroken over them. By
making the spar depth 18% of a wing with a thickness of 20% of the
chord, a wing panel with a span of three times the chord could be made.
This gave complete wings with an aspect ratio of nearly 6·5 when a centre
section or fuselage width was added. Aspect ratios of that order were
commonplace at that time and, as the new wings satisfied the strength
specifications laid down by the Army, cantilever wings were perfectly
practicable.

The modern designer may wonder why Platz made no attempt to utilize
the entire wing thickness for the spars, for it is obvious that he could have
saved weight by omitting the rib capping strips where they passed above
and below the spars. Platz's adherence to his continuous-rib method

stemmed from his pursuit of simplicity, but it demonstrates that his empirical stressing methods had failed to reveal the importance of the depth of beam in resisting bending.

Platz was convinced that cantilever wings should be one-piece, integral structures without joints or divisions. He had never liked the four separate wing panels of the earlier Fokker biplanes with their heavy attachment fittings and bracing that had repeatedly given trouble. In holding this view Platz was more advanced than the designers of the Junkers J.I, which had divided wing panels, and of the N.F.W. monoplane, which had heavy spar joints in the centre of the fuselage. All subsequent Fokker monoplanes, biplanes and triplanes had one-piece wings.

To facilitate component design Platz extended his empirical testing method to tubes, braced frameworks and similar details that might be needed in new aircraft. The results of these tests were recorded in the form of handy graphs giving the ultimate loads that had been determined for certain lengths and sizes. From these graphs interpolations for the dimensions wanted could be made.

These home-made aids to design were the more useful because in all the staff of the greatly expanded Fokker works there was not a single person who was capable of making even the simplest stress calculation such as any engineering student could have made after a year's study of elementary mechanics. This was the outcome of Fokker's dislike of qualified engineers. It was also a source of perpetual frustration for Platz, who could find no-one able to show him how to approach plain design stressing.

Fokker was ultimately compelled by Adlershof to employ a graduate engineer on material control. However, this engineer proved to be a man whose doctorate thesis subject had been the development of artificial limbs. Dr. Ing. Koner did his official job at Schwerin with more enthusiasm than effect. Platz became friendly with him, but in spite of much prodding by Platz the Herr Doktor gave no indication of being able or willing to give Platz the technical guidance he needed. Nevertheless, as noted on page 195, this was the expert who, although lacking aeronautical knowledge, was sent by Fokker to represent the designer at type-test conferences at Adlershof.

The process of designing a new Fokker aeroplane started with a design conference which Fokker himself usually attended. He would present an elementary idea of what today would be termed a design requirement. In the case of the Fokker triplane this was simply "I want a triplane". The rest was left to Platz.

After the basic requirements had been determined at the design conference, a side elevation of the new aeroplane was laid out on millimetre-squared paper, to one-tenth scale. Platz always drew on squared paper; this saved having to measure dimensions. Some of the paper he used at Schwerin had been made by the famous Montgolfier firm.

The positions of the engine, fuel tanks, armament and pilot were put in first. It is worth noting that these, especially the weapons and pilot, were Platz's first considerations. Some designers seemed (and some still seem) to fit these items in as afterthoughts, more or less on the eve of flight testing. The position of the centre of gravity was next determined, using estimated weights for fuselage and tail, and subsequently the fore-and-aft position of the wing. For the latter purpose, Platz assumed the centre of lift to be about 30% of the chord from the leading edge.

The wing location, in its turn, made it possible to determine a fuselage length. Platz found that the best position for the hinge lines of the tail control surfaces was at about 2·25 times the wing chord from the centre of gravity.[1] With this dimension established, the tail surfaces and tail skid could be drawn in. The plan view of the fuselage was drawn directly below the completed side elevation. All this design drawing could be completed by one man within a single day, provided that all details had been settled in advance or repeated previous standard practice.

A few hours of laying-out were next spent on the jig board for the lateral frames of the fuselage structure. When this was completed, the construction of the fuselage could begin.

The design of the wing was straightforward unless it was tapered. In tapered wings, Platz chose a tip chord that was two-thirds of the chord at the wing centre; the thickness/chord ratio of the tip aerofoil was 1 : 9, or approximately 11·2%. The tip aerofoil itself was a derivative of Platz's standard section; both basic sections had the same angle of incidence of the chord of the mean camber line.

Such a wing was easy to produce. Rigging presented no problems, for the wing had all its pick-up points in one plane and could be easily and accurately attached to a cabane structure or fuselage, and the under-surface of the wing at centre or root was always straight and parallel to the fuselage axis. This always facilitated the assembly and repair of Fokker aircraft. The upper surface of the front spar was straight and horizontal from wing-tip to wing-tip; the taper of the spars provided dihedral on the lower surfaces of the wings.

Tireless in his pursuit of simplicity, Platz evolved a simple method of drawing the various ribs of a tapered wing. The contour of each rib, once determined, was laid out on stout drawing paper and transferred to wooden jig boards by pricking pins through the drawing. A skilled draughtsman could do all the drawing work on a wing of 15 to 20 sq. m. area (160 to 210 sq. ft.) in about eight hours.

The rib spacing was almost always the same distance of 310 mm. (12·2 in.). Riblets were fitted to preserve the nose contours and to support a stiffening strip of thin three-ply that was fitted along the leading edge. Wedge-shaped cut-outs were made in this strip between the ribs, both to save weight and to prevent the formation of wrinkles in the fabric covering where the ply terminated. The cut-outs robbed the leading-edge section

[1] Fuselage lengths and tail sizes were often modified during flight testing. Such alterations seldom took more than two or three days.

of torsion resistance, but this mattered little in a two-spar wing of the Platz type.

Platz produced standard aerofoil templates of 1,000-mm. chord; these were divided at 50-mm. and 100-mm. chordwise stations, with the ordinates of the upper and lower profile contours given. A departure from current practice was the use of the chord of the mean camber line as the datum, instead of the chord line of the rib.

When the original one-tenth scale drawing of the project in hand had yielded span, plan-form and area of the wing, a draughtsman needed only to be told to lay out a wing for a chord of, say, 1·95 m. This was a degree of standardization unheard of in those days; but for any of the aircraft designed by Platz up to 1919 (and afterwards) no more detailed information was needed.

Platz always chose chord lengths that were divisible by 3 as well as by 5 (e.g., 1·95 m.). This simplified the lay-out work and kept the drawings free of odd-sized dimensions.

While the lay-out work was proceeding, Platz was using his simple stressing principles to derive the dimensions of the spar flanges. The attachment fittings for the front spar of each wing were designed with a load factor of 4, those for the rear spar with a factor of 3.

In all later Fokker transport monoplanes the ailerons were cut out of the wing when the wing structure was nearly complete. This saved work, both in design and construction, and avoided the need for special jigs. It was the simplest possible way of making ailerons. But, to Platz's chagrin, Fokker insisted, often with sound reasons, on horn-balanced ailerons: these had to be made separately as welded steel-tube structures. Platz, as a non-flying man, was inclined to regard Fokker's insistence on balanced ailerons as a mere fad. Whenever he could get away with it, Platz would fit unbalanced, integrally constructed ailerons—which, often enough, had to be replaced by balanced surfaces, for they tended to be heavy on the Fokker type of wing. Fokker, with his pilot's control feel, had been right.

The tail unit, controls, undercarriage and other fixed components and installations were, like the fuselage, laid out on millimetre-squared paper.

This standardized method of designing aeroplanes was employed for all Fokker prototypes up to 1926, including the famous Fokker F.VII/3m three-engine transport monoplane that made so many outstanding flights. After 1926, workshop drawings of a more conventional kind were made —but from similar project drawings.

In all his designs, Platz used straight lines and right angles wherever possible. Dimensions that could be chosen freely had to be round and convenient values. This single-minded insistence on simplicity and economy never proved to be detrimental to any Fokker type.

We have seen that Platz's total knowledge of the Army's strength requirements for wartime single-seat fighters was limited to what he had managed to elicit from Roland Betsch, the Technical Officer of the

Bauaufsicht at Schwerin. Betsch was an author, and may not have properly understood the official design requirements; or he may not have described them adequately. Whatever the explanation may be, Platz worked to specifications that did not wholly agree with the BLV Design Requirements for Army Aeroplanes.

Because he did not know how air loads should be distributed spanwise and chordwise over wings, it was natural for Platz to assume concentrated air loads. For these he evolved an original procedure of strength distribution over the two wing spars and, notwithstanding his ignorance of the BLV specifications, it proved satisfactory: no wing of any Fokker aeroplane ever failed because it lacked design strength. Such wing failures as did occur were attributable either to poor material, poor workmanship (in particular, reduction of critical dimensions), or to flutter phenomena, about which no-one then knew much. In no case did any investigation or test prove that the dimensions chosen by Platz were inadequate.

All Platz-designed wings were dimensioned as cantilever structures, even when interplane struts were fitted; and the triplanes were capable of flying without struts. This was in fact done, as succeeding chapters will show; however, on fabric-covered wings aileron response was sluggish owing to reverse torsional deformation of the upper wing tips. Interplane struts conferred the necessary torsional rigidity.

Apart from the V.1 and V.2, all Fokker biplanes and triplanes had fabric-covered wings; so, too, did some of the smaller, low-powered monoplanes such as the V.39 and V.40. The wings of the other monoplanes had plywood skins to provide greater strength in torsion. To achieve adequate differential bending stiffness, Platz made the dimensions of the lower flange of the rear spar the same as those of the upper flange of the front spar. All spar flanges were laminated of laths, each 10 mm. (0·4 in.) thick, of good Polish pine (but, on occasion, there was a difference of opinion between Platz and Fokker as to what "good" meant).

In Fokker wings, the front spar was always located at one-fifth and the rear spar at three-fifths of the chord; this arrangement was used in all the V types and later designs. With these spar locations, the proof loading of complete wing structures did not become critical until the applied load approached a value of seven times the specified basic load.[1] When the timber really was of the best quality, the achieved ultimate strength actually exceeded a load factor of seven.

Fokker wings thus had a good strength margin for deterioration after the aircraft had been much used. Wooden structures, however, are scarcely affected by fatigue. In fact, Fokker wings have proved to have a longer service life than metal wings, and to have less need for overhaul and inspection.

When calculating the dimensions of the spar flanges of the V.1, Platz, aware that wood was critical in compression, chose an upper limit of 300 kg./sq. cm. (4,250 lb./sq. in.) for the ultimate compression strength of

[1] The basic load was the all-up weight minus the weight of the wings.

pine. Later designs were based on a value of 350 kg./sq. cm. (5,000 lb./ sq. in.); this was still well on the safe side.

The load on the spars was assumed to be concentrated, in the spanwise direction, at the centre of the wing-plan area outboard of the section under consideration.

The lower flange of a front spar was given 17% of the cross-sectional area of the top flange. With these dimensions it was found that it was unnecessary to check for adequacy in tension.

In each spar, two sections were calculated: one at the root (or wing centre, or cabane pick-up points), the other at about half-span. The spar dimensions established for these two sections were then joined by spanwise straight lines: these yielded the intermediate spar sections and, by extension to the wing tip, indicated the smallest permissible spar sections in the tip region. To provide sufficient areas for gluing the webs to the flanges and in order to resist handling stresses, the spar-flange thicknesses in the tip portion were often increased.

Inside the spars, between the flanges, light diaphragms were glued in at every rib station. This prevented wrinkling of the webs.

The plywood that was then available was considerably inferior to the resin-bonded material of the present day, but it was slightly lighter. Although the same timber (birch for preference) was used in its manufacture, all aircraft plywood till about 1930 was glued with albumin or casein glues. The glue layer was thus apt to decay from mould and fungus. Such plywood was, in strength, quality and moisture resistance, inferior to the best modern plywood. Fokker aircraft of the war period suffered badly from the use of poor plywood.

The design stressing of the steel-tube structure of the fuselage was also made quite simple and reasonably accurate without sacrificing safety.

The *IdFlieg* asked all aircraft manufacturers, from 1916 or early 1917, to supply stress analyses when submitting any new type of aeroplane. Fokker never troubled to do so; nor did he tell Platz (who might have pressed for the employment of a stressman) about it. The *IdFlieg* officials reminded Fokker of the requirement whenever they saw him at Adlershof; he fobbed them off with empty promises. In the end, the Fokker firm was the only one that made no attempt whatever to comply with the *IdFlieg* request. The structures experts were infuriated, for in the circumstances they had no choice but to test every new Fokker type to destruction—at Government expense, of course.

Many, but by no means all, of the test reports are still in existence. They contain ample testimony to the soundness of the design methods evolved by Platz. He, of course, never saw one of these reports: he may not even have known that such tests were being conducted: had he done so he might have asked that the reports be shown to him.

The effectiveness of the methods by which Platz, unversed in engineering, surmounted the intricacies of dimensioning airframe structures is admirably illustrated by the following example, which was related to the author by

214

the late Professor W. Hoff, then Director of the German Aeronautical Establishment, or D.V.L.

When Platz designed his first transport monoplane, the F.II, after the war, the German Air Ministry (Reichsluftamt) demanded that the D.V.L. make a searching investigation of the aircraft's airworthiness in view of its potential importance as a public transport vehicle. The D.V.L. asked for a stress analysis, stating that, if this proved the structural soundness of all vital components, a destruction test of a complete airframe would not be required.

Platz was far too diffident to submit his own calculations for the D.V.L.'s stressing specialists. He therefore asked the D.V.L. for help in preparing an acceptable stress analysis. Hoff lent Platz an expert in airframe stressing. The expert discovered, to his considerable surprise, that his refined methods of strength checking led to precisely the same dimensions that Platz had chosen. Furthermore, when an apparent discrepancy in the strength of certain undercarriage members arose, Platz was able to prove that the D.V.L. expert had worked upon a wrong assumption and that he (Platz) had been correct.

The result of the full stress check was favourable, and the report of the D.V.L. specialist so impressed Professor Hoff that he urged Platz to publish a description of his short-cut methods. Platz, who always shunned any form of publicity and still regarded himself as a humble welder, was completely abashed and failed to respond.

The F.II structure required no modification and, as the aircraft performed well in the air, having viceless handling characteristics, an unrestricted Certificate of Airworthiness was quickly granted. The D.V.L. stressing expert later joined the Dutch Fokker works and became one of Platz's trusted collaborators for many years.

A great advantage of Platz's design methods was that new types could be designed quickly and without needing technicians skilled in engineering design. Furthermore, the construction of a prototype could be started while the design work was still proceeding.

A remarkable example of this unprecedented capability was the hurried design and construction of an experimental single-seat fighter early in 1918. In this instance Platz established, unintentionally, a world record for speed in aircraft design and prototype construction. This record still stands and is unlikely to be bettered.

During the first Adlershof fighter trials in January 1918 (about which more will be said in Chapter XIII), Fokker demonstrated the V.17 cantilever mid-wing monoplane with a 110-h.p. Le Rhône rotary engine. This aircraft impressed influential officers. Alive to this interest, Fokker telephoned Platz at Schwerin on a Saturday night in the following terms: "The V.17 is very good. I would like to show something similar but with the 160-h.p. Mercedes. I shall be here for two more weeks. Can you do it?" Platz thought he could, and set to work.

Fokker can have had little idea of the work involved in the design and construction of a new prototype. The much heavier and longer engine needed a bigger and stronger airframe; it was not merely (as he may have imagined) a matter of putting a different engine into a V.17 airframe.

The design drawings were completed during the Sunday following Fokker's telephone call. On Monday morning the ribs for the tapered wing were drawn and the rib jigs laid out. The laminated spar flanges were glued up, the fuselage welding jigs were laid out and the structure welded up. The engine, airscrew, radiator, and some undercarriage parts such as the wheels, axle and shock absorbers, were borrowed from the Fokker V.11. Workers were brought from the production shops to speed the rib making and to help with the assembly. Casein glue was, of course, used throughout, and the greatest delay was occasioned by the need to wait for glued parts to set and dry.

On Saturday morning the new fuselage was ready, complete with engine cowling, undercarriage, and all installations such as controls, etc.; it was covered too. The plywood-covered wing was french polished by thirty carpenters. Platz had decided on french polishing in order to save the time that the drying of the more conventional dope and lacquer would have demanded. This was the fourth ply-skinned wing to be made in the Fokker Works.

At 2 p.m. on that same Saturday the new type, V.20, was ready for its first flight. Fokker was still at Adlershof, so it was flown by Weidner, one of Fokker's best works pilots. On the following Monday morning, the new V.20 stood on the tarmac at Adlershof, gleaming, immaculate, and ready to participate in the trials.

The whole work of design and prototype construction had taken $6\frac{1}{2}$ days.

CHAPTER XI

THE TRIPLANE ERA

FROM THE beginning of 1916 it had become obvious that the Oberursel Gnôme engine was useless for operational service. Unfortunately, the Oberursel firm had done little to improve upon the obsolete Gnôme design for which they had acquired the licence in 1913, although the need for an improved engine can hardly have escaped the firm's attention. After 1914 no operational aircraft of the Allies employed Gnôme engines with automatic inlet valves; by 1916 even the newer Monosoupape was being superseded by Le Rhône and Clerget rotaries.

Tests of captured Le Rhône engines at Adlershof showed that although none of these engines could pass the 60-hour fault-free run prescribed for aero-engines of the German Air Corps, they were considerably superior to the Oberursel Gnôme: not only were they more reliable, but the power output was greater and less power was lost at altitude.

In 1916 the *IdFlieg* invited all German aero-engine manufacturers to produce the 110-h.p. Le Rhône nine-cylinder rotary. Full facilities would be given and large orders were promised. Even confirmed champions of the water-cooled engine were sent specimens of Le Rhône engines for study; such firms pretended to make appropriate efforts. The Oberursel firm were promised preference in the awarding of bulk orders, with refund of development costs; but development at Oberursel progressed at a snail's pace. No Oberursel-built Le Rhône (UR-type, officially) became available until late 1917. Even this belated effort was only accomplished by securing some of the drawings in underhand ways.

Fokker, now boss of the Oberursel concern, pressed hard for early supplies of the precious rotary. As related in an earlier chapter, he had become sole owner from March 1917, after the firm had paid 35% dividend for 1915–16. Years later, Fokker complained that he had invested no less than £300,000 in Oberursel; but this included money spent on the unfinished development of a Hispano-Suiza variant by Gabriel Becker.

Schwade had dropped out of the aero-engine business for reasons that are still not fully known. Experience with the Siemens-Schuckert D.I indicated that Siemens und Halske had not succeeded in producing a completely satisfactory bi-rotary engine. Dinslage, their designer, and his staff were working on a more powerful version with eleven cylinders. The Gandenberger Machine Factory of G. Goebel (Darmstadt) had

217

undertaken the development of a Gnôme-type rotary with promising new features. But this, too, was still experimental.

Shortcomings in the supply of 160-h.p. Mercedes engines for fighters led to attempts to procure aero-engines from abroad. This was not easy for blockaded Germany. Switzerland had none to offer: later the Swiss supplied licence-built Argus water-cooled engines for training aircraft. Holland and Denmark had no aero-engine industry. But in Sweden, at Landskrona, Dr. Enoch Thulin, a well-known pre-war pilot and engineer, made small batches of 110-h.p. Le Rhônes under licence. The Thulin-made engines were known to be of excellent workmanship and made with the best Swedish materials. As a stop-gap, Germany ordered 700 of these engines, with ample spares. They were imported in strictest secrecy to avoid endangering the firm's licence arrangements with France. For the same reason, these Thulin engines were officially declared to be captured specimens (*Beute* engines), and bore nameplates to that effect.

It is still not known whether the engines were imported direct or went by a devious route via Dutch camouflage firms. This might explain why relatives of the late Enoch Thulin still emphatically deny that engines were supplied to Germany. However, the profits of the Thulin works soared in 1917 to the unprecedented peak of 1,246,000 crowns, whereas in 1918 they dropped to a mere 16,000 crowns. The firm's labour force employed on the production of these rotaries was 800. Thulin was also given orders for the 160-h.p. Mercedes, but none seem to have reached Germany.

Any residual doubts about the origin of Germany's Le Rhône engines can be easily dispelled by trying to calculate how many Allied aeroplanes would have to be shot down to provide the Germans with a harvest of 700 brand-new, fully serviceable 110-h.p. Le Rhônes complete with all spares. At a rough guess, the Allied air forces would have had to be about ten times their actual size to provide so many; and the stores of spares would have defied explanation. In fact, about 99·5% of all *Beute* Le Rhône engines installed in German aircraft had never been in any Allied aeroplane, but were Swedish Thulin type G rotaries.

By the time the Thulin engines were delivered, nearly all German rotary-powered fighters were being withdrawn from operational use; it was therefore decided to use the engines to power training aircraft, which at that time were scarce. The store containing these *Beute* engines was shown to Fokker, with the suggestion that he should produce a good two-seat trainer powered by the Thulin Le Rhône. Fokker had other ideas: he felt certain that the engines could be used to power a very good operational fighter, but kept his thoughts to himself.

With the Swedish Le Rhône engines arriving apparently too late the supply of aero-engines for fighter aircraft continued to be precarious. Germany had relied almost exclusively on six-cylinder in-line engines that had long, six-throw crankshafts of integral construction. And there was a bottle-neck in the drop-forging of these crankshafts. No efforts had been made in Germany to augment or expand drop-forging facilities.

Production had been left to the aero-engine firms. The monopoly enjoyed by Daimler and Benz had, by eliminating competition in crankshaft output, retarded production.

The engine production experts of the *IdFlieg* and the Flz. made great efforts to remove the bottle-neck. They advised engine manufacturers to undertake the development of power units like the Hispano-Suiza which, with its short, four-throw crankshaft, was well suited to quantity production.

The relative importance of stationary and rotary engines can be deduced from the following statistics of engines supplied to the German Army Air Corps:

Period	Stationary engines	Rotary engines
Aug.–Dec. 1914	748	100
Jan.–Dec. 1915	4,544	493
Jan.–Dec. 1916	6,930	892
Jan.–Dec. 1917	10,364	836
Jan.–Oct. 1918	13,542	1,785
Total, 1914–18	36,343	4,106

The Air War on the Western Front, early 1917

During the first quarter of 1917 the Germans succeeded in regaining some parity in air power in the most hotly contested sectors of the Western Front.

The Allies claimed to have shot down seventy-four German aircraft during January 1917; the German claims for the corresponding month totalled sixty-five Allied aeroplanes and three kite balloons shot down on the Western Front.

The German fighter forces began to grow; their morale rose; and in the spring of 1917 their bid for aerial supremacy made itself felt on the Allied side. The situation was not restored until new and better fighter types, such as the Spad, Sopwith Camel and S.E.5, with armament equal to that of the German biplanes, began to arrive in the British and French sectors.

A major contribution to the restoration of German fighter pilots' morale had been made by the Albatros D.III and D.V, which convinced their pilots that theirs was the superior equipment. By this time, air-combat tactics had been developed and were understood; and an air-warning system had been thoroughly organized, thus saving fruitless patrolling and avoiding belated alarms. The aggressive spirit of the pilots grew, and Allied reconnaissance and observation aircraft suffered more than ever, especially the pusher types, which had to be discarded or relegated to night bombing.

In March 1917 the Germans claimed to have shot down 161 Allied aeroplanes. Most of these burned in the air: the general use of incendiary and tracer ammunition had arrived.

Manfred von Richthofen had arisen as Boelcke's successor. Although he was similar to Boelcke in character and outlook he lacked his predecessor's technical knowledge and had little interest in the engineering aspects of aircraft design or in new technical developments. Von Richthofen was and remained the typical cavalry officer with the instincts of a born hunter. Boelcke was always eager to study engineering features or propose new developments; he had the methodical mind of a staff officer; and it was largely thanks to him that the Jagdstaffel formations developed so favourably. To Manfred von Richthofen aeroplanes meant little; he would have preferred a horse and sabre for fighting, had this been possible. Both Boelcke and von Richthofen were born leaders of men, and were immensely liked as well as respected. Both had sound moral background and displayed absolute integrity in their dealings with the aircraft industry. This distinguished them from some of the less scrupulous officers in fighter units.

When the Battle of Arras began on April 9, 1917, British squadrons on the Western Front possessed a total of 365 front-line aeroplanes, of which 120 were fighters. The Germans could muster only 100 fighters out of a total of 195 aircraft. But most of the German fighters had the 160-h.p Mercedes D.IIIa engine and two machine-guns (Albatros D.II, D.III D.V and Roland D.II). Less capable aircraft, such as the Halberstadt D.V and a few Siemens-Schuckert D.Is were operational only in small numbers and were quickly replaced. Few, if any, Fokkers were left; McCudden last met a Fok. D.III on this sector on January 23, 1917; it escaped his attentions. Albatros D.Vs came forward to this sector from the end of April 1917 onwards.

During the early months of 1917, a new and unusual British fighter was encountered by German pilots: a little triplane that appeared to have a phenomenal performance. On April 7, a single triplane flown by Flight Lieutenant R. A. Little of No. 8 Squadron, Royal Naval Air Service, made a surprise attack on eleven Albatros D.IIIs of Jasta 11, and outmanoeuvred them all. Manfred von Richthofen wrote a caustic report on this combat, requesting early re-equipment with aircraft better able to counter the new British triplane; without such new aircraft Germany was in danger of losing air superiority. He had assessed the real value of the new British fighter.

Manfred von Richthofen himself had an engagement with Sopwith triplanes a few days later, on April 20, 1917; he was then flying an Albatros D.III. In spite of their rotary engines and single-gun armament, the triplanes proved formidable opponents, capable of outmanoeuvring and outclimbing the best German fighters flown by skilled pilots. Even the brand-new Albatros D.V with the latest D.III version of the Mercedes engine was no match for the Sopwith. Manfred von Richthofen reported that the new triplane was certainly the best Allied fighter at that time.

In May 1917, the Kogenluft, General von Hoeppner, stated frankly in an interview with representatives of neutral newspapers that in German opinion the best enemy fighters were the Sopwith triplane and the new 200-h.p. Spad.

Startling though it was in its first combats, the Sopwith triplane was not a revolutionary aircraft when considered solely from the aeronautical engineering standpoint. Its three wings were of equal span, chord and dihedral; all had ailerons. Because the chord was narrow the two spars of each wing were sufficiently close together for a single, broad-chord interplane strut to suffice on each side. This allowed the wing structure to be braced as a biplane. The central wing was just below the pilot's eye-level, and had cut-outs in the trailing edge. The triplane arrangement resulted in an aircraft that was small, light, and with a light wing loading. The aircraft was relatively clean and had a reliable and powerful engine. It proved to be quite fast and to have excellent manoeuvrability, a very good climb and a high ceiling.

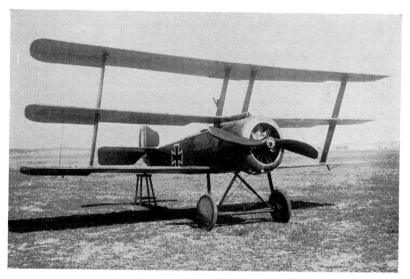

A captured Sopwith triplane.

Inevitably, some specimens of the Sopwith triplane fell into German hands. One that was captured in good condition was rushed to Adlershof, where it was carefully examined by official experts in June and July 1917. On July 27 a circular, signed by Hauptmann Muehlig-Hofmann, was sent by the Flugzeugmeisterei to all aircraft manufacturers, inviting them to inspect the Sopwith triplane at Adlershof. The *IdFlieg* let it be known that promising projects for triplane fighters would be favourably considered, and orders for experimental prototypes would be readily granted. A rich crop of triplanes resulted: it seemed that every aircraft manufacturer regarded it as his duty to provide the Fatherland with at least one triplane fighter. Most of these aircraft were thoroughly bad and too late in appearing.

Fokker's travels to the Western Front

Early in 1917 Fokker again journeyed to the front. Although the German command was far-sighted enough to encourage such activities, in the interests of exchanging technical information between industry and operational units, Fokker was one of the few executives in the German aircraft industry who regularly paid visits to front-line formations. These visits were welcomed by pilots, who were able to air grievances about their equipment unhampered by Service regulations.

Fokker had two purposes for this particular visit: he wanted to find out what kind of fighter design, in continuation of the V.1/V.2 development, would be likely to be successful; and he wanted to discuss with his pilot friends ways and means of overcoming the growing resistance of the Adlershof technicians to his aircraft. He felt that something should be done to curb the slide-rule wielders and stress experts. So he assured one and all that he, Fokker, could give them the finest fighter aircraft on earth if only the thick-headed theorists of Adlershof would let him: his advanced designs were too practical for the chair-borne brigade at Adlershof.

These arguments struck a sympathetic chord; in fact, many of the leading fighter pilots had similar ideas. They had been provided with obsolete aircraft, some proving to be complete wash-outs; the pilots therefore ought to be consulted in the selection of new fighter types. The departmental chiefs of the *IdFlieg* and the Flz. readily agreed to this idea: it had always been a difficult and heavy responsibility for them to choose the best available type of aircraft; time and time again the chosen type, although good at the prototype stage, did not go into operational use until too late, when it was obsolescent. In other instances, new engines had proved disappointing under operational conditions.

For these failures the technical experts were blamed, consequently they were well content to leave the task of selection to operational pilots. It was decided that all new and airworthy prototypes should be sent to Adlershof to be flown in comparative trials by competent fighter pilots. In addition, it was suggested that promising new experimental aircraft should be sent to the front, even before being submitted to a type test. This, it was thought, should help to expedite production and re-equipment with the latest and best types.

These concessions to operational units were, of course, a quite startling innovation in the German Army. It was unheard of for soldiers to be allowed to choose their own equipment: no soldier had ever been invited (officially, that is) to express his opinion on the design or handling of his rifle. But the officers responsible for the innovation, notably Thomsen,

Siegert and Wagenfuehr, did not hesitate to cut red tape in this way; they were confident that the arrangement with the fighter pilots would work well. Fokker hoped so too.

While Fokker was visiting Jagdstaffel 11, commanded by Manfred von Richthofen, he was told about the sensational new Sopwith triplane that had made its appearance at the front. Fokker was shown the first specimen brought down before it was passed on to Adlershof. He was also taken to an observation post, where he saw the triplane in flight. Von Richthofen and his technical officer Leutnant Krefft told Fokker that they needed just such an aircraft. But it had to come quickly and to be at least as good as the Sopwith.

Fokker hurried back to Schwerin. This was the chance he was waiting for. The time was late April 1917. Although he knew that other manufacturers would be invited to submit prototypes designed to counter the Sopwith triplane, he was confident that Platz would be able to get out a design more quickly than his competitors and that it would probably be better. Moreover, Fokker had a start over his rivals because he was the only manufacturer who had seen the Sopwith and knew its capabilities. He also recalled the large store of *Beute* Le Rhônes at Adlershof: this engine would do as well as the Clerget that powered the Sopwith, and it was immediately available in quantity. There would therefore be no hold-up because of shortage of engines.

As soon as he got back to Schwerin Fokker told Platz of his discoveries and ideas. One might think that Fokker would have recorded fully all that he had learned about the Sopwith, with a technical description of the design and structural features that he might have been expected to note with care. Nothing of the kind! As Platz distinctly recalls—and he is quite emphatic about it—Fokker merely told him: "I have seen a good enemy triplane at the front. We must build one too". And that was that. Platz gathered that the new prototype was to have a rotary engine that would be forthcoming from Adlershof almost at once.

Platz did not like the idea at all. He was all for Spartan simplicity: to him, it seemed an outrageous and retrograde complication to give an aeroplane three wings when one would be so much better: he could not understand it at all. But Fokker was the boss; to argue with such a stubborn fanatic was not easy, and Platz was very conscious of the fact that he was just beginning to find his feet as a designer. He could not help it: the triplane was an order: a triplane it had to be!

Platz is also quite certain that while he was designing the Fokker triplane he had no information whatever about the Sopwith triplane. No example of the Sopwith or any of its components came to Schwerin (contrary to the assertion made later by Dr. Sablatnig), and Platz's only wartime visit to Adlershof did not occur until 1918. It is therefore certain that his triplane design, the Fokker V.3, was not influenced by that of the Sopwith; this is borne out by a comparison of the general arrangement and structural design of the two aircraft. How far any advice or suggestions of

Fokker's may have influenced the final development of the V.3 cannot now be ascertained, but any such advice seems to have been confined to points relating to the handling and armament of the new type.

Some small Sopwith influence might be attributed to the use, at a later stage, of a single interplane strut. Platz is emphatic that this strut was quite unnecessary when the prototype was first tested at Schwerin, but Fokker insisted on having it fitted after testing the aircraft. Platz cannot recall the reasons given by Fokker at the time. To the world Fokker let it be known that it was added because the Adlershof experts abhorred cantilever wings (which was quite untrue) and that the operational pilots did not want them either (which probably was true).

The first Fokker triplane, the V.3.

The Fokker V.3 was simpler and lighter than the V.1. With the elaborate streamlining abandoned, the slab-sided, fabric-covered fuselage saved weight and eased production and maintenance in the field. There were small plywood fairings on the fuselage sides to blend the circular cross-section of the engine cowling into the rectangular section of the fuselage structure; a rounded top decking was also fitted.

As on the Sopwith triplane, the three wings were staggered. This was neither coincidence nor imitation; it merely happened to be the best way of getting a decent view from the cockpit. All the wings had the same chord and section, but the top wing was of greater span than the other two; these were of equal span. Thus in each wing the cantilever portion was of the same length, consequently it was possible to make all the spars

224

of the same cross-section. Platz neglected to take into account the actual lift grading over triplane systems. He assumed uniform loading everywhere. All wings were integral structures, the middle wing being attached directly to the upper longerons.

Much attention was given to the evolution of a suitable wing section. Platz thought that thick aerofoils might prove inefficient in a triplane system and that a section with no camber on the undersurface would give a high landing speed. He therefore reshaped, by eye, the V.1/V.2 section to the characteristic undercambered aerofoil of the Fok. Dr.I. This aerofoil was not tested aerodynamically in a wind-tunnel or in any other way when the V.3 and V.4 were designed. Later on, unknown to Platz, the Flz. subjected it to wind-tunnel tests at Goettingen as the Goettingen 298 aerofoil. The results of these tests were circulated by the Flz. to all German aircraft manufacturers. They were, of course, of limited value because of the low Reynolds numbers and the failure to take the turbulence of the wind-tunnel into account.

The results of British wind-tunnel tests of the Fokker aerofoil were largely ignored at the time: the leading aeronautical brains in this country were "positively certain" that thick aerofoil sections must be fundamentally bad. This being so, no-one would have been so unpatriotic as to admit that a German designer might be right with such an outlandish idea.

The two wing spars had to be placed as close together as possible so that the middle wing could be accommodated in front of the cockpit. But, as trials with the V.3 showed, this impaired the torsional stiffness of the wings. To put this right, the gap between the two spars was bridged, above and below, by span-wise plywood strips glued and bradded over the tops and bottoms of the spars. This produced a box structure with four vertical webs and four narrow flanges, covered by plywood flanges. This unique spar-box arrangement of the Fokker triplanes obviated the need for internal drag bracing, yet allowed the wings to be covered simply with fabric.

In such a wing the stiffness of the deep ribs with their plywood web could have been utilized to relieve the torsion strain (by compound action of the rib-spar system restraining the spars from warping). However, it was Fokker practice to make the spar gaps in the ribs large enough to allow the ribs to slide over the web splices during assembly; the ribs were subsequently attached to the spars by triangular corner pieces.

Each wing tip was formed by attaching a wing rib at right angles to the end rib. This was simple and yet gave a pleasing, rounded tip shape; it was also capable of resisting dope stresses and facilitated handling.

The cabane structure for the top wing was much simpler than that of the V.1, but was rather tall because the wing was above the level of the pilot's head. The cabane of the V.3 (and of subsequent Fokker triplanes) consisted of two inverted-V struts with cable cross bracing in the plane of the front members. There was a wide bracket at the apex of each inverted-V strut; this attachment was fixed to both wing spars. The top wing attachment was consequently not so rigid as that of the V.1, but it was lighter, interfered less with the pilot's view, and probably caused less interference drag than the ten-strut cabane structure of the V.1.

Seen from some angles, particularly from the front, the V.3 looked ungainly: neither Fokker nor Platz was much impressed by its lines.

In the V.3 Platz abandoned the peculiar control surfaces of the V.1 and V.2 and fitted conventional ailerons, elevators and rudder. In accordance with his views on simplicity the ailerons and elevators were not balanced surfaces. The standard comma-shaped rudder of the M types was retained. Although balanced, it was simple enough for Platz's taste.

After flight-testing the V.3, Fokker demanded balanced ailerons and elevators. Platz disapproved of these luxuries, which he regarded as a mere fad of Fokker's. But Fokker insisted on them, and was right to do so—every pilot who flew the Fokker triplane praised its effortless response to the controls. Platz returned to plain control surfaces in several subsequent designs. It is regrettable that he never troubled to learn to fly.

It was decided not to submit the V.3 to a type test or to an evaluation at the front. Instead, a re-design under the new designation V.4 was undertaken.

Platz realized that the appearance of the triplane could be improved by increasing the span of the middle wing so that the spans of the three wings decreased regularly from top to bottom. The increased span would mean a higher maximum bending moment at the fuselage, and Platz was not keen on fitting stronger spars to the centre wing on this account.

The Fokker V.4 was a new design with revised wings, interplane struts, and horn-balanced ailerons and elevators.

226

Fokker V.4.

A new middle wing of the desired increased span was subjected to structural tests to determine whether stronger spars were needed. The results proved that the wing had an unusually high load factor for those days and needed no strengthening. Platz now realizes that the V.3 and V.4 spar flanges were generously dimensioned: when he designed the aircraft he failed to take into account the high strength of pine in tension. Had he done so he could have made the bottom flanges smaller.

Despite the favourable result of the structural tests, Platz was glad that the interplane strut was fitted, for it reduced the appreciable flexing of the wing. Although harmless enough in itself, this flexing would probably have alarmed pilots. In front elevation the interplane strut was perpendicular to the wings. Platz now recognizes that it would have been

A "demonstration", Fokker-fashion, of the strength of the middle wing of the Fokker V.4.

more logical to instal the strut obliquely, so as to form equal-span bays in the three wings. This might also have looked better.

The Fok. Dr.I was later flown experimentally without interplane struts by Adlershof test pilots: they wanted to find out what would happen if the interplane strut was hit in combat. The triplane remained manageable but the wings warped visibly and displayed an inclination to flutter during steep glides. This indicated that the interplane strut was subjected to bending fore and aft and was not a mere placebo, as Fokker had claimed. This was also proved by the official sand-loading tests; when the required ultimate load for case C (terminal nose dive) was reached, the fittings of the upper strut began to buckle, a sign of impending collapse from torsion.

The Fokker V.4 emerged with a new set of wings in which the top and bottom surfaces were of greater span than those of the V.3; the middle wing was of intermediate span in order to provide progressively reducing spans. Horn-balanced ailerons were fitted to the upper wings, and the interplane strut made its initial appearance. The horn-balances of the elevators projected outside the tailplane contours, and twin fixed machine-guns were fitted. Fuselage, rudder and installation appeared to be identical with those of the V.3.

The introduction of the Fok. F.I triplane

In June 1917, as a counter-measure to combat Allied air superiority in the Flanders sector, four of the best Jagdstaffeln (Nos. 4, 6, 10 and 11) were grouped together to form the first German Fighter Wing (Jagdgeschwader Nr. 1). The new unit was mobile, for it was intended that it should be moved to any sector threatened by Allied air activity. Its command was given to Manfred von Richthofen.

On July 6 von Richthofen was shot down wounded; he returned to the aerodrome at Marcke on July 25. On the following day he announced to his officers that the unit was to be re-equipped with Fokker triplanes. These he described as being "as manoeuvrable as the devil" and capable of "climbing like monkeys". This re-equipment had been decided upon without waiting for a Type Test.

A possible reason for this hasty adoption of the new Fokker lay in the poor opinion of German fighter aircraft held by their pilots. They were then opposed by Sopwith Pups, Triplanes, Camels, S.E.5s, Spads, Nieuports and Bristol Fighters; the F.E.s and R.E.8s were easy meat for the German fighters. The new S.E.5a was greatly superior in climb and speed. Leutnant Adam, leader of Jasta 6, regarded the S.E.5 as about equal to the Albatros D.V; he regarded the Pup and Triplane as inferior, and thought the Camel might also prove to be inferior. There was no doubt about the superiority of the S.E.5a and the 200-h.p. Spad over the Albatros.

Voss, leader of Jasta 10, differed from Adam: he regarded all contemporary British single-seaters as better than the Albatros in climb, manoeuvrability and ability to dive. Leutnant Groos, the deputy leader of Jasta 11, agreed entirely with Voss. Manfred von Richthofen himself was convinced that re-equipment with better fighters was long overdue.

Fokker had been given an order for the supply of three experimental examples of his triplane design. The V.4 prototype (Military Order No. 101/17) was sent early in August to Adlershof for structural testing prior to operational evaluation at the front. The other two aircraft, No. 102/17 and No. 103/17, were nearing completion at Schwerin. The Flugzeug-meisterei conducted the strength tests with all speed between August 7 and 10, 1917, with Fokker present. The type was, at that early date, referred to as Fok. Dr.I.

The fuselage of Fok. F.I No. 102/17. In the cockpit is Fokker; Platz is standing on the steps. On the ground is Ahrend, a fitter.

For the first time a new Fokker aircraft passed its structural tests without major modifications. It was suggested that the rudder bar should be strengthened, and that the diameter of the steel-tube longerons in the rear fuselage should be increased to 20 mm. The tests appeared to indicate that the undercarriage strength was not up to the required standard but, as there were doubts about the testing rig (which was thought to be some-what unrealistic), the aircraft was not grounded or retarded for this reason, and in fact no Fok. Dr.I ever gave cause for complaint about its undercarriage.

On August 11, the prototype V.4 was tested to destruction in Case A. The ultimate load factor proved to be 7·92, which was highly satisfactory. Fokker asked for the fabric to be removed from the lower wing so that structural deformation could be observed. The ribs began to buckle at a

Fokker, in the cockpit of F.I No. 102/17, speaks to General von Lossberg. To the right of von Lossberg is Manfred von Richthofen (*Photo: Imperial War Museum*).

load factor of 7·75, final failure occurring with the buckling of the webs at the fuselage. Taking into account the lift from the aerofoil fairing of the undercarriage axle, the ultimate load factor could be as high as 8·38. It is doubtful whether any other operational aeroplane of the period possessed comparable strength.

Fok. F.I No. 102/17.

With the type designation Fok. F.I, No. 102/17 and No. 103/17 underwent acceptance flight tests at Schwerin on August 16, 1917. They were taken by Fokker to Manfred von Richthofen's fighter wing at Courtrai on August 21. It is not known with certainty why the two aircraft were designated Fok. F.I. Perhaps the Kogenluft had decided on a new category that followed naturally on the official category letters A, B, C, D and E. But the *IdFlieg* had already settled on Fok. DR.I (or more correctly Fok. Dr.I) at a very early stage, as a Flz. drawing dated August 7, 1917, clearly proves. All doubt about the triplane's official designation was removed by a Flz. order dated August 19, 1917, and signed by Muehlig-Hofmann. This order established the category Dr. for single-seat fighter triplanes; it also created the categories (CL (or Cl) and GL (or Gl) for light two-seaters and light twin-engined aircraft respectively. Thus 102/17 and 103/17 remained the only Fokker triplanes to bear the designation F.I. They differed visibly from the V.4 only in having the elevator horn balances lying within the contour of the horizontal tail surfaces.

On August 26, 1917, no less a personage than Quartermaster-General von Ludendorff, commanding the German armies in the field, came to see the new Fokker fighter. Fokker demonstrated it with his usual skill. On the evening of August 29, Leutnant Werner Voss, leader of Jasta 10, tried it for the first time. He was delighted with the little triplane and its capabilities. He made the first operational flight on F.I No. 103/17 on the following day; during this flight he shot down a British aircraft. Voss's fighting career with the triplane was brief, but with it he scored no fewer than twenty-one victories between August 30 and September 23.

Werner Voss taxying Fok. F.I No. 103/17.

231

He was flying No. 103/17 when he met his death on September 23. He was flying alone on an evening patrol when he saw an S.E.5a, which he attacked. Other aircraft were attracted to the fight. These included the S.E.5a's of "B" Flight of No. 56 Squadron, R.F.C., led by Captain J. T. B. McCudden and including Second Lieutenant A. P. F. Rhys Davids. After a long fight, in which Voss fought superbly, Rhys Davids at last placed a well-aimed burst of fire into the Fokker triplane. McCudden, who was the only witness of the triplane's last plunge to earth, later praised Voss's skill and courage; Rhys Davids bitterly regretted that he had been unable to take such a gallant foe alive.

Werner Voss with his Fok. F.I, No. 103/17.

Manfred von Richthofen flew a Fokker triplane for the first time on September 1, 1917: the aircraft was Fok. F.I No. 102/17. Although he was still suffering badly from his head wound and had little faith in rotary engines, he took instantly to the Fokker. Later that day, again flying the triplane, he shot down an R.E.8 near Zonnebeke. It was his sixtieth victory.

Although that particular victory was an easy one, so much did von Richthofen like the Fokker that on the following day he reported to the Kogenluft that it was distinctly superior to the Sopwith triplane and well suited to the requirements of his Jagdgeschwader. He requested complete re-equipment with triplanes with all possible speed.

Fok. F.I No. 102/17 had a shorter life than its sister machine. On

September 15, Oberleutnant Kurt Wolff (Jasta 11), a frail-looking boy of great spirit who was very popular with Manfred von Richthofen and his brother officers, was shot down and killed while flying it in combat with Sopwith Camels of No. 10 Squadron, R.N.A.S.

About the middle of October 1917, six new triplanes were delivered from Schwerin, all now bearing the designation Fok. Dr.I and differing from the F.Is in some details. The only external difference was the addition of wing-tip skids under the lower wings. The order numbers of these first six Fok. Dr.Is were 104/17, 106/17, 109/17, 110/17, 111/17 and 113/17.

Eleven more arrived three days later, all with *Beute* Le Rhône engines. These were Nos. 107/17, 112/17, 114/17, 116/17, 118/17, 119/17, 121/17, 122/17, 123/17, 125/17 and 132/17. No. 108/17 did not go to the front: it was supplied to Adlershof for flying trials of the new 160-h.p. Goebel Goe. III engine.

Included in the next batch of triplanes was the ill-fated No. 115/17. This Fok. Dr.I was delivered to Jasta 15, on October 22, 1917, where it was taken over by the Staffelführer, Leutnant Heinrich Gontermann. Bad weather delayed his first flight in the aircraft until October 28, 1917. On the following day his second flight in the new triplane ended fatally: an eye-witness description indicates that Gontermann was performing aerobatics at 1,500 ft. over the aerodrome when it became apparent that his triplane was out of control. Several parts of the top wing were seen to break away, and the aircraft crashed. Gontermann was seriously injured and died next day, twenty-one years of age and with thirty-nine victories to his credit.

On October 31, two days after Gontermann's fatal crash, Leutnant Pastor (Jasta 11) crashed in a similar manner while flying No. 121/17. In spite of the promise showed by the triplane all aircraft of the type were grounded immediately. A special commission of experts (Z.A.K. Sturz Kommission) was hastily formed and sent to the front to investigate. Its members were Oberleutnant Dr.-Ing. W. Hoff of the D.V.L., the Flugzeugmeisterei engineers Diebel and Fleckig, and—most important— Dipl.-Ing. Roland Betsch, technical officer of Bauaufsicht 13 at the Fokker works, Schwerin. A more searching structural examination of the aircraft was begun at Adlershof.

Meanwhile, the Richthofen Jagdgeschwader had to revert to Albatros D.Va and Pfalz D.IIIa, both with the 160-h.p. Mercedes and no longer competitive types in the more active sectors of the front.

Manfred von Richthofen had been a witness of Pastor's crash. Immediately after the accident, he and his Technical Officer, Leutnant Krefft, examined all the Fokker triplanes on the strength of Jagdgeschwader I. The result was alarming: they found extensive evidence of bad workmanship. It was obvious that production of the wings had been rushed, and that such inspection as might have been made had been sketchy. When the crash-investigation commission arrived from Adlershof, accompanied by a much-subdued Fokker, von Richthofen showed them his findings. He also impressed upon the commission the urgent need for a speedy investigation and recommendation: the Fok. Dr.I was urgently needed and had shown great promise.

Examination of the remains of both the wrecked triplanes confirmed that the workmanship had been exceedingly poor. On the other hand, the wing spars had not failed in flight; but in each case the ailerons and ribs had come off in manoeuvres that could not be called violent, and this was puzzling. Several theories were advanced. It was suggested that side-slipping might have imposed some hitherto unknown loading on the ailerons, accentuated perhaps by the horn balances. Hoff did not like those balances: might not they, at some point, have produced an abrupt overbalancing force, thus producing sudden and unexpected peak loads? If so, the attachment of the ailerons did not look strong enough to cope with such loads, nor did the ribs that might have to transmit them look substantial enough. Some redesign seemed necessary: this ought to be investigated at Adlershof.

The accidents to Gontermann and Pastor were, by coincidence, investigated on the same day, November 2, 1917, the former at La Neuville, the latter at Kortryk. One eye-witness of Gontermann's crash, a fighter pilot of Jasta 15, had noticed that during a side-slip to port the port aileron had broken away first; immediately afterwards the ribs came off the top wing. Examination of the wreckage showed that the top-wing spar had remained intact until the impact with the ground; the rest of the wing structure was missing. The Z.A.K Sturz Kommission found similar evidence in the remains of Pastor's aircraft. The spar of the top wing and the port aileron were examined, and it was found that all the ribs had come away in the air. The inner portion of the aileron was missing, and the surface had fractured outboard of the horn balance. The hinges were intact; a part of the auxiliary spar to which they were attached was still in place. Manfred von Richthofen stated that Pastor was gliding down. As the triplane tended to drop its port wings Pastor would have applied starboard aileron, thus producing a load on the ailerons that might have caused the failure.

For examination, von Richthofen and Krefft had selected the Fok. Dr.I that had done most flying, and had stripped the fabric from its top wing. This immediately revealed an insecure connexion between the auxiliary spar and the wing-tip former. Moreover, the interior of the wing had been badly affected by moisture: all the plywood webs had warped, and some of the cap-strips of the ribs had come away from the webs.

Removal of the fabric from the bottom wing of another triplane revealed that many ribs had pulled out of the grooves of their cap-strips, and that the triangular-section gusset pieces attaching the ribs to the spar box had come adrift, probably because of moisture and careless gluing. In this instance, disintegration of the entire wing seemed imminent.

After the Kortryk investigation, Oblt. Hoff interviewed Fokker in the presence of Manfred von Richthofen and delivered a stern warning that he would have to improve his production and inspection methods. If he did not do so, drastic measures would have to be taken. Fokker's lame excuse—that his factory had worked day and night to expedite the delivery of the first triplanes because von Richthofen wanted them so urgently—was brushed aside.

On November 6, 1917, the *IdFlieg* wrote to Fokker confirming in detail "the instructions imparted to Herr Fokker by Oblt. W. Hoff at Kortryk". This letter was agreed with the Kogenluft and was signed by Muehlig-Hofmann. It stipulated that existing Fok. Dr.I aircraft were to be provided with new and properly constructed wings without delay: the new wings must be supplied by Fokker without extra charge. All wings of existing Fok. Dr.Is must be sent to the Central Aircraft Acceptance Commission (Z.A.K.) at Adlershof. Until new wings were fitted, all Fok. Dr.Is must remain grounded.

The letter from the *IdFlieg* further directed that all Fok. Dr.I wings already made must be uncovered, examined thoroughly, and modified as follows:

1. Reinforcement of the tip former by adding a second rib to form a box rib.

2. A third box rib to be incorporated in the wing to provide a more solid attachment for the auxiliary spar.

3. Improvement of the joint between the auxiliary spar and the wing-tip former.

4. Omission of the cut-out at the centre of the auxiliary spar.

5. Improvement of the joint between the auxiliary spar and the cap-strips of the ribs that were attached to it.

6. Improvement of the joints between the rib webs and their cap-strips.

7. Stiffening of the rib webs by the addition of vertical stays.

8. Omission of the lightening holes in the rib webs to reduce moisture absorption.

9. The fabric must be sewn to the ribs; it must no longer be nailed on.

10. Provision must be made of means for supporting the fabric, especially in the centre of the upper wing.

11. The wing interior must be protected against moisture by a coating of protective lacquer.

12. The Flz. would experiment on the size of the horn balances of the ailerons: these might have to be modified.

The *IdFlieg* requested that these modifications should be inspected and approved by the Flz. before any wings were accepted. They also emphasized that all wings supplied in the future had to be more carefully produced and must not require further structural modifications.

The crash-investigation commission submitted its report and recommendations on November 15, 1917. It and its associated documents were signed by Roland Betsch.

Critical though the *IdFlieg* letter of November 6 was, Platz never saw it (until the author showed him a copy recently), nor did he learn the findings of the crash-investigation commission. Apart from Fokker's failure to pass this information to Platz, it seems extraordinary that Betsch, who was personally acquainted with Platz, did not consider it his duty to discuss with the designer the technical details of the report. One cannot escape the feeling that at Schwerin conceptions of duty were peculiar, war or no war.

Today, having learned all these technical facts belatedly, Platz is convinced that the Fok. Dr.I could have been made safe with fewer modifications, simply by more careful production and a modification of the rib construction that he had already introduced at that time. After a test flight with a production Fok. Dr.I, the pilot had shown him that the fabric on one of the bottom wings had become loose; there had been no accident of any kind. Platz found that the rib cap-strips had come off the webs. The grooved cap-strips, a relic of the early monoplane, had been insufficiently glued and had parted company with the rib webs. Platz obviated this danger by sandwiching the web between two separate rib-contour runners: this gave a secure joint. The ribs of all subsequent Fokker aeroplanes were made in this way, regardless of whether the wings were fabric-covered or plywood skinned.

Of the other modifications demanded by the *IdFlieg*, Platz agrees that Nos. 1, 3, 5 and 9 were good ideas. His own independent action had met requirement No. 6. Modifications Nos. 2, 4, 7 and 8 seemed to him quite unnecessary, and his arguments against them would probably have convinced the Flz. experts if they had realized that the designer of the triplane was Platz, not the great A. H. G. Fokker who was so curiously inarticulate when questioned about design details.

The effect of the crash-investigation commission's report and the *IdFlieg* letter was to bring Fok. Dr.I production to a standstill. As a scapegoat, the Schwerin works manager was dismissed. The military authorities refused to accept any further aircraft until all wings had been modified and thoroughly inspected.

All this was a considerable set-back for Fokker and his company. The initial order had been for 320 triplanes (with the numbers 101/17 to 220/17, and 400/17 to 599/17), and Fokker had been told, before the wing-failure crashes, that much larger orders might be given: this depended only on engine supplies and, most of all, on the lubricating-oil situation. But now the triplane was in disrepute, and instead of accepting growing orders Fokker had to use up his profits in having all wings stripped, examined and modified.

The original delivery programme envisaged the supply of 173 Fok. Dr.Is by December 1, 1917, the balance of the first contract to be delivered

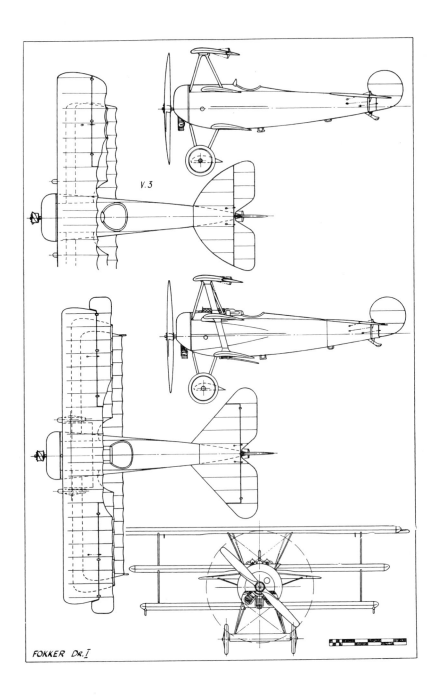

V. 3

FOKKER Dr. I

237

thereafter. The grounding of the type changed this drastically, as the following table indicates:

Date of report	Number of operational Fokker triplanes	Number supplied by Fokker during period preceding date of report
1.9.17	2 (Fok. F.I)	3 (one as type aircraft to Adlershof)
1.11.17	17	None during September; 24 during October
1.1.18	35	6 during November; 47 during December
1.3.18	143	
1.5.18	171	
1.7.18	118	Up to 1.7.18, 150 Fok. Dr. I were withdrawn from front-line units in the major flying sectors
1.9.18	65	
1.11.18	69	Almost all with home-defence fighter formations

The modified wing, when tested at Adlershof, proved capable of withstanding more than 200% of the maximum load specified for the aileron attachment, in spite of an adverse load grading. Being over-strength it was, of course, heavier than it need have been. On November 28, 1917, Fokker was notified by telegram from Hoff that the wing had proved satisfactory on test. The ban on the Fok. Dr.I was then lifted.

A Fok. Dr.I with fabric removed.

238

Deliveries of the modified triplanes started again early in December. By that time, however, the type had lost its temporary superiority and, especially in those sectors where aerial fighting was most intense, something better than the Fok. Dr.I was wanted.

The official report on the strength tests of the modified Fok. Dr.I wing was dated November 28, 1917. It included a description of the way in which the Fokker works had complied with the detailed requests of the *IdFlieg*. The points in the *IdFlieg* letter of November 6 (see page 235) had been dealt with thus:

1, 2, 9 and 10: modifications effected as requested.

3 and 5: the auxiliary spar was joined to all ribs by a triangular gusset piece of plywood; this was glued and pinned in place. Finally, a strip of fabric was cemented over it as a moisture protection.

4: the cut-out had been retained, but local reinforcement had been provided by gluing an additional piece of wood aft of the spar.

6: the joint had been improved by cementing on fabric.

7: web stiffeners had been added; over each of these, a strip of fabric had been cemented reaching over the cap-strip.

8: had been disregarded; this was accepted.

11: all wooden and metal parts in the wing had been given a protective coating of lacquer.

The structural modifications increased the wing weight by 3·5 kg.; that is, 4·25% over the original wing-structure weight of 84·5 kg. (187 lb.).

In the loading tests of the strengthened wing, the lift contributed by the undercarriage aerofoil was neglected, as before. The modified airframe withstood the specified safe loads in Cases A and B without any permanent or excessive deformation. The upper wing deflected by 135 mm. at the tips under a load factor of 5 in Case A, whereas the deflection in the original airframe had been only 127 mm. This was not investigated, possibly because the deflection was wholly elastic.

The aileron strength was tested under a negative load of 150 kg./sq. m. (30·8 lb./sq. ft.) with the control column fixed; simultaneously the wing in front of the loaded aileron was sand-loaded to 200 kg./sq. m. (41 lb./sq. ft.). Again no excessive deformation was observed, but splintering began to occur at the strut ends under this exceptionally severe load.

The auxiliary spar was stressed from a chordwise load of 150 kg./sq. m. on the ailerons; but even at twice this load no failure or permanent deformation occurred.

Finally an overload was applied to the wing tips. In the Case A test the sand was first applied uniformly along the span. When this load (2,345 kg., or 5,160 lb.) proved safe, additional loading was applied, rising triangularly to the wing tips. At 65% of this unrealistic tip load, the spar of the bottom wing failed at a distance of 75 cm. (30 in.) from the port side of the fuselage.

The report concluded that failure of wings or ailerons was unlikely in

Typical section of Fok. Dr.I wing.

service unless glued joints were badly affected by moisture. The Bauaufsicht was instructed to exercise greater care in supervising the production of these aircraft.

After this unhappy interlude the Fok. Dr.I was relatively trouble-free. Two wing failures that occurred early in 1918 might have been attributable to combat damage. On February 3, 1918, Leutnant Wolff (Jasta 11) had to crash-land No. 155/17 after failure of the top wing: the aft spanwise stringer and ribs of the wing had broken. On March 13, 1918, Leutnant Lothar von Richthofen lost his top wing while diving almost vertically from an unfavourable combat position; he managed to crash-land and escaped with minor injuries.

Two days later, on March 15, 1918, following a crash report, the modified Fok. Dr.I ribs were again strength-tested at Adlershof. The rib was fixed at its spar gap and a concentrated lift load applied to it. Failure occurred by buckling of the web under a load of 55 kg. (121 lb.). Two plywood reinforcing pieces were bradded to the web on both sides of the lightening holes. The rib now supported a load of 75 kg. (165 lb.). The test arrangement was far from being realistic: when the report was shown to Platz he considered the reinforcing pieces to be quite unnecessary.

The bogey of wing failure was not completely exorcised: on May 9, 1918, Leutnant Wenzel (Jasta 11) had five ribs fail in the top wing of his Fok. Dr.I during violent combat manoeuvres. He managed to land unharmed, and the failure was found to have been caused by poor workmanship.

Concurrently with the structural testing, the Fok. Dr.I was subjected to flying tests at Adlershof. There, on November 10, 1917, Fok. Dr.I No. 141/17 was evaluated as a typical example of the type. During the final meeting of the test committee and the discussion of the results, the Fokker company was represented by Dr.-Ing. Koner. The standing practice was for the designer of the aircraft to represent his firm at such discussions. The unsuitability of Koner as the Fokker representative has already been commented on.

No attempt was made to measure performance during the November trials: the performance figures that had been obtained during the acceptance tests of No. 141/17 on October 15, 1917, were incorporated in the report. These figures had been established with a military load of 145 kg. (320 lb.), 55 litres of petrol (12·2 gals.), and 8 kg. (17·6 lb.) of oil. Climbing times were:

To 1·0 km. (3,300 ft.)	:	1·6 minutes
2·0 km. (6,600 ft.)	:	4·2 minutes
3·0 km. (9,900 ft.)	:	8·0 minutes
5·0 km. (16,400 ft.)	:	20·6 minutes

The take-off run was 45 m. (50 yd.); the landing run 50 m. (55 yd.). The top speed was stated to be no less than 190 km./hr. (118 m.p.h.), but this was in fact an over-optimistic figure. Careful speed measurements were made in April 1918 at Rechlin: these established a maximum speed of only 156 km./hr. (97 m.p.h.) at an altitude of 2·75 km. (9,200 ft.), decreasing to 138 km./hr. (86 m.p.h.) at 4·18 km. (13,800 ft.).

Thus, D.H.9 pilots were not exaggerating when they claimed that they had been able to run away from the Fokker triplane with ease. In fact, the Fok. Dr.I was appreciably slower than the Albatros D.V, which it was supposed to supersede. But it had a much superior rate of climb at medium altitudes, and it manoeuvred superbly, its instant response to its highly sensitive controls demanding no effort from the pilot.

Fok. Dr.I, No. 141/17, the subject of the official type test.

During the evaluation tests, various minor details were adversely criticized. These included better sealing of the entry of the aileron cables into the wing to minimize moisture absorption; poor attachment of the wing-tip skids (the need for them was not questioned!); the use of coloured anti-rust lacquer; defective cowling attachment; compass badly placed and not easily seen (it was unreliable anyhow); wheel track too narrow; front attachment nuts of the middle wing inaccessible; and so on.

More serious criticism was levelled against the shoddy crash-protection padding in front of the pilot; this should have been of 10-cm. (4-in.) diameter. The aircraft was found to be 25 kg. (55 lb.) heavier than the weight inscribed on the fuselage side (but the Fok. Dr.I was not by any

Fok. Dr.I, No. 141/17.

means unique in this respect). The aileron cables were considered to be poorly arranged, for they chafed in places. The rudder should have had three bearings instead of only two; and the ailerons were of such a length that they should have had one more hinge.

The petrol cock was criticized for being too small, and for allowing petrol to drip into the fuselage. It was thought that the fuel tank should be made of brass, and that its mounting should be more substantial. There was some doubt about the effectiveness of engine cooling and—a curious criticism—the accessibility of the engine installation was queried. This last point was somewhat startling in view of the fact that all other operational German fighters had their engines deep within plywood fuselages.

242

The triplane's exceptional manoeuvrability was praised. But the type could be recommended for Service use only after the wing and aileron design had been passed as airworthy.

At the final meeting no fewer than twenty-seven officers and high-ranking engineering experts of the specialist departments of the Flz. were present. Among them was Roland Betsch of the Bauaufsicht. It could not be said that the final judgment had been lightly or hastily reached.

The detailed report of this test failed to reach Platz, despite the fact that one copy was sent to the Fokker firm and another to the Bauaufsicht for action. Thus he, the designer, remained in ignorance of all the criticisms, suggestions and new requirements; nor did he know that the report was accompanied by a reminder that the required stress analysis of the aircraft was still outstanding and should be submitted forthwith. Apparently Bauaufsicht 13 at the Fokker Works had their own ideas about liaison between a manufacturer and the *IdFlieg*!

The Fok. Dr.I at the front

When the new Fokker made its appearance on the Western Front, most of the German fighter pilots took to it instantly and were full of praise for its flying qualities: it was everything they wanted a fighter aircraft to be. Even after the set-back caused by the wing failures and the subsequent suspicion of structural weakness, the operational pilots demanded that the ban on its use should be raised as quickly as possible. When similar difficulties beset some other fighter types the pilots fervently hoped that the suspect aircraft would not be seen again.

Allied pilots soon had the measure of the Fok. Dr.I. They discovered that it was rather better than the obsolete Sopwith triplane but that it was too slow. The drag of the triplane wing system deprived it of the ability to make swift, surprise diving attacks. As the test results quoted on page 241 indicate, the Germans had overrated the Fokker triplane's speed. Yet it was not lack of speed that was its major shortcoming, even though that allowed the D.H.4, D.H.9, Bristol Fighter and Spad to run away from the Fok. Dr.I if they chose to do so: it was the poor all-round performance at the steadily increasing combat altitudes that mattered most. All Allied aircraft could now fly and fight at substantially greater heights.

On January 14, 1918, the Kogenluft ordered a drastic reduction of the load to be carried by all operational single-seat fighters. The fuel load was cut to provide a maximum endurance of only $1\frac{1}{2}$ hours; during acceptance tests, fuel for only one hour needed to be carried. This load reduction for all fighters in the D and Dr categories[1] was also to apply to all new designs. This was an admission of the serious consequences of the mismanagement of aero-engine development in the immediate past.

In spite of the relief provided by this order, the main combat weakness

---

[1] E-category fighters had long been superseded and none was in operational use.

Fok. Dr.Is on the Western Front in 1918. A photograph taken at the time when the Fok. D.VII was superseding the triplane.

of the Fok. Dr.I continued to be the low power and low compression ratio of its 110-h.p. Le Rhône engine. The Allies had largely withdrawn the Le Rhône from operational use a year or so earlier. A programme with the aim of re-equipping the Fok. Dr.I with more powerful engines of better altitude performance was therefore initiated. Some of the experimental engine installations are described in pages 247–251. None of these variants was put to the test of operational flying before the Fok. Dr.I was withdrawn from first-line units.

Typical of the opinions of the pilots who flew the triplane in its operational heyday are those of von Tutschek and Ernst Udet. Hauptmann von Tutschek claimed that the Fok. Dr.I was superior in dog-fighting to any contemporary Allied fighter, better even than the 200-h.p. Spad single-seater. He himself had dived the Fokker triplane until its terminal velocity was reached in a near-vertical dive: this he claimed to be in excess of 240 km./hr. (150 m.p.h.), which is just possible but not very probable.

Ernst Udet stated, early in 1918, that to him the Fokker triplane seemed to be the ideal fighter aeroplane; he regarded it as superior to the Sopwith Camel in manoeuvrability and rate of climb. He was so fond of the triplane that shortly after the war he wanted a similar aircraft designed for him for exhibition flying.[1]

Less enthusiastic were those pilots who were built on more generous lines than the average mortal. The Fok. Dr.I was no aeroplane for long-legged pilots: E. A. Marquard has recounted the agonies he endured in the triplane's cockpit; a contemporary cartoon depicted him with his legs protruding through the bottom of the triplane's fuselage, his feet

[1] He was disappointed when, after our arguments about the merits of triplanes, I confronted him with a low-wing monoplane. It took him some time to get used to the idea of sitting above a single wing.

resting on a rudder bar mounted on the undercarriage axle. Marquard also criticized the poor view from the cockpit during take-off and when touching down. This was certainly true, because the fuselage was short and the undercarriage tall.

Most pilots of the Richthofen Jagdgeschwader flew the Fok. Dr.I until April 1918; from then onwards it was progressively replaced by the Fok. D.VII biplane. During the first big air battle over Le Cateau, on March 18, 1918, sixty German single-seat fighters took part: the majority were Fokker triplanes, one of which, No. 152/17, was flown by Manfred von Richthofen.

Contrary to all the sensational claims in Allied newspapers during the war and in certain American magazines published since then, Manfred von Richthofen's triplanes were perfectly standard and carried no more than the two regulation machine-guns. He, however, had the privilege of having two or even three reserve aircraft. These were all alike and were always kept ready for immediate operational use in case his usual triplane was unserviceable for any reason.

Occasionally the red wings of his Fok. Dr.I bore leader's streamers similar to those used in British squadrons. He adopted these after a shot-down British pilot had said that during the fight he had looked in vain for the legendary Red Baron as the most desirable target. A Prussian officer could not let this pass.

Production of the Fok. Dr.I ceased during May 1918; after that, no more production triplanes were accepted.

Notes on individual Fokker triplanes appear in Appendix V (page 411), and a full description of the construction of this remarkable aeroplane is in Appendix IV (pages 406–410).

The Fokker triplane seen through Allied eyes

Examples of the Fokker triplane soon fell into Allied hands. One of the best specimens was No. 144/17, which came down in British-held territory in near-perfect condition, its pilot (Leutnant Stapenhorst of Jasta 11) having been wounded by anti-aircraft fire. This Fok. Dr.I had been despatched from Schwerin on December 12, 1917; its engine was apparently an Oberursel-built Le Rhône, or had been given an Oberursel nameplate.

The design features of the triplane were critically studied by Allied experts. At this remove it is difficult to know whether some were so strongly prejudiced that they thought that anything produced by the enemy was inevitably no good, or considerations of national security or propaganda required their reports to imply that that was the case. Others evaluated the Fokker intelligently, but took care not to hurt the tender feelings of the authorities and aircraft designers in this country.

In March 1918, Ministry of Munitions report No. I.C. 620 was published. It was brief, incomplete and inaccurate, its tone being set by the statement "It was felt the machine exhibits few instructive features". The report asserted that the Fok. Dr.I was "one of the poorest of modern German designs", emphasized "the grave structural weakness" of the airframe, and made it abundantly clear that the "expert" who wrote the report had been either insufficiently conscientious to make a rough paper check on the airframe strength or incapable of doing so: it would have cost less than an hour's work. The report must have made remarkable reading for British pilots who had experienced the combat qualities of the Fokker triplane.

But British experts in less official positions thought somewhat differently. In particular, *Flight* took great pains to discuss the design objectively and in great detail: no doubt this description was written by C. M. Poulsen, who was the journal's technical editor at that time. This excellent private effort allowed Allied aircraft designers to judge for themselves the merits of the Fokker triplane.

The *Flight* report criticized the fact that welded joints were stressed in tension. In comparison with other German fighters, the triplane's cockpit seemed cramped and spartan; the seat upholstery and padding were described as of inferior quality, like the rest of the furnishing. This criticism was justified: indeed, the poor finish and workmanship of the Fok. Dr.I may have been partly responsible for the poor impression it created among the British technicians.

The critic erred in objecting to the seemingly weak attachments of the undercarriage struts. As described in Appendix IV, this arrangement was intentional and in conformity with German official requirements.

On the whole, *Flight*'s appraisement was not only intelligent and accurate; it was remarkably fair and far-sighted.

Immediately after the Armistice, the Allies discovered a number of serviceable Fok. Dr.Is in two fighter training establishments at Valenciennes and Nivelles. At Nivelles in particular, British and American officers had ample opportunity to make trial flights before these triplanes were scrapped. They were all astonished by the aircraft's sensitivity, instant control responses, and the effortless ease with which it could be thrown about in the air. They now understood why their erstwhile German opponents had been so disconcertingly agile and elusive in combat. The Allied pilots were the more impressed because, during the war, the British authorities had not troubled to make proper flight tests of any of the captured triplanes. (Captured Fok. Dr.Is had been test-flown in France early in 1918, but the reports of these tests cannot now be traced.)

None of the officers who now had an opportunity of trying out the Fok. Dr.I found any real difficulty in mastering it. Although the specimens they flew were somewhat past their best and their engines were running on a low-grade castor-oil substitute, the triplanes still impressed with their spectacular climbing ability.

A few years after the war, one or two triplane single-seaters were built in Germany. These were more or less variations of the Fok. Dr.I and had

This Fok. Dr.I was captured by the French and flown by them. Apparently the original cowling was replaced by one from a Nieuport.

Le Rhône-type rotary engines. Max Schueler, a veteran pilot and designer, flew one all over Germany advertising Sarotti chocolate. It had a Thulin-built engine, and its career ended in an unfortunate forced landing in 1926. It seems that no genuine Fok. Dr.I exists anywhere today.

Non-standard versions of the Fok. Dr.I

Towards the end of 1917 the Oberursel UR.II engine passed the official acceptance test; it was the Fokker-sponsored copy of the Le Rhône. Engines of this type were from then on installed in the Fok. Dr.I, but the pilots at the front preferred the *Beute* engines, and all kinds of subterfuges were employed to replace the UR.II. Both engines were practically identical, but the Thulin-built version embodied better materials and the workmanship was excellent.

Siemens und Halske had now completed their new eleven-cylinder counter-rotating engine, the 160-h.p. Sh.3. As it had not then passed its type test it remained experimental. This engine was more powerful than the Le Rhône and, owing to its higher compression ratio, had a better altitude performance. The large, slow-running propeller had a high propulsive efficiency.

Fokker received an order for an experimental triplane to be powered by this engine. The Sh.3 needed a different engine mounting embodying a front bearing; the cowling also had to be modified. Even when a four-blade airscrew was fitted it was still of such a diameter that a taller undercarriage was necessary. This not only made the aircraft ungainly in

The Fokker V.7, a Fok. Dr.I with the 160-h.p. Siemens–Halske Sh.3. engine.

appearance but impaired its handling characteristics on or near the ground. It was also heavier. Although otherwise virtually identical with the standard Fok. Dr.I, the triplane with the Sh.3 engine was given the new designation Fokker V.7. Later versions of this triplane had the fuselage lengthened by as much as 55 cm. (21·7 in.).

A. Zeithammer, the Siemens engineer in charge of the field trials with the Sh.3 engine, complained bitterly of Fokker's uncooperative attitude. Fokker persistently found fault with the engine during test flights, yet Zeithammer was unable to trace any trouble. Fokker, of course, was not anxious to see the Siemens-Halske engine achieve success and be adopted. He had instructed his Oberursel firm to develop with all speed an eleven-cylinder Le Rhône development for a more powerful variant of the Fok. Dr.I.

It seems that the *IdFlieg* finally decided to take the experiments with the Sh.3 out of Fokker's hands. One or two further Fok. Dr.Is with the Sh. 3 were sponsored by Adlershof, but these were modifications of existing Dr.I airframes made in the Flz. workshops and by the Siemens und Halske firm.

While these experiments were proceeding, experience with the Sh.3 elsewhere left no doubt that the engine was still a long way from being sufficiently serviceable for operational use. Piston trouble was experienced, and the only available oil was not suitable. Hence, in spite of its magnificent climbing performance and amazing ceiling, the Siemens-engined Fok. Dr.I never reached the front. Besides, as Kurt Student relates, this version was slightly unstable and too sensitive for the average fighter pilot of the time. The approach and landing needed care: the wing-like axle fairing had been omitted in order to reduce the tendency to float near the ground. The torque reaction from the large airscrew was felt powerfully because the wing span was so short; and the blip-switch had to be used with great care when flying close to the ground.

The *IdFlieg* had intended to prolong the operational life of the Fok. Dr.I by fitting more powerful engines. One of the earliest of these experimental installations was of the first Goebel Goe.III engines (Works No. 1) of 170 nominal horse-power. This engine was fitted to one of the earliest production triplanes, No. 108/17, which was test-flown by Schuetzenmeister at Goerries on October 30, 1917. It was fitted with an Axial airscrew of 270-cm. (8 ft. 10¼ in.) diameter and 255-cm. (8 ft. 4·4 in.) pitch: this gave 1,260 r.p.m. on the stand and 1,300 r.p.m. in level flight near the ground. At 5·0 km. altitude (16,500 ft.) the engine speed dropped to 1,130 r.p.m.

The forward fuselage of the Fokker V.7.

Carrying ballast of 60 kg. (132 lb.), 55 litres (12 gals.) of petrol and 10 kg. (22 lb.) of oil, the Goebel-powered triplane climbed to 5·0 km. altitude in only 14·3 minutes. This was an excellent performance for that time and far better than that of the standard Fok. Dr.I. The Goe.III, which was then some way from developing all the power of which it was capable, had an hourly fuel consumption rate of 90 litres (20 gals.) of petrol and 9 kg. (20 lb.) of oil; the latter was *ersatz* castor oil. This was greater than the consumption of the Sh.3 engine for about the same power output.

The Goe.III was a promising development of the Gnôme, with a half-controlled, half-automatic inlet valve, a high compression ratio, and (later) oversized cylinders. Final versions (Goe.IIIa) could produce over 200 h.p. for short periods. This engine was the first to have a separate gear for an auxiliary drive; this was supplied as part of the engine's light alloy mounting.

Some of the Fok. Dr.Is delivered from January 1918 onwards were supplied with this Goebel engine, about thirty aircraft in all. It is improbable, but by no means impossible, that one or other of these triplanes may have been flown on the Western Front. Most of them went to home-defence fighter formations and training units, and experience of the Goe.III was favourable.

When the new 145-h.p. Oberursel UR.III Le Rhône development came out late in December 1917, one of the first examples to complete its bench test was quickly installed in Fok. Dr.I No. 469/17 and demonstrated by Fokker. This variant was not officially adopted, but the aircraft was flown extensively as an engine test-bed for the development of the UR.III.

Three Fok. Dr.Is (Nos. 485/17, 527/17 and 562/17) were fitted with captured 130-h.p. Clerget engines: the engine numbers were 953, 1072 and 1503, the airframes Factory Nos. 2111, 2232 and 2195, respectively. The three aircraft made their acceptance flights on April 24, 1918, at Goerries, flown by Neisen, Grosse and Schuetzenmeister respectively. These Clerget-powered triplanes were not intended for operational purposes, but were, used for an investigation into the Clerget engine's behaviour.

This investigation almost certainly arose out of the serious difficulties experienced by Germany in trying to obtain lubricating oil for rotary engines. Castor oil had become so scarce on the German side that it could no longer be supplied even for the few rotary-powered German aircraft that were then operational. A German substitute (Voltol) had been developed; it was produced by a polymerization of ordinary mineral oil under electric discharges. This substitute was certainly less soluble in petrol than ordinary oil, but its lubricating qualities fell far short of those of castor oil. Worst fault of all, its quality was not consistent. Some at least of the troubles that afflicted German-built rotaries could be blamed on their oil, consequently there was good reason for subjecting captured engines with well-known performance to the torture of running on German *ersatz* lubricants.

During 1918, Fok. Dr.I aircraft were used in a special series of experiments instigated by the *IdFlieg*. The object of this work was the evolution of a supercharger for rotary engines in order to maintain constant power output up to altitudes of 6·5 km. (22,000 ft.) and higher; service ceilings of 9·0 km. (30,000 ft.) were envisaged for 1919, and were within reach when the Armistice supervened.

As a first step, a UR.II was installed in an otherwise standard Fok. Dr.I and fitted with a Schwade gear-driven compressor weighing 47·5 kg.

(105 lb.). This was mounted behind the cylinders, alongside the crankshaft and carburettor. For the drive, Schwade had designed a suitable gear and a coupling embodying elastic clutches. When running at 10,500 r.p.m. the compressor absorbed about 20 b.h.p.

This was the first German direct-coupled aero-engine compressor to fly. Details of the flight tests have never become known, but the results were highly satisfactory. Had the war continued into 1919, Schwade would have received a large production order for a fully developed version to be used in a Fok. D.VIII variant: this would have given these single-seaters a marked superiority early in the year.

A compressor had also been developed by Siemens und Halske for the Sh.3 engine. This had already been flown in an obsolete Siemens-Schuckert D.I, in which it was mounted under the carburettor; the aircraft was turned over to the Flz. in October 1918 for further trials. The *IdFlieg* wanted comparative trials with a more modern aircraft and engine, however. The Siemens people would have preferred such trials to have been made in one of the later Siemens-Schuckert fighters, but none of the modern types could accommodate the compressor.

It was therefore decided to install the three-stage Siemens compressor in a Fok. Dr.I with Sh.3 engine. The compressor weighed 38 kg. (84 lb.) and ran at 8,600 r.p.m. The Fokker works obtained all installation details from Siemens in September 1918. Apparently in addition to the *IdFlieg* experiments with the supercharged Sh.3, the Fokker works intended to apply the Siemens compressor to an Oberursel UR.II in a Fok. Dr.I. This installation was never completed, however.

The V.6 triplane

In pursuit of his policy of developing parallel prototypes with rotary and stationary engines, Fokker wanted a triplane with a Mercedes engine.

The Fokker V.6 in its original form, before the lower wing was faired to the fuselage.

251

In this configuration the result was the V.6, which had a 120-h.p. Mercedes.

Platz designed the V.6 to have approximately the same wing loading as the Fok. Dr.I, consequently its heavier engine inevitably made it a larger aircraft. Its wing span was something over 8 m. (26 ft. 6 in.). The greater chord of the mainplanes dictated larger gaps; this meant that the bottom wing had to be placed a short distance below the fuselage. Aerodynamically this was bad, for it caused interference drag, premature flow separation at the lower wing, and an extensive vortex region aft that reduced the effectiveness of the tail controls. As Fokker soon discovered, the performance and flying qualities were adversely affected.

The lower centre section was later faired into the fuselage, adding considerably to the fuselage depth, but this did little good. The V.6 had other defects. The long six-cylinder engine made it necessary to place the cockpit well aft: owing to this and the larger wing chord, the pilot's view was inferior to that afforded by the Fok. Dr.I. Being a larger aircraft, the V.6 was less manoeuvrable. It was therefore a poor prospect, even if its aerodynamic deficiencies could have been remedied: it was and remained an ungainly aeroplane. Fokker saw no point in pursuing its development and abandoned the design.

One feature of the V.6 that became a characteristic of later Fokker fighters with water-cooled engines was its nose radiator mounted immediately behind the airscrew. There was nothing new or original about the nose radiator, but it had been almost forgotten in Germany when Platz revived it in the V.6. For those days it was an excellent position for the radiator, and much to be preferred to the then-fashionable radiator installations in or at the wings, which were detrimental to the airflow over the wings.

The V.8 quintuplane

Fokker recognized that the triplane fashion had brought him success. The Fok. Dr.I had put him in the lead and his competitors had not been able to catch him up. This gave him a brainwave: if three wings produced such a successful aeroplane, even greater things might be expected from one with more wings.

On the strength of this aerodynamic misconception he shocked Platz with a request for a quintuplane; he was convinced that five wings ought to ensure resounding success.

Platz was perturbed by this proposition. The more he thought about the boss's request in detail, the more his dismay grew. His aerodynamic knowledge at that time was still limited, but he felt instinctively that a quintuplane would be useless as a fighter. It was, of course, an affront to his belief in simplicity, and the complete antithesis of his ideal, the cantilever monoplane.

Platz argued with Fokker, trying to prove to him that it was scarcely feasible to attach five wings satisfactorily to a single fuselage and that the whole thing would be a mass of struts and wings. But Fokker would not listen; he insisted stubbornly on a quintuplane.

In 1917, Platz had not had enough experience as a chief designer to feel sure enough of himself in rejecting an absurd request. With extreme distaste he started the unpleasant task of designing the V.8 at Fokker's behest. Even today he regards the V.8 as such an outrage that he dislikes admitting that he designed it.

Anyone but Fokker would have conducted model tests or wind-tunnel investigations on stability and control before building such a weird aircraft. Ignoring, as usual, such technical desiderata, Fokker had the contraption built without having the slightest inkling of the kind of properties it was likely to display.

The weird Fokker V.8 quintuplane.

Platz did his best. He decided on a tandem-wing arrangement, but retained a conventional tail unit on a long fuselage. This was a reasonable feature, giving better fore-and-aft trim possibilities. It may also have saved Fokker's life. A triplane wing system was mounted at the extreme nose of the aircraft; a pair of biplane wings were attached amidships at a distance of 2·5 times the wing chord behind the triplane structure; neither set of wings was staggered. Balanced control surfaces were fitted to the top wings of both the triplane and biplane systems; those at the front acted as conventional ailerons, those on the midships wings were apparently aligned with the elevators. The centre of gravity was located between the two wing systems; the cockpit was rather far aft, in line with the leading edge of the biplane wings. The engine was a 120-h.p. Mercedes, and a nose radiator was fitted.

When the V.8 was completed, Fokker made a short hop in it: his intimates dignified this exercise by calling it a flight. He demanded some modifications; when these were completed he made another exploratory hop. After this, Fokker decided to scrap the aircraft. He realized that Platz was right; but he did not tell him so.

The V.8 was, of course, entirely a private venture: no type-test commission was confronted with the alarming experience of evaluating it.

Platz confesses that he was immensely relieved when the quintuplane proved such a convincing failure. It if had not been, Fokker would have insisted on aircraft with more and more wings, and Platz would never again have been able to revert to simple and practical aeroplanes.

CHAPTER XII

THE FOKKER–JUNKERS EPISODE

In 1917, the United States of America entered the war on the side of the Allies. Up to that time the U.S.A. had been supplying some aeronautical material for the Allied war effort but, as far as aircraft and aero-engines were concerned, this had been negligible in quantity and inferior in quality. Germany knew that the U.S.A.'s entry into the shooting war would mean, ultimately, an increase in the supply of war material to the Allies. The production capacity and technical ability of the Americans, once applied to the latest proven British and French aircraft types, were likely to produce a substantial growth in Allied air power.

In anticipation of this, the German High Command prepared a comprehensive "America Programme", designed to step up the German war effort. The Kögenluft was charged with building up a much expanded air force, backed by a major production effort.

The America Programme suffered serious setbacks. In November 1917, two extensive fires retarded re-equipment. At Adlershof, stores containing hundreds of new aero-engines, thousands of magnetos and other valuable material were gutted; arson was suspected. An explosion in the Griesheim Elektron Works, the sole producer of magnesium and its alloys, paralysed this source of supply. A coal shortage affected the production of steel for crankshafts in the Rhineland. Aircraft materials of all kinds, from steel tubes to fabric and dope, had become scarce. Substitute materials had to be introduced. Most of these not only created new and serious problems but were downright bad.

Even the manning of the specified new formations of the Army Air Corps proved difficult. Of 15,000 recruits called up during August and November for service with the Air Corps, only 30% proved to be skilled workers instead of the 80% that had been promised and expected.

In June 1917, Major Siegert, in charge of the *IdFlieg*, had appealed to the aircraft industry to make greater efforts. With biting sarcasm he had pointed out that "the casualty list of the aircraft industry has empty pages", and that "complaints about harming the shareholder were much less important than the necessity to harm the enemy".

During the critical summer of 1917, Major F. Wagenfuehr, the capable organizer in charge of aeronautical development and production, decided that it would be a good idea for the Fokker and Junkers Works to join

255

forces. His experts advised this, for they reasoned thus: Professor Junkers, ignorant though he was of flying and aircraft production, had created a revolutionary development in aviation; Fokker, a practical man with wide flying experience, could produce serviceable aircraft. Thus, a combination of the talents of these two eminent men should provide the superior aircraft that were so badly needed at the front. The argument was not unattractive.

So the Junkers–Fokker Works were founded on October 20, 1917, after Wagenfuehr had talked to Fokker and Junkers in his most persuasive manner. Fokker paid his 50% of the capital of six million marks (about £150,000). Junkers instructed his bankers to do likewise. That more or less concluded for good the combined efforts of the new firm to contribute to the war effort.

It was a simple case of Greek meeting Greek. Neither the wily professor nor the egotistical Fokker had any intention of helping each other on a give-and-take basis, or of pooling their resources. Each merely wanted to extract something from the other that he himself was not willing to give. Since both were equally good at this game, a common effort was out of the question. Junkers gave his partner no details of the outcome of his research, and Fokker did not tell Junkers how to make aeroplanes suitable for operational use (the Junkers types suffered from abominable flying qualities, and pilots at the front refused to have them). Finally Fokker withdrew, complaining that the deal had cost him his £75,000. There may have been some truth in this, for at that time Junkers knew far more than Fokker about financial dealings.

Wagenfuehr was nonplussed to see his scheme come to nothing. As a regular officer with a strict upbringing in honesty, he could not understand how leaders of industry dealt with each other.

CHAPTER XIII

IN ERSTER LINIE ALLE APPARATE
D.VII . . . . .

FOKKER'S PERSONAL design inspirations cooled off after the spectacular failure of the V.8 monstrosity, and Platz was able to get on with sensible designs. He wanted to develop a monoplane with a cantilever wing. Fokker was not keen on the idea: monoplanes were out of fashion. A biplane on the lines of the V.4 would probably have a better chance of winning production orders, provided it was as simple as the triplane and its wings were not obvious cantilevers.

A competition for the selection of new fighter types was shortly to be held at Adlershof. Fokker insisted on entering as many types as possible: in his opinion, the broad approach offered the best prospects of success. The *IdFlieg* had indicated their intention of ordering rotary-powered fighters as well as aircraft with stationary engines. The Army had invited attention to the promising new 160-h.p. Siemens engine, and stated that they wished to consider prototypes with this engine.

With all these considerations before him, Fokker again decided on the parallel development of two prototypes, one a light, rotary-powered aircraft, the other a larger machine with a 160-h.p. Mercedes.

It was decided that the new type should be a sesquiplane. Platz's first attempt was the V.9, a small biplane that originally had an 80-h.p. Oberursel engine. After the first flight tests this was replaced by a 110-h.p. Le Rhône. The V.9's direct descent from the V.4 was apparent: its fuselage, tail unit, undercarriage and engine mounting were all virtually identical with those of the triplane. The V.9's lower wing had the same compounded spar arrangement and was located in a recess in the underside of the fuselage. The upper wing was of greater span and chord, and its two box spars were at a conventional distance with drag bracing between them. The cabane structure consisted of two tripods of steel tubes and was somewhat similar to that of the V.1. Both wing spars were bolted to the four apices of the tripods.

Both wings were integral structures covered with fabric, and were dimensioned as cantilevers. Merely to reduce their flexing under load, and to satisfy Fokker, a V-strut was fitted between them. The lower end of the strut was made broad enough to provide an attachment that was

The Fokker V.9.

connected to both the basic spars of the lower wing. Without knowing it, Platz had thereby avoided the structural weakness of the Albatros fighters—the possibility of oscillatory torsion of increasing amplitude in the lower wing under certain conditions of flight. The V.9 cabane structure needed no diagonal bracing, consequently the aircraft was truly *verspannungslos*.

The aerofoil section of the V.4 was employed in both wings. There was no stagger, and the wings were made without dihedral. Ailerons were fitted to the upper wing only; to Platz's displeasure, they had horn balances.

The pilot's forward field of view was unobstructed. The upper wing was somewhat above his eye-level, and a large cut-out was made in the trailing edge in order to improve his outlook. Despite the greater wing chord, the field of vision was better than that of the Fok. Dr.I.

The V.9 was rather a small aeroplane, with a span of about 7·5 m. (24·6 ft.) and a length of less than 5·9 m. (19·5 ft.). It was also very light, and its wing loading was about the same as that of the Fok. Dr.I. In its final form the V.9 was demonstrated at Adlershof, but it was never subjected to an official structural test, nor was it fitted with guns. It remained purely experimental.

The parallel design with 160-h.p. Mercedes was built late in 1917; it appears that it made its first flights late in December 1917. This new biplane seemed to hold considerable promise, and Fokker was most anxious to get it ready for the Adlershof competition.

Designated V.11 (Factory No. 1883), the new aircraft was in some respects an enlarged edition of the V.9. Both wings were of greater chord, the increase of the lower-wing chord being sufficient to require two separate spars with box ribs as compression members and wire bracing

258

The Fokker V.11 in its original form. Note the projecting ailerons and balanced rudder.

between them. This in turn necessitated a different mounting for the lower wing. Interplane struts of N-form were fitted; these were an immensely practical innovation, and became characteristic of many later Fokker biplanes.

The cabane structure was simplified. There were tripod supports for the front spar of the upper wing, but the rear spar was connected to the fuselage by a single strut on each side. Whereas the tripod was welded to the fuselage, the rear single strut could be removed. The front strut

Another view of the original Fokker V.11. There was no central cut-out in the wing trailing edge, and the balance portions of the elevators had straight-edged tips.

of the tripod was connected to the centre of the engine-bearer tube. This gave direct transfer of the inertia load from the heavy engine and produced a strong and light space frame; it reduced drag and improved the field of vision.

The engine was neatly installed, with a radiator similar to that of the V.8 mounted in front of it. In the V.11 the radiator was mounted on the engine bearers and could be exchanged without removing the airscrew. The expansion tank was an integral part of the radiator.

In its original form the V.11 had a tail unit similar to that of the V.9, and horn-balanced ailerons on the upper wing. There was no cut-out in the trailing edge of the wing. Its fuselage was somewhat short, having been designed to have the same proportions as that of the V.9; the greater forward side area created by the long engine had not been taken into account.

As will be recorded later, the V.11 required a major modification before its flying qualities could be regarded as safe and satisfactory. This consisted of lengthening the fuselage by some 40 cm. (about 16 in.) aft of the centre of gravity. To compensate for the resulting tail-heavy moment, the upper wing had to be moved aft; this in turn necessitated a cut-out in the trailing edge of the upper wing. A triangular fin and a new rudder were fitted, and the area of the aileron balances was altered. There may have been a change in the amount of stagger, but this is uncertain.

After these modifications the V.11 was safe and pleasant to fly. It had now become, in all essential features, the design known subsequently as the Fok. D.VII. It appears that a second example of the modified version was built. In February 1918 it became the true prototype of the Fok.

The modified V.11 with revised ailerons and new tail unit. The upper wing has been moved aft, necessitating a small cut-out in the trailing edge to improve the pilot's upward view.

This aircraft is believed to be the second Fokker V.11, modified to production standard. It had a large exhaust manifold carrying the exhaust gases to a level above the upper wing.

D.VII. One of these two experimental aircraft was later converted into the V.24 experimental aeroplane.

A closely related design was the V.18. This too was constructed before the end of 1917 and was intended for the Adlershof trials. In external appearance the V.18 was very similar to the V.11 but probably differed in its internal design or in dimensions. It was also heavier, and may have been designed to be of greater strength. The upper wing had a cut-out in its trailing edge, possibly indicating that the cockpit was further forward than that of the original V.11. The undercarriage had a wider track and the axle had a somewhat longer travel.

The V.18 proved to be considerably inferior to the V.11; in particular

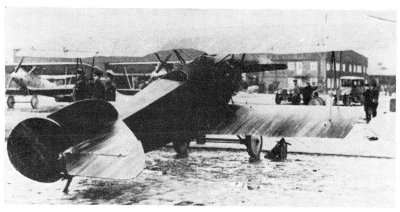

The Fokker V.18.

261

its rate of climb was unimpressive. Its career was brief: apparently it was not rebuilt after being involved in a collision with the Fokker V.13/I during the Adlershof trials.

Yet another experimental biplane fighter was built and tested at Schwerin before the end of 1917. This was the rotary-powered Fokker V.13, which appeared in two versions, each with a different engine.

The V.13 design was intended to have a better climb performance at altitude and a higher ceiling than the V.9. To this end the wing area was increased. The lower wing no longer had the compound spar box of the V.4: it was of greater chord and had separate spars like that of the V.11, consequently N-type interplane struts were employed. The upper wing was also larger than that of the V.9. The V.13 cabane was generally similar to that of the V.11, differing only in having the front strut of the tripod attached to the forward end of the lower longeron. The tail group resembled that of the V.9; there was no fin.

Power for the first version of the design, V.13/I, was provided by a 110-h.p. Oberursel (Le Rhône) UR.II.

The V.13/II had the 160-h.p. Siemens-Halske Sh.3 eleven-cylinder bi-rotary engine, which necessitated a taller undercarriage; otherwise it was a replica of V.13/I. It had an excellent rate of climb and a high service ceiling. Fokker, of course, considered that the ingenious Sh.3 engine was an imposition laid upon him by the *IdFlieg*, and hoped to replace it by the new 145/160-h.p. Oberursel UR.III as soon as the first pre-production engines became available. As far as is known, the V.13/II remained experimental.

Before 1917 ended, Platz found enough time to realize his ambition of building a cantilever monoplane fighter. This, the V.17, was virtually a V.4 fuselage and tail unit fitted with a shoulder-high cantilever wing.

Fokker V.13/II.

262

The wing had two spars, conventionally spaced, and was covered entirely with plywood. This skin took care of the torsion, and was an early example of modern stressed-skin design. The engine was a 110-h.p. Le Rhône.

The first Adlershof fighter trials

The first of the three comparative trials for the selection of new single-seat fighters began late in January 1918. The idea was admirable in theory, but it must be admitted that the results, on the whole, were no more than moderately satisfactory. This was because some of the notable fighting pilots who flew the competing aircraft were in the pay of individual firms, and consequently gave biased opinions in favour of the products of those firms. Three years of war and the insidious growth of bribery in Germany had not passed unnoticed by the young fighting pilots, and it is perhaps not surprising that their conceptions of honour had become somewhat tarnished. Ultimately it became an open secret that certain officers in command of fighting formations received favours from certain firms for "plugging" their products and denigrating those of their competitors.

Among the laudable exceptions was Manfred von Richthofen, who set an example as a conscientious Prussian officer of absolute integrity. At the other end of the scale was Hermann Goering, later a notorious member of the Hitler gang. Officers serving with or under him knew that he could be bought.

The aircraft manufacturers made the most strenuous efforts to capture the bulk orders and went to almost any length to win the approval of the pilots for their products. All firms, Fokker included, had entertainment managers whose job it was to arrange lavish dinners and parties for the pilots. These young men were consequently seldom in any physical condition to assess any aircraft dispassionately. Valuable presents such as gold cigarette cases were distributed; the more "progressive" pilots were paid in cash.

When the competitive flying began, the Adlershof aerodrome—normally strictly out of bounds to all civilians—swarmed with commercial representatives of the aircraft industry. After this impromptu trade fair had gone on for a week or two, greatly impeding the flight trials, the officers in charge of the competition decided to clear the aerodrome of those civilians who had no immediate connexion with the trials. The party-worn pilots could then get on with the real business of sampling the prototypes that had passed the structural examinations or were otherwise assessed as safe enough for familiarization flights.

The ban on civilians applied to Fokker. Not to be outdone, he flew over the forbidden area in one of his old experimental aircraft to have a look at what was going on. He could do this easily enough, for he had retained one of his old sheds on the Johannisthal side. Why this had not been requisitioned in August 1914 is a mystery. In it he had strategically planted his aeroplane and his personal mechanic Schmidt.

One cannot but admire the thorough and extensive preparations that Fokker had made for these trials. He entered no fewer than eight aircraft: four biplanes, three triplanes and a mid-wing monoplane. While the trials were in progress, a further monoplane followed. This was the V.20 which, as described in Chapter X, was designed and constructed by Platz within the space of a week while Fokker was at Adlershof.

The best mechanics of the Fokker works were at Adlershof too. Indeed, the Fokker team was the best organized of all the competitors.

Although Albatros, L.F.G.-Roland, Pfalz, Rumpler, Siemens, Schütte-Lanz and other companies had made efforts to comply with the suggestions of the *IdFlieg*, they had not prepared so comprehensively nor so wisely as Fokker. It soon became clear that he had presented prototypes that were good in all respects that mattered, and had not been developed in one specific direction at the expense of all other considerations. Most of the other types excelled in one aspect of performance but failed to be satisfactory in a general way. It was one of Fokker's great gifts as a pilot to sense how the qualities of an aeroplane should be blended to produce a really practical and useful aircraft. He never sought to have emphasis on any specific quality—say, speed, or climb, or ease of handling—but preferred to achieve a balance that would meet with the approval of operational units.

Of Fokker's four biplane entries, two (the V.11 and V.18) had the latest high-compression version of the 160-h.p. Mercedes, the type D.IIIaü. The *IdFlieg* wanted to compare prototypes with this engine because it had been ordered in quantity from Daimler.

As noted earlier in this chapter, the V.13/II had the 160-h.p. Sh.3 engine for the same reason. However, the Sh.3 had not then passed its type test and was not in quantity production, only small batches being built.

Fokker also succeeded in his desire to oppose the Siemens-Halske engine: he managed to get one of the first of the new Oberursel UR.III rotaries and had it installed in the V.13/I for demonstration against the V.13/II with its Sh.3. He seemed oblivious to the fact that the new Oberursel was inferior in altitude performance and propulsive efficiency. As it was a modification of the well-tried Le Rhône, he was convinced it was better suited to operational needs.

The *IdFlieg* had indicated that two fighter types would be chosen for quantity production, one with the Mercedes engine and another with a rotary engine not yet specified. Fokker hoped it would be the Oberursel: the Siemens people hoped equally that it would be their own engine, which was then being evaluated at the front.

Soon after the trials began, Fokker asked Manfred von Richthofen to try the V.11 He flew it on January 23, 1918. When he landed he told Fokker that it had a good performance and was manoeuvrable, but its flying qualities were unsatisfactory. This was so: it was tricky to handle and directionally unstable; when dived, it had a strong tendency to swing. This was unacceptable in a combat aircraft. Its stalling characteristics were unpleasant and might lead to accidents. If these vices could be remedied, the V.11 stood a good chance of success. Von Richthofen was delighted to note that Fokker had incorporated the control grip and gun triggers that he favoured, in place of the usual press-buttons.

Fokker heeded von Richthofen's criticism: he knew it was justified. He had had little opportunity to fly the V.11 himself, but his brief acquaintance with it had sufficed to tell him that its flying characteristics were unpleasant, and that it needed careful handling.

And so it was that the extensive modifications that have already been described came to be hastily undertaken in the Fokker shed at Johannisthal. Expert welders and other workmen, with tools and materials, were summoned from Schwerin to work all hours over the week-end under Fokker's direction. Fokker took great care to conceal the extent of these modifications from the technical officers and other competitors. This was a wise precaution, for the structural reliability of the aircraft might have been questioned after such extensive rebuilding. Fokker let it be known that the V.11 had had a slight landing mishap and needed some repairs. It was normal practice for minor repairs or engine overhauls to be undertaken during the trials, and any suspicion that might have attached to the V.11's temporary disappearance was further reduced because the job was done at a week-end, when the aerodrome was deserted.

With Fokker's usual luck, everything went smoothly. A trial flight showed him that the V.11's handling characteristics were greatly improved, although at the expense of some manoeuvrability. But it was now really safe to fly, and could be dived without any swing developing. At the first opportunity, Fokker suggested to von Richthofen that he should try the aircraft again: the control gearing had been adjusted, Fokker explained, and the Herr Rittmeister would now find it more pleasant to fly. Von Richthofen was surprised that these "small adjustments" had made the V.11 so delightful to handle; it was now vice-free. He urged other pilots, notably Loerzer, to try it. It seemed to be a really promising aeroplane.

The Trials

The Adlershof trials began on January 21, 1918, a mild day with only a thin layer of cloud at about 13,000 ft. All works pilots were busily engaged on the climbing tests under the control of the Adlershof technicians. These officials weighed every aeroplane before and after flight, noted the type of airscrew used on each (to ensure that the same one would be used in the speed tests), and installed two sealed and calibrated barographs. Refuelling was supervised to guard against the use of any special mixtures. All of these precautions were necessary to avoid cheating by enterprising manufacturers.

The best climbing performance was put up by a Siemens-Schuckert D.III fitted with a special Siemens Sh.3 engine: this gave about 220 b.h.p. on the ground and drove its airscrew at 2,000 r.p.m. instead of the usual

1,800 r.p.m. maximum. This S.S.W. D.III reached an altitude of 6·0 km. (20,000 ft.) in twenty-two minutes. Service pilots, however, found this aircraft rather tricky to land and less manoeuvrable than the Fokker biplanes.

Fokker demonstrated the not-yet-modified V.11 and, later, the V.13/I with its new 145-h.p. UR.III engine at low altitudes. His superb handling of these aircraft made a great impression. Another UR.III engine was tested in a Fokker triplane.

The second day was again mild. The V.9 fitted with a 110-h.p. UR.II, had to make a forced landing outside the aerodrome owing to engine trouble after a climbing trial, and was damaged. The new Junkers D.I low-wing monoplane was flown against an Albatros D.Va, an obsolescent type. The Albatros was flown by Hauptmann Schwarzenberger, the head of the fighter experimental section of the Flz. and its chief test pilot. The Junkers was flown by Fokker, as a director of the Junkers-Fokker Works. To everyone's amazement the Junkers proved the slower of the two. Fokker explained afterwards that the Junkers had an airscrew whose pitch was too fine; his engine threatened to overspeed and consequently he had to throttle down. There was undoubtedly something wrong with the airscrew, for it disintegrated in flight. Fokker managed to land the monoplane undamaged.

Later in the day he tried the V.13/I with the UR.III, but the engine was still running unsatisfactorily.

On the third day the fighter pilots were allowed to try those prototypes that had been structurally cleared. Oberleutnant Bruno Loerzer tried one of the new Siemens-Schuckert D.IIIs but, despite his skill and experience, crashed it when landing. Oberleutnant Ritter von Tutschek turned turtle in an Albatros D.Va fitted with the high-compression Mercedes. As already mentioned, Manfred von Richthofen tried the unmodified V.11; he found it faster than the Albatros D.Va, against which it was flown for comparison of speeds. The representatives of other firms grew uneasy when von Richthofen flew the Fokker V.11 as his first aircraft: a rumour that he "was sold on Fokker" went around. This was quite unjustified. Manfred von Richthofen, then as always, was completely impartial and unbiased.

Fokker's pilot Schuetzenmeister climbed to 4·0 km. (13,200 ft.) in the V.13/I, but the engine failed to give the expected power. Fokker demonstrated the V.17 mid-wing monoplane for the first time. When it was matched against the V.11, the Pfalz D.IIIa and the Albatros D.Va, the monoplane was the slowest of all. It was during the afternoon of this day that Fokker made the telephone call to Platz that resulted in the V.20, which Fokker flew at Adlershof eight days later.

On January 25, misfortune befell the Fokker team. While thick fog covered the aerodrome, a mechanic of the Oberursel works taxied the V.13/I into the V.18. This aircraft and an Albatros standing nearby were extensively damaged.

266

When the fog lifted during the afternoon, the Fokker works pilot Grosse climbed in the V.11 to 5·0 km. (16,500 ft.) in 30·7 minutes, despite unfavourable weather. In a later climb he put up the impressive time of 25·2 minutes to the same altitude.

In their first discussions with the Adlershof technicians, the fighter pilots expressed disappointment with all the aircraft they had sampled. Climbing times of 25 to 30 minutes to reach 6·0 km. (20,000 ft.) were regarded as acceptable, but all the new types were slow. This opinion reduced the chances of those firms who had aimed primarily at producing fast-climbing fighters; it had a particularly adverse effect on the types with the Siemens Sh.3 engine. The conclusion was that fighters with water-cooled engines were preferable for operational purposes; they were faster but did not have such good climbing performances.

Another of the Siemens-Schuckert D.III biplanes made a crash landing and turned over. An identical aircraft, however, made the climb to 6·0 km. (20,000 ft.) in 20 minutes. The Fokker V.13/I, flown by Schuetzenmeister, took 22 minutes to climb to 5·0 km. (16,500 ft.).

Few flights were made during the seventh day because most of the pilots were too fatigued, from one cause or another. Fokker, as a lifelong abstainer, had no hangover, and flew the V.17, climbing to 5·0 km. (16,500 ft.) in 24 minutes. This was a good performance on the low power of the V.17's UR.II engine. The V.18 had been repaired and made a trial climb, piloted by Heide; its time was disappointing, however.

The next day was distinguished by a dense fog and the removal of all unnecessary commercial representatives from the aerodrome.

In the quieter atmosphere that followed, the trials continued with more serious flight testing and sober discussion of the results. Climbing trials, speed comparisons and mock combats were held, interspersed with familiarization flights by the fighter pilots. There were sundry crashes, all in landing accidents. The second Schütte-Lanz D.III, a promising design by W. Bleistein, was written off after a particularly ill-judged landing.

During the first few days of February, the Fokker triplane variants with the 200-h.p. Goebel Goe.III and 145-h.p. Oberursel UR.III engines made spectacular climbs, piloted by Matthias and Grosse. They failed to give the Fok. Dr.I a new lease of life, however, for the type was regarded as much too slow. The climbs served only to demonstrate the capabilities of the new rotary engines.

The Choice

The fighter pilots were now asked to indicate which two of the various prototypes they thought best, one with the Mercedes engine, the other with a rotary.

Two different types had to be selected because the German Army Flying Corps did not believe in complete standardization of its aircraft or engines.

There was the pre-war example of Austria to point the dangers of standardization in a field that was developing rapidly; and there was the further operational proof of the British Royal Aircraft Factory types. The German engineering experts welcomed the official policy which, by spreading responsibility over a number of firms, provided a form of insurance against set-backs.

The Service technicians wished that they could feel equally happy about the question of water-cooled engines for fighter aircraft, but all efforts to break the Daimler monopoly had proved unavailing. The new 185-h.p. B.M.W. IIIa engine had been successfully flown in an Albatros D.Va during the trials and had proved to have an excellent performance, especially when climbing; but quantity production was only beginning. The new 185-h.p. Benz Bz.IIIa had been demonstrated in a L.F.G.-Roland D.VI, and the 195-h.p. Benz Bz.IIIb eight-cylinder engine in an Aviatik D.III; but these engines had not been fully tested, much less put into production. So it had to be the Mercedes.

The choice of an airframe for this engine was a relatively simple matter. Albatros, Pfalz and the L.F.G. had made no real efforts to provide something progressive. The new Rumpler types were promising but so lightly built that their ability to withstand the strains of operational use was questionable.

The matter was virtually decided after Manfred von Richthofen had flown the Fokker V.11 for the second time, after its modification. He had urged Loerzer and Klein to try it. They compared it with the two Rumplers, both of which had a better climbing performance than the Fokker. They flew the V.11 in mock combats against standard Service types and other prototypes. It proved faster and far more manoeuvrable than the Junkers D.I, and had the advantage of still being conventional. The V.11 was delightfully easy to fly. In a dive it accelerated quickly to high speed but remained as steady as a rock. The view from the cockpit was good. All pilots who tried the V.11 seemed to like it.

Points of criticism were that the performance at high altitude could be better, that the aircraft was rather heavy, and that its climb was not impressive. The new 185-h.p. B.M.W. engine ought to be installed. This last point had to be answered by the *IdFlieg* representative's reminder that production of this engine had not yet really started. It had to be the Mercedes, for the next six months at least.

Following their earlier contention that speed at medium altitudes was preferable to spectacular climbing performance, the fighter pilots recommended the adoption of the Fokker V.11 as the basis of the new Mercedes-powered fighter type. It was essential that the new type be supplied quickly and not, as had happened with earlier Fokker fighters, when it had been surpassed by new enemy types. Could the Fokker works cope with rapid quantity production, if the V.11 were chosen?

Precisely the same question was in the minds of the *IdFlieg* officers. Those who knew Fokker's production facilities at Schwerin were certain that he could not possibly cope with a really large order. To achieve early deliveries it would be necessary to have the V.11 produced under licence by two or three firms that had adequate, up-to-date facilities; these firms should be given the bulk of the orders. At that time the Albatros company at Johannisthal and their large branch firm, the Ostdeutsche Albatros Werke at Schneidemühl, had no urgent orders. They had the largest production facilities in Germany. A further possibility was the A.E.G. aircraft factory at Henningsdorf: they had ample experience with welded structures.

A memorandum to the Kogenluft was prepared to enable Thomsen to give his decisions to Siegert and to his personal representative at the trials. The memorandum contained the reasons for the selection of the V.11 and enumerated the production difficulties that had to be resolved before the new type could be put into service at an early date.

There was much less unanimity about the choice of the rotary-powered fighter type. The pilots said that all the prototypes with rotaries were more difficult to handle than the V.11, and their engines gave the impression of being less reliable. This was perfectly true.

Pfalz, the L.F.G. and Siemens had made efforts to produce fighters with a fast rate of climb and high ceiling. These were useful characteristics where interception was the prime consideration, but the engines were all still in the experimental stage. Until these new engines had been developed to an acceptable standard, the well-tried Le Rhône would have to be retained for operational purposes. The Flz experts concurred.

Some pilots expressed preferences that puzzled the Service test-pilots: recommendations were made in respect of aircraft that were obviously inferior and had been included in the trials merely because they were interesting and not unsafe.

There was agreement over the Siemens entries: although they had an excellent rate of climb and were reasonably fast at altitude they were much too tricky and obviously required further development. The Siemens-Halske engine was not yet sufficiently reliable.

The Pfalz D.VII, which unfortunately had the same engine, had given a better account of itself and was considerably faster. It was well built and fairly easy to handle. The Pfalz D.VI won a measure of support by virtue of its 110-h.p. Le Rhône engine, but its performance was inadequate. A majority regarded the L.F.G.-Roland effort as a wash-out.

Finally, Manfred von Richthofen's advice prevailed. He recommended the Fokker V.13 as the best all-round type. It was easy to fly, very manoeuvrable, and otherwise similar to the V.11. As the V.11 had already been recommended, the similarity of the two types would be an advantage when pilots had to switch from one to another.

The V.13/II with its Siemens engine had a measure of support from the *IdFlieg* officials. Little had been seen of it during the trials, partly because it had been damaged, partly because the owner of the Oberursel firm had little interest in promoting the Siemens engine. In a climbing test, Mathias had flown the V.13/II to an altitude of 4·5 km. (15,000 ft.) in 19·5 minutes.

Although this fell appreciably short of Leutnant Mueller's record climb of 5·0 km. (16,500 ft.) in 13 minutes on the Service version of the Siemens-Schuckert D.III with the same engine, it was considerably better than the performance of the Fokker V.13/I with the 145-h.p. Oberursel UR.III.

But the fighter pilots wanted neither the Siemens-Halske Sh.3 nor the Oberursel UR.III: they preferred the 110-h.p. *Beute* Le Rhône which had proved so satisfactory in the Fok. Dr.I. Their final choice of a rotary-powered aircraft was the Fokker V.13, but with the 110-h.p. Le Rhône.

This recommendation was accepted by the authorities, but the type was ordered in small numbers only, pending the availability of a more powerful rotary for operational service.

Hauptmann von Falkenhayn of the Kogenluft's staff told Fokker of the decisions and congratulated him on his double success. Fokker was asked how soon he could arrange for type tests to be made, and how quickly he could supply production aircraft. He retorted that he could promise nothing, for his factory was cluttered up with those A.E.G. C.IV trainers that the *IdFlieg* had inflicted on him.

At that moment Fokker did not know that this very problem had been discussed when the question of giving him direct orders was considered, and the *IdFlieg* had agreed to cancel the A.E.G. contract in favour of the new fighter types. The alternative would have been to order only proto-types from Fokker and place the production contracts with better-equipped firms. This idea was rejected, however; the A.E.G. trainers were not too badly needed, and there was no wish to stifle Fokker's eagerness to get production going.

Fokker was promised, on the spot, a provisional order for 400 V.11-type aircraft, subsequently designated Fok. D.VII, at £1,250 per airframe (1914 value), a very generous price. He was told to initiate production with all possible speed: to expedite matters, the existing prototypes should be modified to production standard for test purposes. This was the biggest order Fokker had received up to this time.

His amazement grew when he learned that his main rivals, the Albatros concern, were to build the V.11 under licence; so were the Ostdeutsche Albatros Werke and the A.E.G. This was a triumph for the little Dutch-man who, at a time when his paternal subsidy looked like being cut off, had thought of offering his services as a flying instructor to the Albatros Werke before the war. For every licence-built V.11 he was to get a standard fee of 5% of the airframe price.

Viewed against the other prototypes submitted for the Adlershof trials, and bearing in mind the supply position in blockaded Germany, no better choice than the V.11 could have been made. Its selection was amply vindicated by its subsequent operational success. The choice of the V.13 was also sensible in the circumstances.

Fokker had succeeded by rights and had arrived at the top of the

German aircraft industry. He had beaten his competitors fair and square in the most exacting competition ever held, for the largest German contracts ever awarded. All he now had to do was to keep Reinhold Platz at work and not let him feel too important!

Fok. D.VI, 110-h.p. Le Rhône.

The Fokker D.VI

The V.11 still needed detail improvements and minor modifications. Fokker hoped to improve its climb, reduce the weight a little, and improve the flying qualities even further. A second specimen of the V.11 was built for Adlershof.

The V.13 was therefore the first of the two successful designs to undergo an official type test. The aircraft that was tested was re-converted to have the 110-h.p. UR.II engine. Early in February 1918, a few days before the fighter trials ended, a V.13 airframe was tested to destruction at Adlershof. A report dated February 18, 1918, cleared the airframe without restriction. Even the (formerly rare) Case C loading had been sustained without any structural failure. Platz had accomplished the near miracle of complying with all BLV requirements without even knowing of their existence.

The type test of the 110-h.p. version, the Fok. D.VI, took place on March 15, 1918. In the climbing test an altitude of 5·0 km. (16,500 ft.) was reached in 29·9 minutes: the service ceiling was 5·6 km. (18,500 ft.). This was not good enough for service on the Western Front, and only limited production was recommended until a development with the 200-h.p. Goebel Goe.III engine could be evaluated. Single aircraft with the first pre-production Geo.III engines were ordered. Take-off and landing of the UR.II-powered Fok. D.VI were surprisingly good, the runs being 35 m. (37·5 yd.) and 40 m. (44 yd.) respectively. The empty weight was

Fok. D.VI.

now 427 kg. (940 lb.), whereas originally the unarmed V.13 had weighed 393 kg. (865 lb.) empty. The standard armament consisted of two LMG 08/15 machine-guns synchronized by the Zentral-Steuerung.

The V.13/II with 160-h.p. Siemens Sh.3 was type-tested on May 15, 1918. It was not accepted for production, however, because operational trials of the Siemens-Schuckert D.III had shown the engine to be troublesome. Moreover, the Goe.III-powered version of the Fok. D.VI was then in production and was to be operationally tested by home-defence fighter units. The first Goebel-powered Fok. D.VI (D.1643/18, Factory No. 2625, engine No. 66) underwent its acceptance flight-test at Schwerin-Goerries, flown by Grosse, on May 21, 1918.

Some three weeks earlier, a production Fok. D.VI (D.1631/18, Factory No. 2613) had been delivered for engine trials with the 145-h.p. UR.III (engine No. 2884). Few examples of this variant were supplied, however.

The Fok. D.VI saw little operational use on any major front. Its performance in speed and climb was not good enough; and it was slow to accelerate in a dive. On July 1, 1918, only twenty-one Fok. D.VIs were in

Fok. D.VI.

operational use; on September 1 the total was twenty-seven. After this date all aircraft of this type were relegated to home-defence and training units.

Seven Fok. D.VIs with UR.II engines were sold to the Austrian Army on August 19, 1918. They were shipped without acceptance flight tests. These aircraft had the Factory Nos. 2614–2617, 2623, 2624 and 2628; they were part of a block originally ordered by the *IdFlieg*, consequently their allotted Order Nos. (D.1632–1635/18, D.1641/18, D.1642/18 and D.1644/18) were cancelled. The Austrian D.VIs differed from standard in their armament: they had a fixed, synchronized Schwarzlose machine-gun on the fuselage, and a free Mannlicher on the upper wing.

All the airframe details of the Fok. D.VI so closely resembled those of the D.VII that no separate detailed description is needed. Its engine installation was similar to that of the Fok. Dr.I. The D.VI undercarriage was almost identical with that of the early production D.VII, and it was identical with that of the Fok. E.V or D.VIII.

In all, about sixty Fok. D.VIs were supplied to the Army under contracts covering the Order Nos. D.1621/18 to D.1700/18; none were acquired by the Navy. Production ceased early in June 1918.

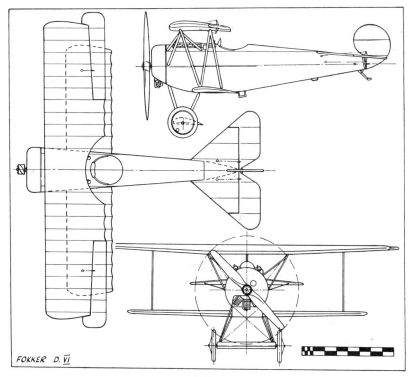

FOKKER D. VI

273

Fokker V.33.

The Fokker V.33

Development of the basic V.9 design did not cease with the termination of D.VI production. Late in the summer of 1918 a further development was built as the V.33. It was smaller and lighter than the production Fok. D.VI but was intended ultimately to take more powerful rotary engines. The V.33 was first flown with a 100-h.p. Oberursel; subsequently a 110-h.p. Le Rhône was installed.

In its original form the V.33 had a V-type interplane strut, although it had two separate spars in the lower wing. This was soon replaced by an N-strut, however. The wing-tips were more rounded than those of the Fok. D.VI; they resembled those of the V.26. Like most rotary-powered Fokker types, the V.33 had no fin, but its rudder was larger and of a more angular shape. The ailerons were not horn-balanced.

The V.33's performance seems not to have warranted further development or a type test. Fokker liked the little biplane, however, and he took

Fokker V.33.

it with him to Amsterdam when he cleared out of Germany after the war. He tried to sell it as a sporting single-seater but, failing to do so, he seems to have flown it for pleasure at Schiphol until about 1922.

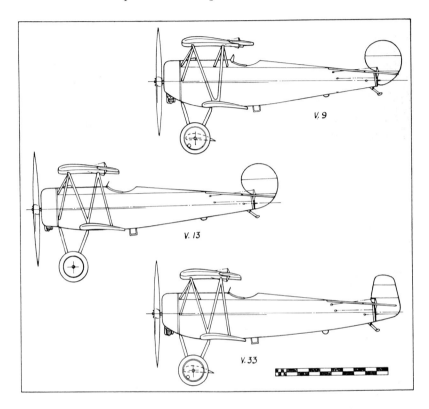

Acceptance tests of the Fok. D.VII

Until Fokker's success in the Adlershof trials, the outlook for his Schwerin factory had been gloomy. The triplane was too slow; its repeated structural failures had destroyed all future prospects; and no further orders could be expected. Production of the A.E.G. C.IV was progressing but did not bring much profit; moreover, as a low-priority contract, the supply of engines and materials was somewhat erratic. By 1918 a strict system of rationing according to priority was in force: part of it was operated by the Association of German Aircraft Manufacturers, which was not exactly biased in favour of the Fokker works.

During January 1918, fifty-four Fok. Dr.I, twenty-four A.E.G. C.IVs, and the three remaining Fok. D.IVs were supplied to the Army. The D.IVs were special long-span, large-area versions for high-altitude experiments; they had waited a long time for their high-compression Mercedes engines.

275

On February 4, 1918, the V.11 underwent its type test. The empty weight was found to be 655 kg. (1,445 lb.) and the operational all-up weight 845 kg. (1,860 lb.); the wing weight was 125 kg. (277 lb.). The aircraft was recommended for adoption, subject to the submission of a production-type aircraft and its ability to pass a structural test. This sample production-type D.VII, numbered D.230/18, was completed during March 1918.

Meanwhile, modifications of the V.11 proceeded in attempts to improve the original aircraft still further. By now Fokker had learned to value patience and application in test flying. He had at last found that it was well worth while to try and try again, in painstaking test flights, in order to get the best out of an existing design; he had seen what could be done when he modified the original version of the V.11.

Fokker had certain preferences in the handling qualities of aircraft, and liked to attain them in his own products. He liked aeroplanes to be slightly tail-heavy in level flight and slightly nose-heavy when gliding. He disliked an aircraft that "hunted" in the pitching plane: that is, that suffered from pitching oscillations or overbalanced elevator control. Control-force harmonization he regarded as important, and he was seldom satisfied with the aileron controls of his aircraft (indeed, the ailerons were usually heavy on Fokker types). Fokker disliked undercarriages that induced bouncing when landing.

On the other hand, discomforts such as draughts, cold, oil splashes, and so on, did not trouble him; he tried to convert other pilots to his point of view, even when they might have to endure such conditions for hours at considerable heights, whereas Fokker flew for quarter-hours at low altitude. He rarely saw the need for providing any form of crash protection: to him, such things were luxuries and he thought too much fuss was made about them.

In pursuing the development of the V.11, Fokker had two main objects: to improve its climb and its handling qualities. He did not want to hand over to Albatros an aeroplane that they might be able to improve. In climbing performance the aircraft compared unfavourably with other types—the Rumplers, for instance—that had the same engine. It did not occur to Fokker that the Rumplers climbed so well because they were of exceptionally low weight.

A new experimental aircraft, the V.21 (Factory No. 2310), was built; it had tapered wings. This modification was not worth the complication it entailed. The V.21, fitted with a high-compression Mercedes engine (the D.IIIaü), took part in the second D-aircraft trials. At 840 kg. (1,830 lb.) its flying weight was slightly less than that of the Fok. D.VII, but its climbing performance was poorer. It took 45 minutes to reach an altitude of 5·9 km. (19,400 ft.), and its ceiling was only 6·3 km. (20,800 ft.). The experiment was therefore fruitless.

The V.22 had dihedral on the upper wing and a four-blade airscrew with the blades set at 120°/60° like the Austrian Baudisch propeller. Fokker

Fokker V.22.

hoped for improved stability and manoeuvrability, and for improved thrust and climb. The improvements were negligible and, to Platz's relief, all these complications were dropped. All the ribs in each wing could remain identical, and the spars could be built with straight tops.

The structural test was made on one of the original V.11 airframes (Factory No. 1883) early in February 1918. When the sand load on the ends of the upper wing reached the specified load factor of 5 in Case A, the tips flexed by 180 mm. (7·1 in.). This deformation proved to be wholly elastic, however, and returned to zero on removal of the sand load. Structural failure did not begin until a load factor of 10·52 in Case A was reached, when the joint at the interplane strut failed. Thus the Fok. D.VII was stronger than any other operational aeroplane used during the war; indeed, no structural failure has ever occurred in the air with a D.VII.

The German pilots quickly gained full confidence in the type, for they found that it would not break up even when badly shot about. There were no vital lift cables to be severed by bullets or shell splinters. Fok. D.VIIs were landed safely even with cabane or interplane struts severely damaged.

Few new types passed the Adlershof structural tests with the ease of the Fok. D.VII. The only modification requested by the Flz. was a local reinforcement of the lower wing spars at the point of union with the interplane struts. This was easily done and made no significant addition to the weight.

An interesting feature of the tests was that the fuselage failed under 112% of the specified load when both lower longerons buckled. This was further proof of the reliability of Platz's experimental stressing methods.

The results of the strength tests of the Fok. D.VII were convincing evidence of the great changes that had taken place since Platz became Fokker's designer. He had produced an aeroplane that was not merely the best operational fighter but was also the strongest and had passed the searching structural tests without criticism. This was quite an achievement.

Later, in June 1918, Fokker-built wings were again tested in Case C (terminal-velocity dive), this case having been found to be critical in other aircraft types. The Fok. D.VII again showed its robustness. Even at 200% of the prescribed load (load factor of 2·5) no undue deformation was observed. However, when moist sand was used, the leading-edge ply strip deformed. This discovery led to tests of ribs that had been wrapped in wet cloth for 24 hours. When load was applied to them the plywood folded and tore easily.

The Flz. informed Fokker that, although the D.VII was satisfactory when dry, it deteriorated dangerously under the influence of moisture. They strongly advised Fokker to ensure proper production control. The protection of all plywood surfaces by thorough varnishing was vital. Moreover, the Adlershof experiments had proved beyond doubt that the plywood used by Fokker was brittle and generally inferior to that used by the Albatros firm. Fokker was again warned to use good-quality material.

As a further consequence a structural examination of a service Fok. D.VII was made in August 1918. The aircraft was D.272/18 (Factory No. 2358, Mercedes engine No. 37,650), which had been sent to the front with the first production batch in early April. It had served in the field for three months under the worst conditions. The purpose of the investigation was to discover how the strength had been affected.

The test D.VII was found to weigh 68 kg. (150 lb.) more than the original specimen aircraft. Unfortunately, this was not an uncommon occurrence during the war.

The sand loading proved that the strength of the wing structure, fuselage and control surfaces was entirely adequate. The tests proved, however, that certain components were of less than the specified strength, and these were parts that could not have been affected by operational use. The control column, for instance, was not strong enough, and the rudder bar did not withstand the prescribed load; the strength deficiencies were 12% and 13% respectively. The anchoring of the fuel tank was not strong enough, nor was that of the undercarriage. There was too much friction in all the control circuits. In general, however, the aircraft was considered to have remained operationally serviceable.

The condition of the control circuits led the *IdFlieg* to suspect that the Fokker works were not pre-stretching control cables in accordance with regulations. The report also pointed out that Fokker had failed to submit a reinforced undercarriage as requested during the type test. It went on to require the strengthening of the lower fork of the control column and the bearing tube of the rudder bar; the fuel tank was to be mounted in steel straps as required by the BLV.

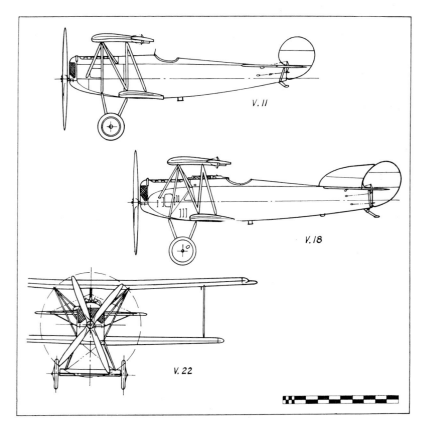

In September 1918, when Fok. D.VII production was nearing its end, two further structural tests were made on details. On one occasion the wing-like axle fairing had tilted back in flight: this led to the suspicion that it might not stand the stress of diving. A sand-loading test dispelled the doubt: the fairing did not collapse until 228% of the drag load had been applied.

The second test was of the rudder. The rudder cables had been doubled because several instances of shot-away cables had been experienced, and the test was made to determine whether the severing of one cable would be harmful. The rudder withstood 150% of the required load; beyond this value the main tube began to distort. So the rudder was also above suspicion, even with one control circuit severed.

The engine question

The Daimler monopoly of water-cooled engines used in fighter aircraft and the Army's desire to break it have already been mentioned. This matter had assumed vital importance by 1918, when enemy fighter types had good-quality engines of 220-h.p. and more, and others of greater power were being developed. Allied two-seaters had engines of 350–400-h.p. whereas none of the German long-range reconnaissance aircraft had power units of more than 260-h.p. The Hispano-Suiza and Rolls-Royce designs were exemplary and far in advance of anything on the German side.

In Germany the development of new and more powerful engines was officially encouraged. Even radically new designs were given support. The end of the six-cylinder in-line engine was predicted. But no-one went so far as to suggest the development of high-power air-cooled engines as the contemporary British technicians did.

The old 150-h.p. Benz Bz.IIIa of 1914–15 was redesigned with a higher compression ratio; this pushed its output up to nearly 200 b.h.p. It saw operational use in the Roland D.VIb fighter, to which the Benz gave a good climbing performance; seventeen of these Rolands were in use on the Western Front in July 1918.

The high-compression Benz Bz.IIIa was never tried in the Fok. D.VII, but one was experimentally fitted with the 240 b.h.p. Bz.IVü; this engine was a similarly improved version of the 220-h.p. Benz, which had become obsolete for bombers and two-seaters. The D.VII with the Bz.IVü was designated Fokker V.24; it had the Factory No. 2612, and Grosse flew it on its acceptance trials on April 24, 1918. The V.24 had an impres-

The Fokker V.24.

sive climbing performance but did not handle well; its manoeuvrability had been impaired, and its high wing loading made it unacceptable for use from the small, rough airfields at the front.

The V.24 was sent to Adlershof for engine trials, but probably remained the property of the Fokker Works. With its heavy Benz engine it participated in the second fighter trials of June 1918. Soon afterwards it was converted to take the B.M.W. IIIa.

The Benz Bz.IVü was subsequently the standard power plant of the Pfalz D.XIV, only a few of which reached the front before the Armistice.

Of the existing higher-powered six-cylinder engines, the 260-h.p. Mercedes D.IVa and the much better Maybach Mb.IV were never tried in fighter aircraft. They were badly needed for bombers and long-range reconnaissance aircraft. The D.IVa was never really successful, although it was widely used; it was heavy and its performance at altitude was poor.

All Argus and NAG engines in production were suitable only for trainers and communications aircraft. The Argus company made some notable efforts to regain its former position but none came to fruition before the Armistice.

Of the new designs, only the 195-h.p. Benz Bz.IIIb V-eight engine was sufficiently developed to be submitted for operational trials. The design was based on the Hispano-Suiza but did not compare with the French engine.

Several other promising V-eights passed the official 60-hr. test, but none had gone into production by the time of the Armistice. None equalled the standard of contemporary British and French engines: Germany had fallen behind in the field of water-cooled engines for fighters, and had no air-cooled engine to offer.

This was attributable to the short-sighted policy pursued by the military authorities who, in spite of pre-war warnings by German technicians that more powerful engines would be necessary, had insisted that 100 h.p. would be enough for their two-seaters, and that no greater power would be needed in the future. This attitude discouraged development and the German aero-engine industry never made up the lost leeway during the war.

Thus, thanks to the improvidence and incompetence of the Army authorities before and during the early part of the war, German airframe designers could not look to more powerful engines as a means to increased performance: they had to achieve their results by their ability to design efficient aircraft.

There was, however, one engine that proved especially effective in the Fok. D.VII. This was the 185-h.p. B.M.W. IIIa, which was the outcome of a successful attempt to break the Daimler monopoly.

Camillo Castiglioni, the financial genius from Trieste, had learned from his German firms (notably the Hansa-Brandenburg Aircraft Works) how difficult engine supplies were. His engineering adviser, Dr. W. Lissauer, assured him that an aero-engine firm would be a worthwhile acquisition.

Castiglioni decided to buy up a small engine factory near Munich, the Rapp aero-engine works, and to re-organize it with enlarged and up-to-date production facilities as the Bayrische Motoren-Werke, abbreviated B.M.W. He was able to lure away from Daimler a team of able engine designers, led by Frietz. They were glad to free themselves from the static policy of their former firm and to work on new designs and developments.

This design team quickly evolved a six-cylinder in-line engine, generally similar to the 160-h.p. Mercedes but with oversized cylinders and a new carburettor system that compensated for altitude. As mentioned earlier, this new 185-h.p. B.M.W. IIIa engine flew during the Adlershof trials and showed excellent climbing capabilities in an obsolete fighter type.

Fokker was able to obtain one of the first B.M.W. engines, with a promise of further supplies. This was installed in the second officially ordered Fok. D.VII, D.231/18 (Factory No. 2314). The installation differed very little from that of the standard Mercedes, but a slightly larger radiator was required because the engine was able to develop up to 240 b.h.p. for very short periods near the ground.

The B.M.W. IIIa was an immediate success in the Fok. D.VII. The aircraft powered by this new engine was given the official type designation Fok. D.VIIF.

After flight testing by the works pilot Neisen the D.VIIF was delivered to the Flz. for evaluation. The climb and ceiling were so much improved that it was quickly decided to fit the B.M.W. engine to as many production Fok. D.VIIs as possible; the limiting factor would be the rate of production of the engines. The Fokker works were granted a provisional priority in the supply of B.M.W. engines.

Thirteen Fok. D.VIIFs were supplied in May, twenty-eight in June, and forty in August. Even in November, when Fok. D.VII production was about to cease, eighteen D.VIIFs were delivered.

Fighter pilots were delighted with this new Fokker: everyone wanted to exchange his D.VII for a D.VIIF. All kinds of subterfuge were employed to get hold of one of the precious B.M.W. engines for installation.

The B.M.W. IIIa was built under licence by the Opel Works, but this version was not so highly thought of. After the war it gave trouble in Fok. D.VIIFs and Fok. C.Is in service with the Dutch Army.

The B.M.W. IIIa had a compression ratio of 6·55 and was designed to run on a fuel mixture of 60% benzene and 40% petrol (of 0·86 specific weight). Benzene was home-produced in Germany from coal, and was in better supply than petrol. Allied experts who tested examples of the B.M.W. failed to use this high-octane fuel, and were led to make unjustified criticisms of the engine. It was one of the most economical engines then in use: when properly adjusted, its fuel consumption was only about 180 gr./h.p./hr. (0·4 lb./h.p./hr.).

Had the war continued into 1919, the B.M.W. IIIa would have been obsolete. It would have been replaced by the 220/260-h.p. B.M.W. IV, which was basically similar to the IIIa but had cylinders of 10 mm.

greater bore and stroke. Only five examples of this engine had been made by the time of the Armistice; but years later it proved its excellence.

Fokker felt that he was not getting enough Mercedes and B.M.W. engines for his factory's production of Fok. D.VIIs, and complained to the authorities. To his discomfiture, he was curtly informed by *IdFlieg* officials that his facilities at Schwerin seemed to serve the war effort best by concentrating on experimental and development work; it was not in the interests of the Service to place major production contracts with the Fokker works.

Thus officialdom acknowledged Fokker's failure to invest part of his immense profits in the improvement of his production facilities. He still had no proper factory, and this fact is recorded in an official *IdFlieg* report of March 1918, dealing with industrial capacities and development of production. This report stated that the factory premises at Schwerin mostly consisted of temporary accommodation such as sheds and hutments. The *IdFlieg* had been unable to determine the size of the available working space, for the production facilities were spread widely over the Schwerin district. The total labour force was about 3,000 workers. No other major aircraft production plant in Germany resembled the Fokker works. In the *IdFlieg* report, the proprietor was named as designer and test pilot of the firm.

The first production Fok. D.VII, wearing cross-patée markings. (*Photo: Peter M. Bowers*).

The Fok. D.VII in production

The Albatros aircraft works were the largest manufacturers of aircraft in Germany at the time of the first Adlershof trials. Their management were not exactly pleased at having to build the Fok. D.VII under licence. Once, their products had swept the Fokkers from the fighter market; now the situation had been reversed. Nevertheless, the Albatros people made the best of a bad job, and energetically set about the production of the Fok. D.VII.

Their technicians were somewhat daunted to learn that there were no

Standard Fokker-built Fok. D.VII, No. 507/18.

workshop drawings of the new Fokker, nor were any likely to be forthcoming because the Fokker works produced from jigs and assembly
sketches. They therefore obtained from Schwerin a complete airframe
and settled down to make their own drawings, using the airframe as the
basis, together with sketches provided by Platz's department. Production
jigs were laid out accordingly. In addition, foremen were given instruction in the Fokker workshops, notably in the welding techniques used in
making the fuselage and cabane structure.

After this preparation, Albatros and the sister works at Schneidemühl
quickly started production of the Fok. D.VII. Their production soon
overtook that of Schwerin, and Fokker was jealous of their output and
its quality. This largely inspired his complaint that Albatros were given
preference in the supply of Mercedes engines; but it was only natural that
the greater part of the supplies of available engines should go where the
aircraft were produced most quickly.

Albatros-built Fok. D.VII (Alb) No. 527/18.

Owing to the circumstances in which the licence production of the Fok. D.VII was initiated, components made by the three principal contractors were not interchangeable. For example, it was impossible to replace the undercarriage of a Fokker-built D.VII with the corresponding component made by Albatros. Even the products of the two Albatros works differed. Large spares depots, notably one at Maubeuge, had to be organized to cope with the enormous quantities of spares required for the three versions of the "standard" Fok. D.VII. If any A.E.G.-built Fok. D.VII had materialized, a fourth version would have had to be catered for.

Fok. D.VII (O.A.W.) 2010/18, built by the Ostdeutsche Albatros Werke.

The A.E.G. made no D.VII, however. Their Henningsdorf works were fully engaged on production of the Riesenflugzeuge that were assembled at the A.E.G. Stettin works. These A.E.G. types were regarded as of prime importance, and it appears that the *IdFlieg* did not press for the production of Fok. D.VII.

The Fok. D.VII at the front

The first example of the Fok. D.VII to go to the front went to Manfred von Richthofen's unit, Jagdgeschwader I, early in April 1918. Von Richthofen was seen flying it when visiting neighbouring aerodromes. Against the enemy, however, he flew his Fok. Dr.I until his death on April 21. Jagdgeschwader I was then in the Somme area with its base near Foucaucourt.

During May 1918, Jagdstaffeln 26, 2, 27, 36 and 3 were fully equipped with the Fok. D.VII. The pilots were delighted with their new mounts, and their victory scores mounted.

On May 1, nineteen Fok. D.VIIs were operational; on July 1 the total was 407; two months later, 828. In November 1918, forty-three Jagd-staffeln were equipped with a total of 775 Fok. D.VIIs.

After the first three months of operational use, however, the standard version with the high-compression Mercedes ceased to be adequate to

The nose of a standard Mercedes-powered Fok. D.VII. Engine cowlings differed slightly in detail, and several forms of exhaust manifold were fitted.

deal with opposing Allied types, particularly in its performance at high altitude. Above 4·5 km. (15,000 ft.) the manoeuvrability deteriorated; and at heights above 4·0 km. (13,200 ft.) the new Siemens-Schuckert D.IV proved to be considerably faster. This was the first time that a rotary-powered fighter had a better altitude performance than one with a Mercedes engine.

The Fok. D.VIIF was, of course, much better and was eagerly sought after. As already noted, however, only limited production of the B.M.W. IIIa was possible; consequently the majority of Fok. D.VIIs had to have the unwanted Mercedes.

General criticisms of the Fok. D.VII related to bad manufacture (for instance, in Fokker-built aircraft, fuel tanks opened at the seams). How-ever, serious operational trouble was caused by overheating of the ammunition boxes in flight (see Appendix VI). Several fires in the air, some of them tragic, resulted from it. On July 15, 1918, Leutnant Friedrichs' aircraft (D.304/18, a Fokker-built machine) was seen to be on fire at a time when enemy action could be excluded as a cause: the characteristic whitish smoke of burning phosphorus was seen. Friedrichs bailed out, but his parachute failed to open. Next day, Leutnant Bender of Jagdstaffel 4 succeeded in parachuting from his burning Fok. D.VII. He stated that he heard reports; there was no doubt that his incendiary ammunition had ignited. An hour later another D.VII of Jagdstaffel 45 suffered the same fate.

On July 17, incendiary ammunition was forbidden for use in Fok. D.VII aircraft. Some pilots had been able to land their burning aircraft and to prove beyond doubt that the fire originated in the phosphorus ammunition. A new kind of incendiary-cum-armour-piercing ammunition had been introduced, but this was not the principal cause of the trouble.

Several schemes were tried to prevent the overheating of the ammunition container. Insulating layers and increased ventilation were tried. A better idea was the ducting of cooling air over the containers from an air intake in a modified radiator.

It was, of course, unpleasant for pilots to know that their aircraft could be set on fire by their own ammunition. Not all of them had taken to wearing parachutes: many of those who did learned too late that the parachutes were of *ersatz* materials and untrustworthy. Even the parachute harness consisted of a kind of paper yarn that would disintegrate when moist.

When the Fok. D.VII appeared on the Western Front it created a sensation among Allied pilots. Lacking the more graceful lines of the Albatros and Pfalz scouts, it looked clumsy and inferior. Soon, however, two-seater crews brought back startling accounts of the new German

Fok. D.VII aircraft on their way to the front, June 1918. The recess in the fuselage underside that accommodated the lower wing can be seen.

fighter that appeared to be able to stand still in the air with its nose up, in which attitude it would pour a stream of bullets into the two-seater from the blind spot. Those Allied airmen who escaped from an encounter with a Fok. D.VII were inclined to overrate its ability in speed and climb.

The Fok. D.VII could not, of course, stand still in the air. German pilots had quickly learned now to exploit the qualities of the thick wing section, which stalled gradually and at a rather high angle of attack. Thus they could approach a two-seater from below, where the observer could not bring his guns to bear, and make their attacks with the D.VII in a nearly stalled condition, with full throttle and nose high.

This manoeuvre was safe and simple, for the Fok. D.VII was not prone to fall into a spin. In fact, it needed skill and forceful handling to compel it to spin. When it did so, the motion was steep, with the nose well down, and the aircraft exhibited a strong tendency to come out of its own accord.

It was not long before examples of the Fok. D.VII fell into Allied hands. One of the first was Fok. D.VII (O.A.W.) No. 2009/18, which made a forced landing intact in French territory in May 1918; it had a Mercedes engine. Its performance was carefully investigated at Villacoublay.

The captured Fok. D.VII (O.A.W.) 2009/18, apparently at Martlesham Heath (*Photo: Imperial War Museum*).

Another, Fok. D.VII (Alb.) No. 1450/18 (Factory No. 2455) was brought down by an S.E.5a on June 6, 1918; it landed slightly damaged, behind the British lines. Its new high-compression engine attracted the attention of British experts, apparently more than did the far more significant airframe. The engine was removed and bench-tested, and a comprehensive report was issued. The airframe was merely examined, although it might easily have been repaired. The report on the aircraft was rather more

288

objective than the earlier one on the Fok. Dr.I. It was admitted that the Fok. D.VII was a perfectly practical and interesting aeroplane, even if some of its design features appeared to be unorthodox or risky.

The journal *Flight* printed its own appraisement of the aircraft, and very sensibly urged aerodynamicists in Britain to investigate the properties of thick aerofoils in cantilever wings before dismissing them as unsatisfactory. The designer of the Fok. D.VII persisted in using such aerofoils, and the performance of his aircraft was by no means bad; in fact they were obviously better than many other fighters then in use. And the serviceability of the D.VII in the field was obvious.

Clear evidence of the high regard that the Allies had for the type is provided by the well-known paragraph of the Armistice conditions, which demanded the immediate surrender of all aircraft of the Fok. D.VII type.

The Allies had expected to collect about 2,000 Fok. D.VIIs, but their intelligence reports must have been inaccurate, for only about half that number had been produced. No more than 700 or 800 can have been in operational use. Many of these were not handed over, for their pilots preferred to crash them or to fly them back to Germany, sometimes loaded with personal luggage of all kinds. Of the aircraft thus "saved", a considerable number landed at Schwerin. Fokker gave instructions for them to be hidden for future use.

Other Fok. D.VIIs were handed over to Switzerland, Holland, Denmark and Sweden. Thanks to this action the type survived for many years, but those aircraft that were handed over to the Allies were mostly allowed to rot. Some were hidden in Germany, but most of them were traced for destruction by Allied agents, or decayed in their hiding places.

Variants of the Fok. D.VII

At the time of writing, it is virtually impossible to trace and record all the many variants of the Fok. D.VII. The various two-seat conversions and developments will be discussed separately.

Some of the modifications of the basic design were made for purely experimental purposes. These included the daring experiments made at Adlershof by von Heidelberg, a university-trained engineer who served as a first-rate experimental pilot on full-scale research work at Adlershof. He it was who flew a D.VII with interplane struts removed. Flights were also made with full cable bracing on the wings for drag-determination tests.

Development work on the D.VII was pursued in four places; most of it aimed at improving the aircraft. Fokker's own efforts at Schwerin resulted in the V.36. The Albatros concern carried out tests of their own. Although the A.E.G. did not produce the type in quantity, G. Koenig of that company conducted aerodynamic experiments that entailed some modifications, as a preliminary to production.

The Flz. made a series of modifications, some in attempts to improve

K   289

the flying qualities still further, others for basic research in controllability. Unfortunately, little information about these experiments has come to light. The modified aircraft were apparently designated 1D7, 2D7, 3D7, and so on. Modification 6D7, for example, had no fin and a modified balanced rudder; the undercarriage axle fairing was not fitted. The 7D7 had an enlarged fin and no axle fairing. Another experimental version had a lengthened fuselage.

Platz, of course, knew nothing of this Adlershof experimental work, nor was any of it inspired by Fokker.

A version of the Fok. D.VII powered by the 210-h.p. six-cylinder Austro-Daimler engine was in production at the Allgemeine Ungarische Maschinen-Fabrik A.G. (MAG) of Budapest towards the end of the war; it was intended for use by Austrian fighter units. The MAG-built Fok. D.VII was slightly shorter than the standard German aircraft but did not differ significantly in weight. Its climb was claimed to be better than that of the Fok. D.VIIF, but this is unlikely because the Austro-Daimler engine was less suitable than the B.M.W. for high-altitude work. No Fok. D.VII was used operationally by Austria.

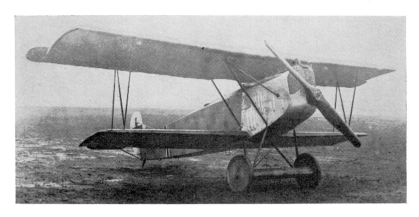

Fok. D.VII with 210-h.p. Austro-Daimler engine, photographed at Schwerin. (*Photo: Peter M. Bowers*).

The Fokker V.36

Fokker's own development of the basic D.VII produced new types in the V series. Of these, the V.22 and V.24 have already been mentioned (see pages 276 and 280).

In the summer of 1918, the Fokker V.34 and V.36 (Factory No. 2656) appeared. It seems probable that their development proceeded more or less simultaneously. It is believed that the V.36 at least was originally powered by the high-compression 220/240-h.p. Benz Bz. IVü engine, but was soon converted to have the 185-h.p. B.M.W. IIIa. In this latter form

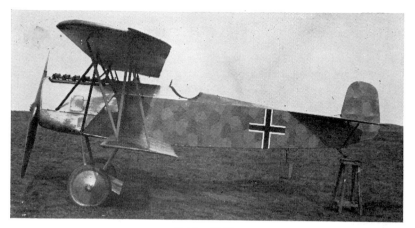

Fokker V.34.

of the V.36, its fuselage was apparently identical with that of the V.34, which also had the B.M.W. IIIa.

In these two aircraft, the B.M.W. installation had an oval radiator of a new type, and the engine was more cleanly cowled. The wings had the same span as those of the Fok. D.VII, but were of smaller area; the new aircraft were also shorter, the V.36 being roughly the same length as the D.VI.

The V.34 had a rudder of the same shape as that of the V.33, whereas the vertical surfaces of the V.36 resembled those of the Fok. D.VII. The undercarriage of the V.34 appeared to be virtually identical with that of the D.VII.

The V.36 aircraft had a better climbing performance than the D.VII, and was Platz's final development of the basic V.11 before the end of the war.

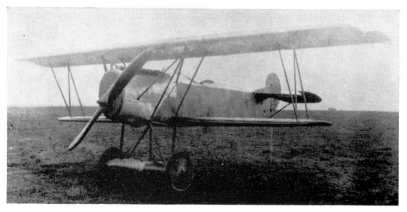

Fokker V.36.

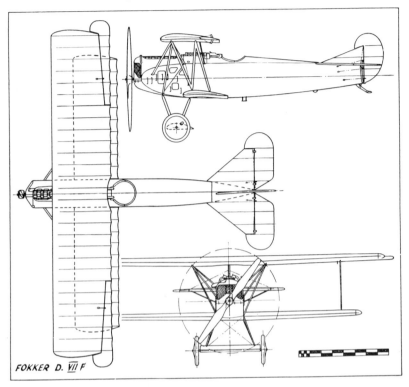

FOKKER D. VII F

One major innovation distinguished the V.36 from its predecessors. In this aircraft, the radical step of transferring the main fuel tank from the fuselage to the undercarriage axle fairing had been taken. This would have been warmly welcomed by every pilot. By 1918, owing to the widespread use of tracer and incendiary ammunition, the number of aircraft shot down in flames had increased alarmingly.

In face of this obvious threat to morale, the *IdFlieg* was pressed to do something to reduce the fire risk. Inventors were encouraged to produce ideas, and the *IdFlieg* stipulated that all future fighter aircraft should embody adequate safeguards against fire, both from enemy action and from crash damage.

Platz suggested the transformation of the undercarriage wing into the fuel tank. Fokker thought it a good idea. If such a tank were struck by incendiary bullets, no burning petrol would reach the pilot or damage vital parts of the aircraft, such as the tail unit. This offered a good chance of escape from such a situation; and in the event of a crash landing the tank was too far from the engine for there to be a risk of fire. It seemed an excellent solution.

Fokker conducted ground tests at Schwerin, using coloured water and

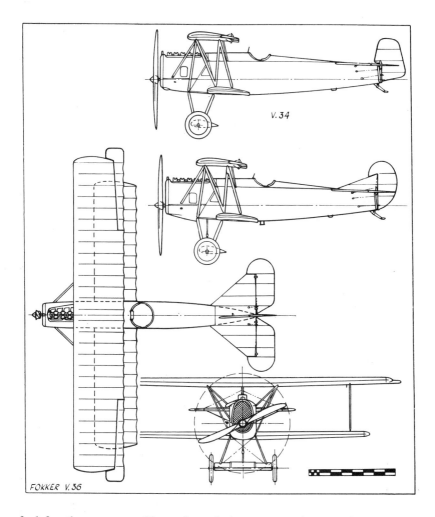

V. 34

FOKKER V. 36

fuel for the purpose. These showed that no escaping petrol was likely to reach the cockpit or tail surfaces. The V.1 fuselage was resurrected for the tests. Fokker also seems to have made some demonstrations in flight, using coloured water.

He took out several patents on undercarriage tanks. His German D.R.P. 332,048 of April 6, 1918, related to the location of fuel tanks within the axle fairing; there were two tanks, one in front of and one behind the axle. D.R.P. 356,749 of December 24, 1918, covered the final version in which the tank was a one-piece component of streamline cross-section, and the axle passed through it in a box-type housing. All undercarriage tanks had a streamline section; the lifting-aerofoil section of the early axle fairing was abandoned.

Standard Fok. D.VII undercarriage before fitting the aerofoil fairing to the axle.

There was, of course, one obvious disadvantage in this arrangement of the petrol tank: considerable pressure was required to force fuel up into the small gravity tank. Submerged fuel pumps were unknown at that time; had they been available, they would have provided an ideal solution. Another fault that emerged after service experience had been gained by the Dutch Army was a proneness to leak after rough landings.

However, when Fokker demonstrated the V.36, its undercarriage tank was welcomed as the solution to a difficult problem. It was sufficient to make the aircraft and subsequent types popular. Influential pilots made great efforts to secure undercarriage tanks for their own aircraft, but as far as is known, no Fokker aircraft was ever flown operationally with such a tank.

The V.36 participated in the third fighter trials held at Adlershof during October 1918, and proved to be distinctly better than the Fok. D.VIIF. It was faster at altitude, and its flying qualities were better, although the aileron control was still considered heavy. In climb it was inferior only to the Rumpler Ru.D.I. This was a biplane of exceptionally low weight and elaborate structural features; it had been designed by

Experimental undercarriage tank for Fok. D.VII with plywood fairing removed.

J. Spiegel in collaboration with F. Budig and E. Rumpler (but was claimed to be Rumpler's personal brainchild). The final version of the Ru. D.I was scheduled for quantity production at the time of the Armistice.

Undercarriage tank for Fok. D.VII with plywood fairing in place.

295

Good though the V.36 was, it was not ordered in quantity before the war ended. In any case, its production was unlikely, because much faster fighters would have been needed in 1919.

Fok. D.VII (Alb.) 541/18 with plywood fuselage.

An Albatros development

At the instigation of the *IdFlieg*, an experimental order was given to the Albatros Works for a plywood fuselage for the Fok. D.VII. This was done, not out of mistrust of the original steel-tube structure, but simply because it was felt necessary to insure against any interruption in the supply of steel tubes. Deliveries of the Fok. D.VII were so vital to the fighter squadrons that interruption of production must be avoided at all costs.

The plywood fuselage was an Albatros development, but the aircraft itself was assembled, finished and put through its acceptance flights at Schwerin. These test flights were made on April 27, 1918, by the works pilot Grosse. This may have been done because Albatros-built wings were not then available or had not yet been approved. The aircraft had no Fokker factory number; it was Fok. D.VII (Alb.) No. 541/18, fitted with a Mercedes D.III engine No. 40720. The wings and tail unit were standard D.VII components.

This Fok. D.VII variant underwent a type test at Adlershof on May 15. It was cleared for operational use and recommended for front-line service. The empty weight differed little from that of the standard aircraft.

However, the supply of steel tubing sufficed for all aircraft-production needs until the Armistice, consequently it was never necessary to produce the plywood-fuselage D.VII in quantity.

This illustration is believed to be the fuselage of the Fokker V.35. The undercarriage fuel tank and its leads can be seen.

Two-seat developments of the Fok. D.VII

It was obvious to Fokker and Platz that it would be easy to convert the Fok. D.VII into a two-seater. If the guns and ammunition boxes were removed, a seat for a passenger could be installed in front of the pilot, close to the centre of gravity. The undercarriage tank of the V.36 would permit the use of a smaller fuselage tank, thereby making more space available.

The completed aircraft whose fuselage appears in the preceding illustration. It bore a form of "Fok. D.VII" marking on the fuselage side, and this photograph appears to have been taken after the Armistice.

The wings had ample strength, even for aerobatics in the two-seat configuration; the only modification needed was the provision of a large cut-out in the trailing edge of the upper wing to enable the passenger to enter and leave his cockpit. The landing speed remained acceptable; and the performance with a B.M.W. IIIa was still good, though not what would be expected of a combat aircraft.

These modifications were made, and the resulting aircraft was designated V.35. The main fuel supply was carried in the undercarriage tank, but an additional tank was installed between the cockpits.

Ernst Udet in the pilot's (rear) cockpit of the two-seater.

The type was flown by Ernst Udet, and in it Platz was treated to aerobatics by Fokker. He enjoyed the experience.

Another experimental two-seater was designed specifically for military purposes. This development had been suggested, for infantry liaison and observation duties, by the *IdFlieg*, who were possibly hoping for an aircraft embodying major Fok. D.VII components. Production of such a machine could have been quickly initiated.

The Fokker V.38 was not a simple conversion of the Fok. D.VII, however. It was a larger aircraft with extensive modifications to make it suitable for its intended duties. The only truly common factor between the V.35 and the V.38 was the B.M.W. IIIa engine.

In the V.38 the pilot occupied the forward cockpit and had a single fixed gun, the ammunition box for which was close behind the engine

298

and was without ventilation. A deep cut-out was made in the wing trailing edge. The main fuel tank was in the undercarriage, and there was a small gravity tank just behind the engine. Fuel feed was by air pressure supplied by an engine-driven pump via a pressure-regulating valve. There was also a hand pump in the pilot's cockpit.

The fuselage structure was not fundamentally different from that of the V.38's predecessors. The observer's cockpit, surmounted by a ring mounting for a movable gun, was immediately behind the pilot.

Owing to its military load, the V.38 was heavier than the V.35; consequently its wing area was increased by about 30%. The span of the V.38 was nearly two metres greater.

The maximum speed of the V.38 was stated to be 175 km./hr. (108 m.p.h.), and it was claimed to have reached a height of 5·0 km. (16,500 ft.) in 21·5 minutes. It is doubtful whether this latter figure was achieved with full military load.

The V.38 was later converted for the towing of gliders. This development is discussed in Chapter XIV.

There was one special V.38. This one had a large supplementary petrol tank in the fuselage, containing enough fuel for six hours' flight. Fokker had it built in September 1918, and it was kept in readiness for his use at the Goerries aerodrome under the watchful eye of de Waal. It was Fokker's escape vehicle in which he intended to flee to Holland if the necessity arose. The Fok. E.V affair and its possible consequences (see Chapter XIV) had made it clear to him that some such provision was necessary.

Unfortunately for Fokker, however, it seems that the people working at the aerodrome had guessed his intentions. When he found himself up against the revolutionary Schwerin workers about November 9, the special V.38 was put under guard by the workmen. Fokker did not dare to go near the aerodrome, but made an undignified disappearance in disguise; he travelled to Berlin by rail, where he engaged some communist deserters as a bodyguard.

In view of the satisfaction that the D.VII was giving, and of the fact that the *IdFlieg* had suggested a two-seat development of the D.VII, Fokker was confident of substantial orders for the V.38. He therefore put a batch of sixty aircraft into production in anticipation of a contract.

But the prototype failed to pass its type test and was not recommended for Service use. There was no room for parachute stowage, and the observer's cockpit was too cramped for observation and infantry-liaison duties. The ammunition box was again too near the engine, and the troubles experienced with the D.VII would be repeated. Adverse criticism was levelled against the aileron control.

All in all, the V.38 compared unfavourably with the latest Hannover and Halberstadt two-seaters. Fokker was told to improve his aircraft before submitting it for a further type test, but the Armistice supervened.

The so-called Fok. C.I.

Although the Service designation Fok. C.I was applied to this two-seater it was not justified, because the type was never officially adopted.

After the Armistice, the sixty premature V.38s were smuggled into Holland, where most of them were readily bought by the Dutch Government as a speedy means of filling the Dutch Army Air Service's requirement for modern two-seaters and light bombers. The first batch, ordered in 1919, were redesigned "Fok. C.I" with B.M.W. engines.

These Fokkers gave excellent service for at least three years, whereafter, although they were still perfectly serviceable, they were replaced by later Fokker types with more powerful engines. Numbers of these surplus Fok. C.Is were exported, notably to Colombia and the U.S.A.

In service, the biggest trouble with these aircraft was the undercarriage tank. Its soldered seams split open, creating leaks: this was a frequent

Fok. C.I.

One of the three Fokker C.Is that were delivered to the U.S. Navy after the war. (*Photo: Peter M. Bowers*).

occurrence after bumpy landings. The undercarriage structure itself was not really robust enough for military use, and stronger wheels had to be fitted.

And yet the Fok. C.I earned quite as much praise for its safety in crash

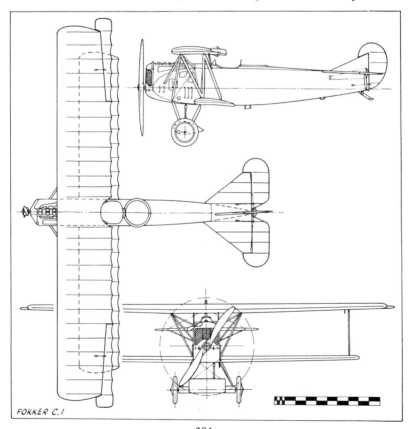

FOKKER C.I

landings as for its flying qualities. The Dutch Air Force did not have a single serious injury from any Fok. C.I crash landing.

Late in 1918 Fokker's Budapest branch told him that the Austrians were enquiring about the possibility of a seaplane version of the Fok. D.VII. Fokker felt sure the German Admiralty would also be interested, so he had a pair of stepped floats designed by a yacht designer and fitted them to a version of the V.35. In this aircraft the passenger sat behind the pilot. Several successful flights over the Schwerin lake were made with various passengers, including de Waal and Platz. No production ensued, but during 1920 similar floats were fitted to a Fok. C.I and further successful trials were made. However, the Fok. C.I remained a landplane.

Fokker and de Waal in the experimental floatplane version of the Fokker C.I.

The Fokker C.II was a three-seat conversion made by Spijkers in Holland during 1920–21. This variant had two seats for passengers under a cabin top; the passengers had to sit facing each other in rather cramped conditions. One C.II was used by the K.L.M. for years; it was used for aerial photography. Another was used by Sherman Fairchild in the U.S.A.; it was flown by E. P. Lott in the "On to Dayton" race in 1924. The type was also used in Canada, on skis when necessary.

The Fokker C.III of 1922 was more or less a trainer conversion of the C.I with a 220-h.p. Hispano-Suiza. The type was supplied in small numbers to Spain.

There were other two-seat variants and conversions of the D.VII, mostly made after the war by various organizations or people, usually without consulting the designer. But during the war a few clandestine conversions were made by enterprising officers commanding fighter units. These aircraft were made from unofficially resurrected Fok. D.VIIs that had been officially written off.

After the war, the Deutsche Lloyd Flugzeug-Werke at Adlershof, under the supervision of the D.V.L., redesigned a Fok. D.VII into a two-seater. This variant was given the designation DLFW. D.VIII. Unfortunately, the prototype was crashed by F. von Koeppen while performing aerobatics too near the ground. Several more examples of this

A German post-war two-seat conversion of the Fok. D.VII. (*Photo: Peter M. Bowers*).

conversion were turned out by G. Hueffer at Krefeld. One served as a flying laboratory for research conducted by the Technical University of Hanover; it was wrecked when landing in fog, but the crew were unhurt.

The DLFW. D.VIII had the 160-h.p. Mercedes engine, but it was moved forward and the fuselage lengthened. The wing span and area were the same as those of the Fok. D.VII.

After the war

For all the victors' insistence on the handing over of all Fok. D.VIIs, they made little enough use of the examples they acquired. Britain apparently took no notice of this product of a defeated enemy, but stuck to wire-braced wing structures with thin aerofoils for nearly twenty years.

One of the Fok. D.VIIs that were taken to the U.S.A. after the Armistice. This aircraft was flown at McCook Field with the Project No. P 127.

An American post-war two-seat Fok. D.VII with 200-h.p. Hall-Scott L-6 engine. (*Photo: Peter M. Bowers*).

Many British aerodynamicists regarded thick aerofoils as bad; structural experts regarded cantilever wings as dangerous; and the A.I.D. cordially disliked welding, for had not a welded rudder failed on a B.E.2 in 1914?

In France, welding was accepted, but the advantages of the welded steel-tube fuselage were not appreciated. French designers in the post-war years were more interested in developing metal structures for wings, consequently they took no real interest in the Fok. D.VII.

The D.VII's influence on American design thinking was considerable, however. In 1918–19, a total of 142 Fok. D.VIIs were shipped to the U.S.A., where they were thoroughly tested in a variety of forms and with a variety of engines. Some had the 230-h.p. Liberty 6, one the Packard 1A-1116. A report on the Liberty-powered D.VII dated February 13, 1920, by the Service test pilot L. P. Moriarty, stated that the flying qualities of the aircraft were exceptionally good. Manoeuvrability and control

This U.S. Army Fok. D.VII two-seater had a large cut-out in the trailing edge of the upper wing. (*Photo: Peter M. Bowers*).

U.S. Army two-seat Fok. D.VII with 290-h.p. Liberty 8 engine. (*Photo: Peter M. Bowers*).

response were very good; the high stalling angle permitted near-vertical firing; and the field of view was better than that provided by most bi-planes. The performance at altitude was somewhat inferior to that of the original Mercedes-powered Fok. D.VII.

The German radiator was not big enough for the Liberty engine, however, and it lacked shutters. Lubrication suffered from surging because the oil pump was at a higher level than the tank.

Two Mercedes-powered D.VIIs took part in the U.S. Army Air Service's First Transcontinental Reliability and Endurance Test, held between October 8 and 31, 1919. The final report recommended aircraft designers to study the features of these aircraft; and the Mercedes engines were reported to have given "a wonderful performance".

In 1922 the Dutch Fokker works were asked to build for the U.S.A. a

U.S. Army Fok. D.VII with 350-h.p. Packard 1A-1237 engine. (*Photo: Peter M. Bowers*).

Fok. D.VII development with the 300-h.p. Hispano-Suiza engine, which was then being manufactured in the U.S.A. under licence by the Wright-Martin Co. The resulting aircraft was designated Fokker D.IX by its makers. It was slightly larger than the D.VII, had a flat frontal radiator and the undercarriage petrol tank, and its angular rudder was somewhat like that of the V.33 and V.34; it had no fin. To the U.S. Army Air Service it was known as the PW-6.

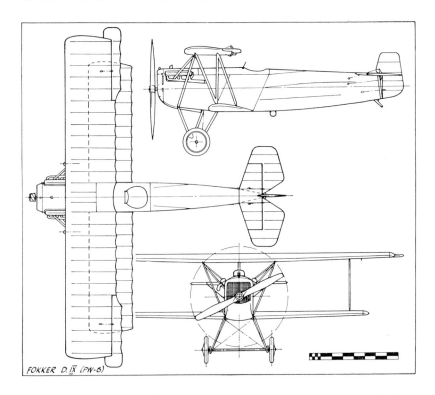

FOKKER D.IX (PW-6)

The influence of the Fok. D.VII structure on American design thinking was far-reaching. Many of the biplanes built in the U.S.A. until the mid-1930s followed the box-spar-and-N-strut formula of the Fokker.

In Germany, the few Fok. D.VIIs that had been salvaged one way or another were employed on meteorological work until at least 1930. These regular flights, entailing climbs to heights of 7·0 km. (23,000 ft.), were conducted by the Deutsche Seewarte at Hamburg. Other countries used Fok. D.VIIs on similar meteorological duties with equal success.

Most of these aircraft were German-built and embodied *ersatz* material; nevertheless, no case of structural failure in the air was reported. But it was no mere coincidence that the Albatros-built Fokkers were preferred and lasted longest.

The Fokker D.IX, known in the U.S.A. as the PW-6.

The air forces of Holland, Belgium and Poland used the Fok. D.VII; and specimens found their way to Switzerland, Sweden, Denmark, Italy, Spain and to countries even farther afield. They proved to be excellent advertisements for the Fokker firm.

Those that were used by the Dutch Army came from the 120 Fok. D.VIIs that Fokker smuggled from Germany to Holland when he fled from Schwerin. Sales to other countries were so good that additional batches of the type had to be made in Holland.

By December 1922, Dutch military pilots had flown over 2,000,000 km. in 11,000 hours on Fok. D.VIIs without a single fatal accident, in spite of many forced landings in difficult country. Some of these veterans were flown until the outbreak of the Second World War. When one Dutch pilot crashed in a Fok. D.VII owing to engine failure in 1938, he was amazed to find that the carburettor of his B.M.W. engine was stamped with a guarantee valid until 1918. The makers of this item had underestimated the quality of their products.

Fok. D.VII in Dutch service, fitted with a 230-h.p. Siddeley Puma engine.

Fok. D.VII in Dutch service. This aircraft has a belly radiator and much-modified engine cowling, steel airscrew, enlarged windscreen, and metal cowling panels as far aft as the cockpit. (*Photo: Peter M. Bowers*).

For want of B.M.W. engines, some of the Dutch Fok. D.VIIs were fitted with Siddeley Puma engines. These were less reliable and less popular.

The Schwerin works

The Schwerin works could not expand rapidly enough to keep pace with incoming orders. The strain upon the staff was made the greater by Fokker's reluctance to spend money on improving facilities, and by the accumulated effect of more than three years of wartime shortages.

Fokker was forever demanding that deliveries be speeded up. He promised impossible delivery dates and expected them to be met: as in 1914 he was naïve enough to accept every order offered him, leaving the production difficulties to his staff. He still thought that all he had to do was to goad his people into frantic activity. Anyone who did not co-operate was liable to find that his way to the trenches was suddenly made easy. As an employer, at that time Fokker was not popular.

In his autobiography he modestly described his wartime activities as follows:

"My business began as a one-man proposition and throughout the war practically remained so. I had to do everything, from designing the smallest part to negotiating for the largest contracts. Never have I worked so hard. What with making frequent trips down to Berlin and the front, supervising the training of Army pilots, designing new aeroplanes, refining the operation of the machine-gun, scheming to outwit my competitors, and a hundred other things as well, I was busy from morning till late at night. Practically the only things I didn't do or supervise were the book-keeping and the purchase of materials."

Which, of course, begs the question: what did Fokker's staff (apart from the buyers and book-keepers) do during those hectic times? With nothing to do all day, must not they have been immensely bored? Platz, who was one of the key members of the staff, has the clearest recollection of being overworked on the design of new aircraft.

Equally dubious were Fokker's protestations that "unfortunately, financial considerations took up little or no part" of his precious time. He was in fact a shrewd, far-sighted business-man who, in spite of all laws and regulations, managed to accumulate his profits in ready money. This was far from easy in wartime Germany.

Fokker had early recognized the possibility of a German defeat, and prepared for the day when it would come. It was difficult for a manufacturer of war material to hoard cash in foreign currency or in realizable valuables. The wartime Government had made many stringent regulations designed to restrict the hoarding of cash; people were compelled to invest earnings and profits in war loans. Fokker must therefore have been exceedingly busy, attending to this aspect of his activities. These matters, of course, were of such a delicate nature that a man of his distrustful nature would not allow any of his employees to deal with them.

In 1917 Fokker acquired an interest in the Axial propeller works; this company produced airscrews to the design of P. Westphal, a well-known pre-war designer of the Johannisthal community. Fokker had also bought the Flugzeugwerft Travemuende. This was a small aircraft works with a good aerodrome, excellently situated right on the coast.

The Travemuende works were a purely private acquisition by Fokker; they were in no way linked with the Fokker Aircraft Works. In them, Fokker saw a means of circumventing the official decree that the output of the Fokker Works was reserved for the Army. He intended to build aircraft for the Admiralty at Travemuende, possibly with components made at Schwerin.

Looking further ahead, Fokker was thinking in terms of closing the

The Fokker works at Schwerin.

309

Schwerin works after the war and concentrating his activities at Trave-muende. He wanted to keep a foothold in Germany. However, in December 1918, Fokker sold the Travemuende factory to Dr. Karl Caspar, a wealthy German pioneer of aviation.

So by the summer of 1918, Fokker's industrial empire extended from Schwerin (aircraft design and production), to Reineckendorf (weapon production and development), Dessau (metal aeroplanes), Budapest (air-craft production for Germany's allies), Travemuende (seaplanes), and Berlin (propellers). Altogether, about 6,000 workers were employed by Fokker.

On July 16, 1918, the name of the Fokker Flugzeug Werke was changed to Fokker Werke G.m.b.H. (Fokker Works, Ltd.). This was probably done to emphasize the more general activities of the firm.

The output of the Schwerin works during the war years was as follows:

Up to the end of 1914	32 aircraft
In 1915	261 aircraft
In 1916	629 aircraft
In 1917	798 aircraft
Between January and March 1918	261 aircraft

Thus, the monthly output had increased from not quite 22 aeroplanes in 1915 to over 87 in early 1918. The figures above were officially quoted, but they sound somewhat optimistic for the years 1915–17.

Surviving acceptance lists give the following monthly production figures:

Month (1918)	A.E.G. C.IV	Fok. Dr.I	Fok. D.VI	Fok. D.VII	Experi-mental	Total aircraft
April	3	13	1	69	3	89
May	—	10	23	118	—	151
June	—	—	25	83	—	108
August	—	—	6	96	No record	102
November	—	—	—	46	No record	46

This, of course, is not the entire output: the lists fail to account for experimental types and variants that were built as private ventures and therefore did not undergo official acceptance tests. The monoplane pro-duction that began in June 1918 and expanded during the following months is not included; these additional production figures are given in the following chapter.

All flight-acceptance tests at Schwerin-Goerries were controlled by de Waal, who had remained a Dutch national. He negotiated all deliveries to the Army and took a hand in checking doubtful aircraft; he also supervised all experimental flying at Schwerin.

Bauaufsicht 13, the establishment of the resident technical officer at the Fokker works, has already figured in this history. In March 1918 it was commanded by a Leutnant Rohde, who was obviously no technician but probably an officer who was medically unfit for front-line service. His subordinates were Roland Betsch, two other officers, and an attached Service test pilot. This last was the N.C.O. Parge who, after the Armistice, became a test pilot for Platz at the Fokker Works.

In addition, the establishment included four Service technicians, two N.C.O.s and eleven privates. What all these people did will forever remain a mystery. As the affair of the Fok. Dr.I proved (and as will be shown again in the next chapter in connexion with the Fok. E.V) the Bauaufsicht scarcely performed the duty indicated by its name: viz., the surveying of production. As far as this was concerned, they might as well have been non-existent.

The Fokker V.17.

CHAPTER XIV

THE FLYING RAZOR

PLATZ CLUNG to his ideal of simplicity: the cantilever monoplane. He had had to comply with Fokker's demands for biplanes, triplanes, and even a quintuplane; in these designs his aspirations towards cantilever wings had to be suppressed as he watched the fitting of interplane struts. He remained convinced that one wing, unencumbered with struts or bracing, was all that was necessary.

Fokker turned down all Platz's monoplane ideas; he even went so far as to say that neither the fighter pilots nor the Adlershof theorists would accept such aircraft. But Platz went on expounding his conviction, and finally had his way when Fokker wanted him to design new types for the first fighter trials.

The first Platz monoplane was the V.17, powered by a 110-h.p. UR.II engine. Despite his long opposition to Platz's cantilever-monoplane ideas, Fokker liked the V.17. He flew it and liked it even more.

There was no time to design and build a parallel type with a water-cooled engine before the Adlershof trials. But the V.17 went to Adlershof with the other Fokker prototypes to participate in the competition.

The V.17 possessed all the significant features of the V.4 triplane without its top and bottom wings. The monoplane was a completely new design, however; the only Fok. Dr.I component it contained was the engine mounting. The one-piece wing had two box spars at a normal spacing. The fuselage was designed to accommodate the spars.

There were fourteen main ribs on each side, and the entire wing skin was of plywood; thus the wing was inherently stiff in torsion. Its span was about 9·5 metres (31·4 ft.) and it had rounded tips.

312

Fokker V.17.

A novel structural feature, often repeated by Platz in later types, was the making of the ailerons as integral parts of the wings; they were simply cut out of the wing structure before the skinning was completed. This simplified manufacture and obviated the need for separate aileron jigs. Such ailerons, of course, could only be plain, unbalanced surfaces: the horn-balanced ailerons fitted to so many Fokker types were welded steel-tube structures. In the V.17 the aileron-hinge axis was skewed.

The weight of this experimental monoplane was reasonably low; but its low-powered engine kept performance down. The V.17 took 35 minutes to climb to an altitude of 5·5 km. (18,000 ft.). Even for early 1918 this was not good enough.

At Adlershof, Fokker personally put the V.17 through the climbing test in order to obtain the best possible time. This climb was made on January 27, 1918, the Kaiser's birthday.[1] Fokker rounded off the festive day with a perfect demonstration of the new monoplane in daring man-oeuvres at low altitude. This created such an impression that he felt the type might be adopted if its rate of climb could be improved.

The parallel development of the V.20 with the 160-h.p. Mercedes and its completion within the space of a week, have been related in Chapter X.

The V.20 wing had a different shape, possibly because lack of time precluded refinement. The tips were nearly square, and the hinge-lines of the horn-balanced ailerons were parallel to the trailing edges. The wing covering aft of the rear spar was of fabric, possibly to save weight. Plywood covered the remainder of the wing as far outboard as the last rib; the tip itself was fabric covered. The weight saving may have been aimed at improving the climb.

With a monoplane wing to accommodate, the fuselage naturally differed from that of the V.11, but the same radiator was used. The V.20 undercarriage was a slightly modified V.11 component.

The V.20 was not the success that Fokker and Platz had hoped for.

[1] A date celebrated by every patriotic German, and a most important day in the life of the Army.

313

The Fokker V.20.

It was, of course, larger and heavier than the V.17. Fokker considered it a promising type, yet he did not submit it for a type test. Both the V.17 and the V.20 would have passed the searching official strength tests with ease.

Next in the monoplane line of development was the V.23 (Factory No. 2443), again a mid-wing monoplane. Platz says that it came nearest to his ideal, and he could not understand why neither Fokker nor the *IdFlieg* fell for it.

In its general appearance, the V.23 looked less angular than any type since the V.3. The wing had rounded tips; and the ailerons were un-balanced, apparently having been made as integral parts of the wing and subsequently cut out. The same low-compression 160-h.p. Mercedes D.IIIa engine and wedge-shaped frontal radiator were used, but the engine cowling was neater and the drag-producing exhaust manifold of the V.20 was discarded in favour of a single downward outlet. There was no fin.

The V.23 took part in the second fighter trials at Adlershof, during

Fokker V.20.

The Fokker V.23.

which it was mostly flown by the works pilot Kulisch, one of the pre-war Johannisthal aviators.

In flying trim the V.23 weighed 839 kg. (1,850 lb.). It climbed to 5·1 km. (16,800 ft.) altitude in 31·5 minutes. It was turned down without a type test, mainly because the pilot's field of vision, severely limited by the expanse of the wings, was regarded as insufficient for combat. Perhaps, too, it was thought that the climbing performance was not promising enough.

As usual, Platz was unable to extract from Fokker any technical information as to why the V.23 was completely rejected. He suspected that the risk of injury to the pilot if the aircraft overturned might have been a reason. In fact, this is unlikely, as the official interest in the Junkers low-wing monoplane indicated. Had the authorities been seriously interested in the V.23, they would merely have insisted upon the addition of a crash pylon.

It seems that the V.23 was preserved by Fokker, later taken to Amsterdam, and finally handed to the German Air museum in Berlin. If this

Fokker V.23.

315

is so, the aircraft must have been destroyed during the bombing of Berlin during the 1939–45 war.

A low-wing monoplane

Platz's suspicions that the V.23 was rejected because of the lack of crash protection must have been dispelled when Fokker asked for another experimental monoplane, this time of low-wing configuration.

As a director of the Junkers-Fokker works, Fokker had repeatedly flown the Ju. D.I low-wing monoplane. He had noticed that the field of vision was much better than that provided by the mid-wing and shoulder-wing monoplanes that Platz had designed. Fokker also found that a low-wing monoplane was by no means unstable, even when it had much less dihedral than his own pre-war low-wing types.

The Fokker V.25.

That Professor Junkers had secured a patent (DRP. No. 310,619 dated March 12, 1918) on low-wing arrangements embodying one-piece wings, did not worry Fokker. This time right was on his side and he was justified in ignoring this unreasonable German patent, for it had no substance and should never have been granted. Blériot, Levavasseur and Fokker himself had in fact anticipated this "invention" by the sage of Dessau.

Platz was not happy about Fokker's latest request. This was not because any serious design problems were involved: he felt that a low-wing monoplane could not be sufficiently stable and safe in the air. Indeed, he is still unconvinced of the advantages of the low-wing arrangement, although he has designed several such monoplanes since 1918. He still regards the low-wing monoplane as deficient in stability and dangerous in the event of overturning on landing. If Platz had been a pilot his views might have changed. And the high-wing monoplane is not without its dangers in the event of a crash.

In spite of his misgivings, Platz designed the V.25 low-wing monoplane (Factory No. 2732), powered by a 110-h.p. UR.II rotary. In appearance

316

it was ahead of its time; twenty years later, with a contemporary engine, it would still have looked up to date. Yet Platz's inhibitions were to lead him to abandon this promising line of development.

The V.25 had a strong crash pylon behind the cockpit; it was faired over, and provided a streamlined head-rest for the pilot.

The wing was tapered and had square tips with rounded corners. It was covered entirely with plywood. No attempt was made to give it greater dihedral than its predecessors had had; the upper surface of the front spar was quite straight. Possibly Fokker told Platz that a larger dihedral angle was unnecessary, for Platz himself seems to have feared that the low-wing arrangement might cause the aircraft to be stable in the inverted attitude.

As usual, the mainplane was an integral structure. It was mounted in a recess in the bottom of the fuselage, like the bottom wing of the V.13.

The Fokker V.25.

The wing attachment was so designed that the incidence could be varied on the ground for experimental purposes; three positions were possible.

A somewhat novel feature, for the time, was the inset position of the ailerons; that is to say, they did not extend to the wing tips. In accordance with Platz's practice, they were cut out of the wing when it was partly skinned. They too had plywood skin. The ailerons had no form of balancing; this may have prejudiced some pilots against the aircraft.

The V.25 differed from its monoplane predecessors in having a triangular fin. Its rudder was generally similar in shape to that of the Fok. D.VII.

There was no cable cross-bracing of the undercarriage. In its place an inverted-V strut was welded in.

The V.25 took part in the second comparative fighter trials, but it had little chance of success, owing to its low-powered engine. It is a matter for great regret that Fokker did not see fit to try the aircraft with a more powerful engine. As it was, the V.25's climb and speed were not impressive, although it was slightly lighter than the V.17.

317

Fokker abandoned this advanced design without pressing for any further development. This was a case of his intuition letting him down: although he was on the right track and perfectly able to beat Junkers in the fighter contest, he failed to see the possibilities. Apart from the obvious move of fitting a more powerful engine, he could have beaten all his competitors by mounting the machine-guns in or underneath the wing, where they would have needed no synchronizing mechanism. He would then have had the simplest aeroplane of all, highly manoeuvrable and with superior fire power.

This was probably the last time that Fokker imposed upon Platz a design formula to which the latter was opposed. And yet, this time, Fokker had been right!

The second fighter trials

A second fighter-aircraft competition was held at Adlershof in June 1918. The Kogenluft had urged the holding of more such trials to speed up the equipment of front-line units with the best types. Aircraft development was moving rapidly; in quantity and quality the Allied air forces were making great strides.

Imperial Germany was fighting with her back to the wall. Superior weapons were urgently needed; in spite of all the shortages in Germany, industry had to produce these weapons. Thomsen and Siegert realized that frequent changes in aircraft equipment could no longer be avoided. They did not expect wonder-weapons, but they were confident that better aircraft and engines could be made.

Hauptmann Kurt Student had been made responsible for the organization of the trials. He imposed strict but sensible rules, taking all possible precautions against interference by industrial interests. No civilian was admitted to the aerodrome while the trials were in progress, apart from essential mechanics. Each aircraft with a stationary engine was allowed two mechanics; each rotary-powered machine was allowed three.

When E. Rumpler, the arrogant director of the Rumpler works, was spotted in the forbidden area, Student had him removed instantly: he was marched out between guards with rifles and fixed bayonets. Rumpler's undignified expulsion provided all the pilots with immense amusement.

This was the same Kurt Student who, six years later, became one of the founders of the Reichswehr Luftwaffe. Later, he formed the first parachute and glider airborne forces. During the Second World War he became known as the conqueror of Eben-Emael and of Crete, and as commander of the defence at Arnhem.

Fokker learned of Rumpler's discomfiture and deemed it politic not to show up at Adlershof while the ban on civilians was in force.

As a preliminary, Student and two other experienced fighter pilots tried all the competing aircraft in flight. They then agreed upon their qualities and drew up a kind of short list of the most likely types. These were the

318

Fok. D.VII, Zeppelin D.I, Pfalz D.XII, and Rumpler D.I, all with the 160-h.p. Mercedes.

The operational pilots, among them Reinhard, Loerzer, Goering, Udet and von Schleich, had three tasks to perform. First they were to fly the various aircraft and give their opinions on flying qualities, manoeuvrability, diving performance, field of vision, and combat qualities. To this end they had to complete forms immediately after landing, in the presence of the duty officer.

Secondly, they were to participate in the group flying of aircraft having the same engine. This included a climb to 5·0 km. (16,500 ft.), at which altitude the aircraft had to race each other for an assessment of their relative speeds. They were also to be raced at a height of 1·0 km. (3,300 ft.). All aircraft were weighed beforehand; all had to carry the same load, which included three barographs.

Finally, the pilots were to attend the concluding discussions and hear technical reports on the aircraft by Adlershof specialists, flying assessments by the official test pilots, strength characteristics, maintenance features, and the like. The results of the competitive flying by the firms' test pilots were also to be made known at these discussions.

Hauptmann Student gave the findings of himself and his officers, based on their test flights. Staff Engineer Eydam reported on the strength of the aircraft concerned; Oberleutnant G. Madelung gave the results of the type tests.

It was considered that these arrangements would prevent the final selection from being influenced by anything but strictly military considerations.

A total of thirty-nine single-seat fighters, either prototypes or variants, took part in the competition, entered by a dozen firms. Fokker's entry included Fok. D.VII biplanes, Fokker-built and licence-built, and the V.24 with the 220-h.p. Benz Bz.IV. The few monoplanes came from Fokker and Junkers only.

Fokker's monoplanes included Platz's latest creations, the parasol-wing monoplanes V.26, V.27 and V.28. These were generally similar, but differed in their engines and engine installations. The V.26 had the 110-h.p. Oberursel UR.II, the V.28 had the 145-h.p. UR.III. The V.27 was a parallel development, but was much larger and had the 195-h.p. Benz Bz.IIIb, a water-cooled V-eight engine.

The initial comparison flights divided the competing aircraft into seven groups; all the aircraft in any one group had the same type of engine.

The 160-h.p. Mercedes group was the largest. It included Fok. D.VII No. 230/18, the type-test aircraft, and two Fok. D.VIIs built by Albatros and Ostdeutsche Albatros; the new Albatros D.XII; the Rumpler D.I, Junkers D.I, Zeppelin D.I, Pfalz D.XII and the Schütte-Lanz D.VII. It was also to include the Naglo D.I quadruplane, but this was withdrawn at the request of the Albatros works.

A promising type of advanced design was the Zeppelin D.I, an all-metal cantilever biplane designed by C. Dornier. But while being flown on July 3 by Hauptmann Reinhard, Manfred von Richthofen's successor as leader of Jagdgeschwader 1, the upper wing broke away and Reinhard, who had no parachute, crashed to his death. He had been pulling out of a dive when a wing bolt sheared; the wing folded back and broke away.

This accident had two consequences. Front-line pilots were under even more stringent prohibition from flying types that had not passed the structural tests at Adlershof. The darker consequence was that the notorious Goering was made successor to Reinhard: the Kogenluft had yielded to the pressure of his influential friends.

The second-largest group of aircraft comprised those with 140/160-h.p. rotary engines. These were the Fokker V.28 parasol monoplane (Factory, No. 2735) with the improved UR.III; four Siemens-Schuckert biplanes, all of different types and with various versions of the Sh.3 engine; two Pfalz D.VIIIs; and two L.F.G. Roland biplanes. A Roland D.XVI parasol was expected but was not ready in time. The Goebel Goe.III engine was also represented.

The group of aircraft powered by the ungeared Benz Bz.IIIb engine included the Fokker V.27 parasol (Factory No. 2734), and four biplanes by Albatros, Aviatik and the L.F.G.

The fourth group embraced all the aircraft with geared V-eight engines. In it were the second version of the Fokker V.27, and biplanes by Albatros, the L.F.G. and Daimler. The Daimler D.I (designed by H. Klemm) was the only entrant with the 185-h.p. Mercedes D.IIIb.

Aircraft with the 185-h.p. B.M.W. IIIa engine formed another group. There were only three, by Fokker, Pfalz and the L.F.G.

Two biplanes had the high-compression 220-h.p. Benz Bz.IVü engine: these were the Fokker V.24 (Factory No. 2612) and the Pfalz D.XIV (Factory No. 2800), which was similar to the Pfalz D.XII.

The last group consisted of four aircraft powered by the 110-h.p Oberursel UR.II. These were the Fokker V.25, Fokker V.26 and two Kondor biplanes designed by W. Rethel.

The heaviest aircraft present were those with the 220-h.p. Benz Bz.IV six-cylinder engine. This power unit was an emergency solution to relieve the shortage of Mercedes and B.M.W. engines. With a weight of 1,032 kg. (2,280 lb.), the Pfalz D.XIV was heavier than the Fokker V.24, which weighed 1,006 kg. (2,210 lb.). At the other end of the scale were the Fokker V.25 (564 kg.: 1,240 lb.) and Fokker V.26 (556 kg.: 1,120 lb.). Among the 160-h.p. Mercedes group, the Rumpler D.I was decidedly the lightest.

During the flying by firms' pilots, the Flz. weeded out a number of types that were obviously out of the running. These included the taper-wing Fokker V.21 (Factory No. 2310) with its high-compression Mercedes D.IIIaü engine; its climb was poor, and it took 45 minutes to reach a height of 5·9 km. Also rejected was the Fokker V.23 mid-wing monoplane (Factory No. 2443) with the ordinary 160-h.p. Mercedes D.IIIa. Kulisch made two officially observed climbs in it.

The V-eight engines were too new and gave a good deal of trouble, even when flown by the firms' pilots. The hotted-up versions of the Sh.3 in the Siemens biplanes also proved troublesome, but the standard engine performed well in other firms' aircraft, and produced amazing climbs.

Schmarje, one of Fokker's pilots, made an excellent climb in the Fokker V.28 with the 200-h.p. Goebel Goe.IIIa, on June 5. He reached a height of 5·0 km. (16,500 ft.) in 10·7 minutes, and 6·0 km. (19,700 ft.) in 16 minutes. The aircraft had an oversize airscrew of 2·7-m. (8·9-ft.) diameter, and its take-off weight was 626 kg. (1,380 lb.). This climb was a record. Schuetzenmeister, another works pilot, put up a slightly better time but with less than the prescribed military load. The V.28 was well thought of, but its engine had not yet passed the official trials.

Other Fokker works pilots who made officially observed climbs were Neisen, Grosse and Kulisch. Fokker himself did not take much part in this competition flying.

The aeroplane with the best climbing performance was the Rumpler Ru. D.I with the high-compression Mercedes D.IIIaü engine. It even surpassed the Pfalz D.XIIf with the B.M.W. IIIa engine. The Fok. D.VIIF could not improve on third place among the fighters with water-cooled engines.

On June 17, demonstration flights were made in the presence of the Kogenluft, General von Hoeppner, accompanied by other high-ranking officers of the German Army Flying Corps. On this occasion, representatives of the industry were admitted.

The best of the Fokker, Junkers, Pfalz, Rumpler and Siemens-Schuckert types were flown in mock combat by officers of the Adlershof establishment, all of them experienced fighter pilots. "Defeated" aircraft were required to withdraw and land.

Among the rotary-engined aircraft the last survivors were the Siemens-Schuckert D.IV and the Fokker V.28 with UR.III engine; the Siemens was flown by Leutnant H. J. Rath, a specialist on Siemens types.

When the Siemens-Schuckert D.IV, with its amazing manoeuvrability and controllability, appeared to be superior, Fokker asked to be allowed to fly his parasol monoplane against the biplane flown by Leutnant Mueller. But even Fokker's skill was not enough to beat the Siemens. After landing he explained that he had less experience of the V.28 than Mueller of the D.IV. This was true enough.

However, the general impression created by the Fokker V.26/28 design was so good that a substantial production order was placed with the Fokker works. The production aircraft were to be equipped with the 110-h.p. Le Rhône engine until the 145-h.p. UR.III and the new 200-h.p Goebel Goe.IIIa were cleared for operational use, when these more powerful engines would be installed. The fighter pilots were in complete agreement with this proposal of the *IdFlieg*.

The selection of a fighter with a water-cooled engine provided a surprise. It was a foregone conclusion that the engine would be a B.M.W IIIa; in fact, the Mercedes-powered prototypes had been asked for solely to provide comparisons. Since no major modification was required to interchange the Mercedes and the B.M.W., all the Mercedes-powered aircraft could be included in the final reckoning.

The Flz. officers confidently expected that the front-line pilots would choose either the Rumpler D.I or the Fokker D.VII. But Udet seemed to be much taken with the Pfalz D.XII, and his opinion carried so much weight that the other pilots reluctantly agreed with him. To the surprise of the Flz. experts, they chose the Pfalz D.XII.

This type climbed well and was fast, but it was definitely not so easy to fly as the Fok. D.VII. Its flying qualities were very much like those of the Spad: it had an abrupt stall and would spin with little provocation. The Pfalz D.XII also somewhat resembled the Spad in appearance; this proved to be an embarrassment in combat.

The Pfalz D.XII was adopted and a large order was placed for the type. Subsequent events proved the Adlershof experts correct in their judgment. When the Pfalz D.XII reached the front, pilots tried to get rid of it as quickly as they could. Udet was one of the first to discard it. It was rumoured that he had been too much in favour with the financial backer of the Pfalz firm.

Although Fokker was gratified to hear this rumour and to learn how little the Pfalz D.XII was liked, he was angered to find that the major part of the output of the B.M.W. engine now went to Pfalz for the Pfalz D.XIIf. His ration of these precious engines for the Fokker D.VIIF was growing smaller and smaller.

Fokker claims in his autobiography that pilots deliberately crashed Pfalz D.XIIf's to get their B.M.W. IIIa engines for installation in Fokker

The Fokker V.26, the prototype of the Fok. E.V./D.VIII fighter.

322

D.VIIs. There are no records to prove this, but it is not unlikely: faulty or unsatisfactory aircraft were occasionally disposed of in this manner, and some pilots were quite skilled at damaging aircraft sufficiently to ensure that they would be written off without sustaining personal injury. On the other hand, the Pfalz D.XII was tricky to fly, and the crashes may have been merely a symptom of inadequate training.

Fokker V.26. (*Photo: Peter M. Bowers*).

The Fok. E.V. (*V.26 and V.28*)

One reason why Fokker had wanted a light monoplane with a rotary engine was that production would not be affected by delays in engine supplies. There was still a large store of excellent Le Rhône engines at Adlershof, to be had for the asking, and Oberursel could produce many more for him.

The Fokker V.26 was more or less a V.13 with the bottom wing removed. The parasol arrangement gave the pilot a field of view that surpassed all earlier efforts; Platz was also convinced that it made the aircraft more stable.

The V.26 wing was structurally similar to that of the V.25; it had a plywood skin and inset, unbalanced ailerons. The spar flanges were a little lighter than those of the V.25 because the cantilever span outboard of the cabane structure was comparatively short. The flanges were laminated by gluing together planks of 10-mm. (0·39-in.) thickness. Platz took great care to ensure that splices in such laminated members were staggered.

The wing-attachment fittings were bolted to filler blocks that were glued into the spars between the flanges. These blocks were built up of glued pine laminations. There were diaphragm bulkheads between the spar flanges at each rib-attachment point.

The trailing edge of the central cut-out was stiffened by a laminated former. In the central portion of the wing the ribs were pitched at a

323

distance of 300 mm. (11·8 in.); outboard of the cabane structure the inter-rib distance was 320 mm. (12·6 in.). The skin, of 1·5-mm. plywood, was attached to ribs and spars by glue and by ½-in. steel pins.

Platz set great store by perfectly smooth wing surfaces. All protuberances were avoided; the surface was carefully polished and lacquered. On the V.26, the cantilever span was 2·88 m. (9·5 ft.) on each side.

The ailerons were small but effective. They were 160 cm. (63 in.) in span, 20 cm. (7·9 in.) in chord. The spar of each aileron was a steel tube, each end of which was plugged and bore a steel pin. These end-pins engaged with bearing sockets let into the rib tails between which the ailerons lay, and thus acted as pivots; each aileron also had a central hinge close to the control horn.

The absence of national markings suggests that this may be the Fokker V.28 with the 145-h.p. Oberursel UR.III engine.

Structurally, the fuselage was simple, for it had to provide no direct wing attachment; it retained its basic rectangular cross-section. The wing supports consisted of two rigid, widely-splayed tripods for the front spar mounting, and two adjustable struts for the rear spar.

The engine mounting, tank installation, controls, and the tail unit, were essentially similar to those of earlier monoplanes and the Fok. D.VI. A single fuel tank was fitted, immediately behind the engine, which it fed by gravity. The tank was divided, one section containing the oil.

Platz could rightly claim that this parasol type was the simplest and cheapest single-seat fighter ever built. He had achieved his aim.

The V.28 was very similar to the V.26, apart from having strengthened spar flanges and different engine mountings. It was to have rotaries of up to twice the power of the Le Rhône; some of these needed a fore-and-aft mounting. The fuel capacity was enlarged.

Although the official strength tests were carried out on an aircraft of V.28 design, the production Fok. E.V had the 110-h.p. Le Rhône.

324

The Fokker V.27

The parallel development with a water-cooled engine was the Fokker V.27 (Factory No. 2734). It was generally similar to the V.26/28 but somewhat larger and heavier. As the V.27 was also intended for the second fighter trials, Fokker chose the new 195-h.p. Benz Bz.IIIb V-eight engine, both geared and ungeared. This engine was, at that time, the most advanced of the various high-speed eight-cylinder developments that were more or less based on the Hispano-Suiza.

This Benz engine was shorter than the Mercedes and permitted a more compact installation. In the V.27 advantage was taken of this fact, and the Benz was neatly installed and cowled, with a circular frontal radiator that was fitted with shutters. Fokker was very pleased with it.

Fokker V.27.

It seems that both versions of the Bz.IIIb engine were fitted to the V.27. In its original form the aircraft had the direct-drive engine; in its ultimate form, as an armoured trench fighter, it had the geared version.

The V.27 wing was wholly covered with plywood; the ailerons were plain surfaces, inset from the tips as on the V.27's contemporaries. The cabane struts were widely splayed to reduce the cantilever span as much as possible.

Schuetzenmeister made two officially observed climbs on the V.27 on June 5, 1918. The time recorded for the first was poor because the engine was not running properly, but the second was a fully competitive effort; better, in fact, than the performance of other fighters with the same engine.

The report on the V.27's handling characteristics stated that landing was easy and the stalling speed low, but the aircraft had an unpleasant tendency to spin abruptly when stalled. Possibly the centre of gravity was rather far aft.

After the fighter trials, Fokker learned that the Army wanted an

The armoured V.27, which was re-designated V.37.

armoured single-seat fighter for the protection of infantry support aircraft and for ground-attack duties. A design requirement was that the aircraft structure must be able to withstand hits without collapsing. A new Service type category DJ had been created, and the A.E.G. were building all-metal prototypes.

Fokker thought the V.27 might meet this requirement if it were armoured. The radiator seemed to be conspicuously vulnerable, but Platz produced an idea for protecting it. This consisted of a disc of armour plate that was fitted to the airscrew hub and faired by a large-diameter spinner. The armour disc completely covered the radiator, consequently six radial blades were attached to its rear surface to drive cooling air through the radiator. This cooling fan seems to have worked so well that Fokker wanted to use it on a new interceptor fighter that needed no armour.

Later, Fokker obtained a patent (D.R.P. 335,745 of October 2, 1918) for a simplification of this arrangement. The patent drawings show a flat piece of armour plate bolted to the airscrew. The armour could be of different shapes and had various slots in it; apparently there were to be neither spinner nor fan blades. Platz recalls that a scheme of this kind was tried but remained experimental.

The armour on the V.27 fuselage consisted of 2·5-mm. steel plate on the sides and bottom of the fuselage and behind the cockpit. The pilot's seat had been moved forward to reduce the area that required armour

326

plate, consequently the wing cut-out had to be enlarged. The armoured version of the V.27 was given the new designation V.37. The V.37 was either too late for consideration or not promising enough to warrant adoption as a Service type. It does not seem to have undergone a type test, nor was a structural examination made.

The Fok. E.V in service

In June 1918 the Fokker V.26 was officially adopted for the use of the Germany Army Flying Corps. It was given the Service designation Fok. E.V in its basic form with the 110-h.p. Le Rhône engine. It was to be superseded by the V.28 as soon as suitable engines were approved and in production. The Admiralty also decided to equip naval fighter squadrons with the Fok. E.V.

Before these decisions were taken, the V.28 with UR.III engine was subjected to a type test on June 6 and recommended for production as Fok. E.Ve, subject to clearance of the engine. Final trials to determine the serviceability of the eleven-cylinder Oberursel had still to be undertaken. In fact, however, only *Beute* Le Rhône or UR.II engines were flown in Fokker fighters on the Western Front until the end of the war.

After the obligatory structural tests had been satisfactorily passed, 400 parasol-wing fighters were ordered from Fokker. The order was given to the Schwerin works on Fokker's assurance that he could meet the rate of production demanded by the *IdFlieg*. The stipulated rate of delivery was to be eighty aircraft per month after an initial period of two months, allowed for the organization of production. Fokker promised to dispatch the first small batches within two weeks or so. He kept his word—at a dreadful cost.

Apparently unnumbered, this aircraft may have been the V.26 brought up to production E.V. standard.

327

Six Fok. E.V were rushed to the front late in July, and a total of twenty had been supplied before the month was out. On August 7, the Jagdgeschwader I von Richthofen received six Fok. E.V; others went to Jagdgeschwader II for Jagdstaffel 19, and to other units.

After the new type had been in operational use for only a few days, Leutnant Rolff of Jagdstaffel 6 (of the Jagdgeschwader von Richthofen) was fatally injured when his E.V sustained a wing failure at a height of 300 m. and crashed near Bermes. Two days later, Fok. E.V No. 107/18 of Jagdstaffel 19 lost a wing: it broke 10 cm. outboard of the cabane struts immediately after the unfortunate pilot had done three rolls at a height of 600 m. The starboard wing was salvaged and sent to Adlershof. A day or two afterwards, a third wing failure caused another fatality.

The Fok. E.V was immediately grounded; an Aircraft Crash Investigation Commission was set up and ordered to report its findings urgently. At the Flz., a technical investigation was initiated. The whole procedure was precisely the same as had been adopted in the case of the Fok. Dr.I crashes. Acceptances of further Fok. E.Vs were postponed until the type was cleared. No acceptance flights were made after August 23, 1918; no more flight tests were made until the last week in September, when the Fok. D.VIII emerged.

Goering, then commander of the Jagdgeschwader von Richthofen, was unable to prevent these drastic measures, which were bound to annoy his friend Fokker: he happened to be on leave at the time. His deputy, Ernst Udet, acted resolutely and correctly. It was therefore not possible to hush things up, and full evidence was available to the investigating commission.

Before discussing the findings of the commission it will be relevant to consider the results of the official structural tests, which had produced very reassuring results. All specified load factors were attained without failure or excessive deformation. The starboard wing had sheared at the cabane struts only when 140% of the specified load factor of 2·5 in Case C was applied: this was more strength than was required.

The Fokker Works were asked to replace the rear struts (which were of streamline section, $45 \times 22 \times 1·0$ mm.) by struts of $55 \times 22 \times 1·0$ mm. section. This was merely a precaution against the possibility that one of the struts might be damaged by a bullet or shell splinter. The firm readily agreed to this modification. Platz was not consulted.

As a precaution, being mindful of their past experience of Fokker quality, the Flz. technicians subjected the Fok. E.V wing to a weathering test. The strength and safety of the Fok. E.V depended, more than in any other aircraft, on glued plywood structures; and the Flz. had noticed that such structures, when made at Schwerin, were badly affected by moisture and consequently lost strength and rigidity.

For this good reason they took the Fok. E.V wing that had undergone the static test, and exposed it to the weather for four weeks from June 23. Water was poured over it several times a day during this period. Finally

328

the plywood skin blistered and wrinkled, and could be crushed by hand; in some places the laminations had separated.

And yet this damaged wing still had an ultimate load factor of 5·92 in Case A when tested (the required factor was only 5·0); at this value both spars failed at the strut attachments. The safety of the Fok. E.V under adverse conditions was thus established; the only suggestion that was made was to recommend better lacquering inside the wing, to reduce moisture absorption still further. This weathering test was quite separate from the basic structural test; it had nothing to do with the accident investigation, either.

Fok. E.V No. 138/18.

In the full structural test, the fuselage longerons buckled when subjected to 115% of the specified maximum loads. The elevator control circuit and the undercarriage were not tested because they were identical with those of the Fok. D.VI. A minor item was a request for the strengthening of the forked tube that held the rudder bar.

On the basis of these favourable results, the Fok. E.Ve had been given a full clearance by Hauptmann Dr. W. Hoff on June 25. Coming so soon afterwards, the evidence collected by the Crash Investigation Commission was a severe shock to the *IdFlieg* and the Kogenluft.

The Inquiry

The officer in charge of the Crash Investigation Commission was Leutnant von Mallinckrodt, an engineering test pilot of the Flugzeug-meisterei. He had flown the first Junkers monoplane on its initial flights in December 1915. The other members of the commission were Staff Engineer Henzel and Sergeant Schubert (a chief mechanic and, in civilian life, a professional engineer).

329

On August 24 the commission met at the staff HQ of the Jagdge-schwader von Richthofen, and began to sift the evidence. Fokker, who had been instructed to inspect the wreckage of the crashed Fok. E.V, was requested to attend this preliminary discussion.

As a possible cause of the wing failures, the theory was advanced that the wings might have failed in torsion from twisting at a high lift loading; this could have produced greater incidence towards the wing tips (i.e. wash-in) with a correspondingly adverse loading gradient. Fokker grasped eagerly at this theory, feeling relieved that a "hitherto unsuspected aero-dynamic wing loading" could be held responsible. It was clear to him that only such crass oversight by the aerodynamicists could have caused the wings to fail.

To make the Fok. E.V safe, the commission recommended that external cable bracing be fitted to prevent the wings from twisting. As a further safeguard, the front spar should be made stiffer, the rear spar less stiff: this, it was thought, would prevent the wing tips from twisting to a greater angle of incidence under load. Of less comfort to Fokker was the added comment that new wings should be more carefully built, and their interior better protected against moisture by lacquer or varnish.

That the emphasis in the commission's opinion was misplaced was made grimly obvious when the production Fok. E.V wing was subjected to a physical examination at Adlershof. The starboard wing of E.V No. 107/18 had not been completely destroyed, and it was thoroughly inspected.

The workmanship was at once seen to be deplorable, and defective timber had been used for the spars. The wing of another machine, No. 110/18, showed the same deficiencies. Fok. E.V No. 127/18 was even worse: water had collected inside the wing, the wood of which was rotting. When the plywood skin was cut, a stream of foetid water flowed out, indicating that the casein glue was perishing.

Closer investigation of the remains of the wing of 107/18 showed that the plywood was of acceptable quality. But the pins that attached the skin to the ribs had been driven in carelessly; most of them had missed the rib cap-strips or had merely splintered them. The glued joints were likewise defective. In fact, the plywood skin was adhering only in parts to the wing structure.

Similar carelessness in pinning was found in the attachment of the plywood webs to the wing spars; moreover, the material used for the spar webs was inferior. The pine used for the flanges of both spars was brittle: it was still "green" and had been insufficiently seasoned. Most glued joints were poor and it was obvious that they had been ineffectively clamped.

It was incredible that so many blatant defects had managed to pass any kind of inspection.

But there was worse to come. When the cross-sections of the wing spars of this production wing were compared with those of the aircraft that had undergone the type test, it was discovered that the lower flange of the front spar of the crashed aircraft was only 7·5 mm. (0·295 in.) thick, as against 13 mm. (0·515 in.) in the type-test aircraft. The rear spar of the salvaged wing was missing and could not be checked.

Fokker was asked to come immediately to Adlershof to attend discussions and loading tests on these production wings. Sensing that something unhealthy was in the offing, he took Platz along with him to act as a kind of lightning conductor in case a storm should break. It was Platz's first and last visit to the Flugzeugmeisterei; and he had, of course, only a vague idea why his presence was required.

A meeting to clear the technical aspects of the matter was held on August 30, 1918. This was primarily to discuss a redesign of the wing. In the chair was Leutnant von Mallinckrodt; Fokker and Platz were present. Two staff engineers from Adlershof attended: Krueger of the Central Acceptance Commission (ZAK) and Stelmachowski, the strength expert of the experimental department of the Flz.

Von Mallinckrodt (who had been on good terms with Fokker and later became his demonstration pilot in international military competitions) pointed out that the Fok. E.V wing had to be redesigned and strengthened. Fokker jumped up, referring to a letter that he had sent to the *IdFlieg*; he complained that he had received no reply. It was in fact an impudent letter, in which Fokker had laid all blame for the wing failures squarely on the Adlershof technicians. These had, so Fokker alleged, failed to take account of wing loadings that actually occurred in flight: they had laid down absurd loading cases for the strength-testing of military aircraft: their sand-loadings were unrealistic. And this was why the wings of the Fok. E.V had broken.

Fokker's hypocritical outburst was as far-fetched as it was unfounded. Its only purpose can have been to act as a kind of smoke screen and to evoke the sympathies of his old benefactors, the regular officers.

Von Mallinckrodt, who had enough technical knowledge to recognize Fokker's accusations as ill-founded, merely referred to the written report of the experimental department of the Flz. This indicated that the wing spars of production Fok. E.Vs were weaker than and different from those originally approved. This, and the obviously bad workmanship present in the wings, were the only subjects for discussion.

After this, Fokker had no more to say. He was told that two more of the existing production wings would be tested. If they too had weaker spars, then all wings already built would be condemned. These wings would be withdrawn from front-line units at Fokker's expense. Also at his expense, they would have to be speedily replaced by redesigned and satisfactory wings.

It was stipulated that all new Fok. E.V wings must be at least as strong as the wing of the type-test aircraft. Stelmachowski wanted wider spars. Fokker protested that the existing spar width provided enough strength (he was right), and that a change would necessitate the design and manufacture of new ribs and fittings: this would hold up deliveries. Stelmachowski admitted that the original spars had been satisfactory. It was therefore left to the Fokker works to decide how the requisite strength should be achieved; but any redesigned wing would have to be proofloaded in the presence of Adlershof representatives before it could be accepted. The *IdFlieg* would define, in writing, the exact conditions for such a test.

Fokker was required to give an undertaking that the utmost care in supervision of production would be taken in future, and that materials and workmanship would be satisfactory. The Bauaufsicht would be given a reminder to perform their duties more strictly.

The replacement wings were to be supplied with the minimum of delay. Again, stress was laid on the need to protect all internal and external surfaces of spars, ribs and skin against moisture.

Stelmachowski's report mentions that Fokker was accompanied by one "Ingenieur Schlotz", but it does not record any utterance by the thus-misspelt Platz. Possibly the *IdFlieg* and Flz. representatives thought Fokker's burly, taciturn companion was either a kind of bodyguard or a police shadow provided by a security department. The Army men were never closer to the solution of the mystery of who designed the wonder aeroplanes of the uncouth Dutchman. And they missed it!

Platz did not in fact open his mouth, and his opinion was never invited. No-one attempted to find out who he really was, and why he sat there with Fokker.

If Fokker had attended the secret conference of all aircraft designers held by the Flz. on August 23, he might have hesitated before delivering his misguided philippic a week later. An invitation to send a representative had been sent to the Fokker works but of course Fokker had ignored this opportunity to increase his firm's technical knowledge. Platz was unaware that any such conference was being held.

At the conference Stelmachowski had communicated the new loading conditions that were incorporated in the BLV 1918 edition. These had been formulated specifically to cover cantilever wings. It was prescribed that such wings should not only withstand the direct drag load of twice the weight: the revised Case C conditions required torsional stiffness of the wing under a torque of 1·75 times the chord times the weight. This was to represent the case of a terminal-velocity dive; under this torque the wing should not twist by more than ten degrees at the tips. Distortion at the wing tips under sand loading to the limits of Cases A and B should not exceed five degrees. Furthermore, the Flz. would henceforth examine front and rear spars separately to determine their behaviour in bending and twisting.

The conference of aircraft designers had accepted the new proposals after a lengthy discussion of their implications.

As far as Fokker and his outburst were concerned, the important fact was that the draft of BLV 1918 had been prepared in the spring of 1918; it was therefore obvious that the Adlershof technicians were fully aware that wing deformations in flight could lead to abnormal aerodynamic loadings. The new requirements had in fact been derived from the original theory of the Fok. Dr.I accidents and from wing failures on Albatros sesquiplanes.

When the meeting broke up, Fokker thought that the storm was now over. The affair had cost him a considerable sum, but at least he had given those Adlershof theorists a severe shaking. But on September 3, the Fok. E.V wings were sand loaded in the presence of Fokker and Platz. Platz had memorized the principal dimensions of the spars and was horrified to see by how much the production spars differed from his original design: their lack of strength was obvious. The flanges were smaller and wrongly laminated. To make matters worse, the more highly stressed upper flanges, which had to withstand the greatest compression load, were even thinner than the lower flanges. The spars had evidently been made upside down.

Platz discreetly conveyed this alarming information to Fokker and let him understand that production at the works must have slipped up badly, for the wings must be seriously under-strength. This did not seem to impress Fokker greatly: he hoped that these little discrepancies would cause no undue fuss, and that perhaps the slide-rule pushers would not notice them. For him it was good enough that the Crash Investigation Commission had established the primary cause of the wing failures as a hitherto-neglected aerodynamic effect. The rear spar was too strong and too stiff: the commission had said so. Besides, wings did occasionally fail, especially when roughly handled by ham-fisted pilots.

While Platz experienced acute discomfort, Fokker was airily unconcerned. He brazenly denied any possibility of careless manufacture and poor workmanship: no blame for these tedious crashes could be imputed to his factory.

A standard sand-loading test was made of the wing of the undamaged production Fok. E.V No. 127/18. It began to fail at only 77% of the specified load in Case A; complete collapse occurred at 108%. The deflections measured at the wing tips differed from each other. This was peculiar: it indicated different spar sizes in the port and starboard halves of the wing. Platz's discomfiture grew. Fokker merely grumbled about the futile activities of busybodies while there was a war on.

Two days later, another wing was sand loaded. It had been taken direct from the Schwerin production shop by the Bauaufsicht at the behest of Hauptmann Hoff. It collapsed when 74% of the specified load in Case A was applied.

The Fokker firm was now requested to supply an experimental wing at the earliest possible moment. The port half of this wing was to be of standard production quality; the starboard half was to be reinforced in accordance with the official recommendations. Platz quietly ignored this specification and had the entire wing made to the standard of his original design.

This "experimental" wing was delivered on September 7. Its weight was 73 kg. (161 lb.), compared with the 69 kg. (152 lb.) of the wing of the type-test aircraft. Under test it sustained no less than 191% of the specified sand-load in Case A; that is to say, it proved to have an ultimate load factor of 9·5. When fully loaded, its tips twisted by no more than one or two degrees in Cases A and B. It resisted 112% of the specified load in Case C.

The Flz. technicians were satisfied that a wing of this strength could not possibly break. They were also certain, now, that the wing failures had not been caused by twisting under load.

In view of the urgency, experiments were conducted to determine whether the addition of cable bracing to the available, under-strength wings could make them acceptably safe until properly constructed wings were made. A new wing from the current production batch was sand loaded. One side was left cantilever, the other was braced by lift cables that ran from the undercarriage-attachment points on the lower longerons to points on the spars 2·7 m. (9·0 ft.) from the centre line.

The cantilever half of the wing deflected by 144 mm. (5·68 in.) at the tip, the braced half by 86 mm. (3·38 in.). The wing resisted an ultimate sand load of 133% in Case A. The cable bracing could therefore be accepted as an emergency solution.

Yet another production Fok. E.V wing was tested to destruction; this one was one of the wings withdrawn from front-line units. It started to break up at only 82% of the specified load in Case A and failed completely at 128%.

In their reports to the *IdFlieg*, the Flz. technicians demonstrated beyond any shadow of doubt that the wing spars of the production Fok. E.V were materially weaker than those of the approved type-test aircraft, and differently made. The *IdFlieg* regarded as indefensible the supply of fighting aircraft that were structurally weak, even if some few were just capable of supporting the specified loadings. This was a gross breach of trust: the Army could not overlook it.

Moreover, as the Flz. pointed out, even although some undersized spars could just withstand the loadings, such wings flexed and twisted more easily. This threw additional strain upon the skin which, carelessly glued and pinned as it was, failed before the specified loading limit was reached. The Flz. would never have passed any of the production Fok. E.V wings: they ought never to have been fitted to any aeroplane.

With the atrociously bad workmanship thus exposed, the Flz. recommended that all existing Fok. E.V wings should be scrapped. If this could not be done immediately, lift cables would have to be fitted as a temporary measure until the wings could be replaced. However, it is doubtful whether any Fok. E.V was ever flown operationally with such cables.

The final report on the Adlershof investigations was signed by Ober-leutnant G. Madelung in the absence of W. Hoff.

Fokker in trouble

Now the fat was in the fire. Such blatant disregard of official standards, such flagrant breach of trust, had never happened before in the supply of aeroplanes for the Army. The matter was made very much worse by Fokker's persistent denials that he or his works were in any way to blame. To the Prussian soldier of that time, rigorously trained to be at all times truthful in matters of duty and to admit blame unhesitatingly when instructions had been violated, Fokker's attitude was incomprehensible.

But the Dutchman was shocked out of his blustering self-justification when he received an official letter, dated September 3, 1918, from the *IdFlieg*. It was signed by Major F. Wagenfuehr, the all-powerful chief of the new Inspektion des Flugzeugwesens (Inspectorate of Aeroplane Equipment).

This communication made it plain that criminal proceedings against A. H. G. Fokker were under consideration, because he had knowingly supplied dangerously defective equipment to the Army, thereby causing the deaths of military personnel at the front.

The letter had been composed by Hauptmann W. Hoff, an officer in the reserve, a quiet man of scientific mind and not at all an arrogant militarist. He expressed Wagenfuehr's views thus:

"I am amazed to learn from memoranda and reports how your firm has carelessly and irresponsibly endangered the lives of fighting pilots, and of the incredible way in which you have tried to shift responsibility for this on to other persons. Contrary to your contentions, the facts at my disposal establish: either
(1) you have deliberately had the wing spars made weaker than those of the type-test aircraft, although you as the designer knew the consequences; moreover, you have concealed this modification although it has been the cause of the wing failures; or,
(2) because workshop drawings were not available, you and your personnel failed to know the correct dimensions of the spars of the prototype aircraft; but instead of determining them correctly, you deliberately and without further investigations ordered incorrect dimensions to be used in production wings.

"No other explanation can be found for your action. To give you the benefit of the doubt, I presume the second alternative. But this, too, must be deemed criminal.

"You now claim to have conducted, *after* the fatal accidents, tests proving that your production wings had insufficient strength. Such tests should have been conducted *beforehand*, instead of—to use your own words—advancing senseless statements unsupported by facts."

This official communication upset Fokker. It was the last thing he expected from his friends in the Army whom he had served so well in the past. He would have felt even more upset had he known that Hauptmann Hoff, the principal aircraft expert, had specifically advised the institution of criminal proceedings against Fokker and the Fokker works.

However, the public prosecutor took no action before the Armistice. While the war lasted, reasons of expediency and policy may have prevailed against prosecuting the young Dutchman. He was a kind of popular hero with a world-wide reputation: to put such a man in the dock might have been damaging to the war effort. It would have been harmful to the Army Flying Corps. Even under wartime secrecy, unpleasant facts might leak out.

Inevitable though the attachment of guilt to Fokker was, he was not personally so guilty as the accusations suggested. It had never occurred to him that it would pay him to tell the truth.

The root causes of his troubles were avarice and his childish desire to maintain the make-believe image of himself as a great engineer and an aircraft designer of genius. For these faults he could justifiably be blamed—but not for deliberately making a criminally dangerous modification of the wing spars. He might also be blamed for lack of responsibility, but not for deliberately endangering the lives of front-line pilots.

All that he had wanted was quick, cheap production of the Fok. E.V. As usual, he had failed to understand that this was impossible with the facilities at his disposal. The best that could be expected of his ramshackle and ill-equipped production shops was the construction of small batches of aircraft, each one virtually hand-made. His arrogance and his ignorance of engineering led him to believe that he could attain the exaggerated delivery figures that he had quoted (by guesswork) merely by goading his assistants and workmen.

Furthermore, good workmanship and the best materials had never interested him; nor had he troubled to engage trained production engineers. In short, his attitude towards aircraft production had not changed since 1911. In 1918 this outlook was archaic and dangerous.

At the Perzina works, which made wings for Fokker's aircraft, supervision and inspection were lax. Speedy production was all: everything made was good enough for aeroplanes regardless of its condition or how it had been made. This policy of quick production suited Fokker.

That the Bauaufsicht continued to tolerate such skimped and shoddy workmanship was indefensible. So seriously did this official body fail in its duty that its members inevitably seemed to be suspected of being in Fokker's pay.

The spars for the Fok. E.V wings had been made without proper jigs. While the plywood webs were being joined to the flanges by gluing and pinning, the webs had been allowed to move down the faces of the flanges, leaving the flanges projecting outside the webs. This made the spars too deep to pass through the ribs, so the "excess" material of the flanges was simply planed away, thus reducing the thickness of the flanges. In this way, some spars had half the thickness of their flanges planed away.

Apparently no-one noticed that the designer had made the top and bottom flanges of different thicknesses, consequently the spars were assembled in random fashion, and not a few had the weaker flanges on top, where the greater strength was required.

The Perzina management neither noticed nor cared about these things. All they cared about was the production of something that, from the outside at least, looked like a Fok. E.V wing.

So it had not been a case of wilfully revising spar dimensions or lack of production drawings. Fokker personally had no reason to change the spars, nor would he have done without consulting Platz. This was a simple case of lack of supervision, inspection and production organization: the rest of the Perzina Works production was just as bad. For quickness, holes in fittings were punched instead of drilled; timber for spar flanges was not selected and inspected before being laminated; and so on.

Platz was shocked when he discovered the whole truth. Now that things had taken such a bad turn for him, Fokker too was alarmed by these discoveries.

Fokker now relinquished engineering responsibility for production work; he left it to Platz. Platz took over the management of the Perzina factory, in addition to his other responsibilities. A satisfactory inspection organization was introduced, and a lot of dead wood was cut away.

Fokker's own story

One would have thought that after such an episode Fokker would have kept quiet about his Fok. E.V experience. Not a bit of it! In his autobiography he brags about it and would have the unsuspecting reader believe that he had scored a resounding victory over the Adlershof technicians. And yet, Fokker may even have believed this, after so many years of presenting his personal version of the facts.

Fokker wrote (or allowed his biographer to write) that the rear spar of the Fok. E.V was strengthened on the instructions of the technicians; the first six parasols were modified accordingly and rushed to the front. This, he claimed, was the cause of the wing failures.

The documentary evidence, extracts from which are incorporated in the foregoing account of the Fok. E.V investigation, contains no vestige of support for Fokker's story. The Fok. E.Ve that had been subjected to the initial strength tests at Adlershof had been found to be completely satisfactory. No request was made for any spar to be strengthened. The failures occurred solely because the spars of production wings had been badly made and were consequently too weak.

In his version of the matter, Fokker tells the reader that the investigation found neither defective workmanship nor inferior materials. This is palpably untrue, for it is in direct contradiction of the actual recorded

337

and photographed findings of the Crash Investigation Commission and the engineering investigators at Adlershof.

The measure of Fokker's "truthfulness" lies in his assurance:

> "All spars had been fully up to dimensions, and the workmanship was the usual high standard."

Hoff and Wagenfuehr had thought otherwise.

> "A demand was made that all wings be replaced and reinforced. This seemed pointless, and would mean an enormous loss to the factory."

What else could the German authorities have done, faced with such criminal mismanagement—faced again with the negligence that, at least once before and less than nine months earlier, had cost the lives of gallant pilots?

> "Not satisfied, the engineering department tested half a dozen more wings before reluctantly admitting that we were not to blame for the weakness."

Wagenfuehr's letter conveys a different impression.

Hoff was a man of great integrity and would have been the last to deny any mistake made by his engineering department. He would never have accused Fokker if there had been a shadow of doubt in the matter. In fact, he had defended Fokker when the safety of the Fok. Dr.I was in doubt. It was Hoff who had saved Fokker's skin by pointing out the possibility that aileron loadings might have occurred that the BLV failed to take into account.

Fokker makes his genius as an aircraft designer plain in this passage:

> "I took a new wing out of production and treated it to a sand-load test in our factory . . . the deflections of the wing were carefully measured . . . I discovered that with the increasing load, the angle of incidence at the wing tips increased perceptibly. I did not remember having observed this action in the case of the original wings, as first designed *by me*. It suddenly dawned on me that this increasing angle of incidence was the cause of the wing's collapse . . . It was the strengthening of the rear spar—ordered by the army's technical bureau—which had caused an uneven deflection along the wing under load . . . The resultant torsion caused the wing to collapse . . . At first the army technical bureau wouldn't give in . . . Eventually, it was agreed that the old specifications were correct."

Comparison of this extract from *Flying Dutchman* with the true facts of the episode will show that the quoted passage contains a careful mixture of fact and fiction that creates a credible distortion of the truth.

It has already been shown that the Flz. technicians knew, long before Fokker could have known, that unfavourable wash-in of a wing under load could produce adverse load gradings. What is even more significant, in view of Fokker's version of the facts, is the extent to which the Fok. E.V wing distorted under the limit loadings: the proof-loadings at Adlershof showed the actual change of incidence to be only 1·08 degrees in Case A and 2·17 degrees in Case B. Since the BLV 1918 allowed as much as 5 degrees in both cases, the distortion of the Fok. E.V was comfortably within the acceptable limit. Fokker could and should have known this, because copies of the reports reached him through the Bauaufsicht.

During 1922, Dr. W. Hoff, the Director of the German Aeronautical Research Establishment (D.V.L.) and in charge of all airworthiness investigations in Germany, published the findings on Fok. E.V wings as DVL Report No. 36 (and in English as an N.A.C.A. report). Fokker made no attempt to challenge Hoff's statement that the measured deformation of the Fok. E.V wing was perfectly tolerable.

Platz explains that even if the rear spar had been strengthened and stiffened, the twisting of the wing under load would have varied very little because the plywood skin made it so stiff in torsion. This was, in fact, borne out by the Adlershof tests. Platz thinks, however, that the load factors stipulated in the BLV 1918 for fighters may have been on the low side. This is not a relevant factor, for Platz-designed wings always had a comfortable safety margin in strength.

As soon as Platz took over responsibility for production, the new specimen E.V wing requested by the Flz. was supplied to Adlershof. As previously mentioned, this wing was identical with that of the type-test aircraft. It was tested from September 7 to September 10 at Adlershof and gave complete satisfaction under all loading conditions.

As an additional safeguard against manufacturing errors, the Flz. requested that the thickness of all spar flanges be increased by two millimetres. This modification was agreed on September 24. Production of the parasol-wing fighter could now be resumed.

The Fok. D.VIII

Acting on the suggestion of the Kogenluft, the *IdFlieg* changed the type designation from Fok. E.V to Fok. D.VIII for the aircraft with the properly made wing spars. This change was effected by issuing an order that all single-seat fighters, regardless of wing number and arrangement, should belong to the D category. The former E and Dr categories were thereupon abolished.

No Fok. E.V could be flown, even by training units. All existing aircraft had to be modified with new wings and redesignated as Fok. D.VIII. All new Fok. D.VIIIs were carefully built under a system of strict supervision organized by Platz. He also set up a technical office for production

Fok. D.VIII.

design matters. This was responsible for minor modifications and the lay-out of production jigs.

The effect of the wing-failure investigation was to delay the appearance of the Fok. D.VIII at the front until October 24, 1918. The first unit to receive the type was Jagdstaffel 11, led by Ernst Udet. The Fok. D.VIII also equipped Jagdstaffeln 1 and 23, and the naval Marine Land-Jagdgruppe Sachsenberg, where Theo Osterkamp's squadron received it.

Production aircraft came along quickly, and the front-line formations were perfectly happy with their new fighter. During its brief operational career, the Fok. D.VIII gave a convincing demonstration of its capabilities, even with its low-powered engine. On November 6, 1918, three Spad fighters were shot down in a single combat with Fok. D.VIIIs, and American fighter pilots had sorry tales to tell about encounters with the "Flying Razor".

On November 1, eighty-five Fok. D.VIIIs were operational on the

A Fok. D.VIII of Jasta 36.

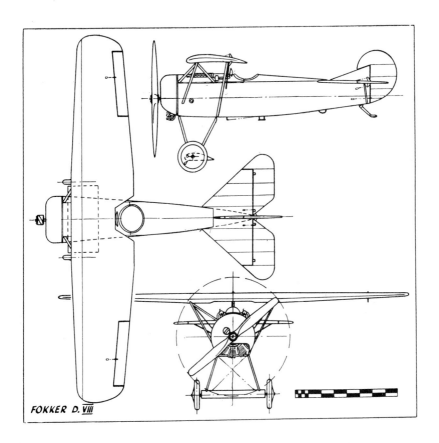

FOKKER D. VIII

Western Front with army Jagdstaffeln; perhaps twenty more were with
naval coast-defence units. No specimen of the type fell into Allied hands
while the war lasted. Immediately after the Armistice many were flown
into Holland and surrendered there. The Dutch Army was glad to
receive these up-to-date fighters, which gave excellent service in Dutch
hands, especially after installation of the 145-h.p. UR.III engine.

Had the war gone on, the Fok. D.VIIIe (145-h.p. UR.III) and Fok.
D.VIIIg (200-h.p. Goebel Goe.IIIa) would have been in service before
the end of 1918. Most of these aircraft would have been fitted with the
new undercarriage tank. However, it seems that no example of these
advanced variants reached the front before the Armistice.

The undercarriage tank had been tried during August. The first installation was made in Fok. E.V No. 238/18 (Factory No. 2879, with UR.II
engine No. 3063). This aircraft was put through its acceptance flights
by Matthias at Schwerin on August 21, 1918. It was intended for
Udet.

By the time of the Armistice the Fokker works had delivered 381

Fok. D.VIIIe, No. 697/18, with 145-h.p. Oberursel UR. III engine.

aircraft of the Fok. E.V/D.VIII type. Some of those built during November were not flight-tested and remained at Schwerin. Some of them may have found their way to Holland. Others were hidden away, but were found to have deteriorated badly when resurrected a few years later for experimental and training purposes by the Reichswehr.

The rest, some with UR.III, Goe.III or Goe.IIIa engines, were handed over to the Allies in new condition. The U.S.A., France, Britain, Italy and Japan received numbers of Fok. D.VIIIs. In general, little was done with these aircraft: the Allied occupation authorities had heard about the wing failures of the Fok. E.V, but they had not troubled to find out the truth of the matter. Consequently, pilots were discouraged from flying these "dangerously fragile" monoplanes with their untrustworthy cantilever wings.

In France and Britain the Fok. D.VIII monoplanes were simply allowed to rot. Nothing at all seems to have been done with these advanced aircraft, not even a trial loading to determine whether they were safe.

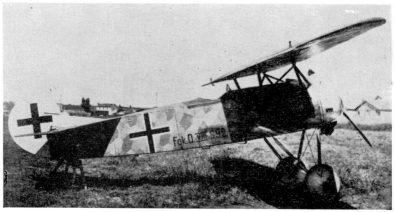

Fok. D.VIIIg, 200-h.p. Goebel Goe.IIIa.

342

Italy was more sensible. As late as 1925 a number of Fok. D.VIIIs were to be seen at the official experimental establishment in excellent flying condition. Except for some harmless play in the lugs of the wing-mounting bolts, these aircraft were as good as new.

As already noted, the Dutch Army was well satisfied with its Fok. D.VIIIs. After 1923, however, it was considered that rotary-powered fighters were obsolete.

The type was flown for experimental purposes in the U.S.A. In May 1921 the U.S. Army Air Service made a comprehensive assessment of a late production Fok. D.VIII, built in November 1918 in the D.520/18 to D.540/18 range (McCook Field Report No. 1676, Air Service Information Circular Vol. III, No. 288). This aircraft still had the 110-h.p.UR.II engine.

The test pilot, First Lieutenant Leigh Wade, described the aircraft's flying qualities as follows:

"The aircraft has a tendency to turn to the right in taxi-ing, takes off very quickly, climbs very rapidly, and is very manoeuvrable. It is easy to fly, and the controls are sensitive. It is tail-heavy but so light on the controls that it is not tiresome to fly. The visibility is very good. The machine-guns are so placed that in the event of a crash the pilot would undoubtedly be injured by being thrown against them. The aircraft

The Fok. E.V No. 238/18 with an undercarriage fuel tank. In the cockpit is Ernst Udet.

343

lands very slowly with a slight tendency to drop the right wing, and to turn to the right on the ground."

A British official report of March 1920 had been much less explicit. It was a second-hand description in vague terms of what a "representative of the British technical press" had stated after seeing a Fok. D.VIII flying at Amsterdam in August 1919.

All who flew the Fok. D.VIII praised its flying qualities and its combat capabilities. It was not quite so manoeuvrable as the Fok. Dr.I and perhaps slightly inferior to the Siemens–Schuckert D.IV, but its pilot had a much better field of view. It was less stable than the Fok. D.VII, but more tractable.

One of the Fok. D.VIIIs that were flown experimentally in the U.S.A.

Undercarriage failures after heavy landings were not infrequent occurrences, but usually the resulting damage was slight, and the pilot was seldom hurt so long as he was strapped in and avoided striking his head against the butts of the guns. To the end Fokker failed to realize the need for adequate crash protection, and in this respect the Adlershof requirements were not strict enough.

The more powerful versions of the type had somewhat different flying qualities. The Fok. D.VIIIg was reported to have good manoeuvrability, but its wings began to vibrate in steep turns. During prolonged spells of combat manoeuvring it also displayed a tendency to slip.

It was a pity that these observations failed to reach Platz. What the test pilot had experienced was most probably a classic case of incipient wing flutter induced by aileron unbalance. This trouble was likely to occur because the centre of gravity of the plywood-skinned ailerons was well behind the hinge axis; moreover, the aileron control circuit was resilient. For these reasons the monoplane tended to develop flutter as soon as the critical speed was approached.

In a later Fokker parasol-wing fighter, the D.X, wing failure occurred from this cause during 1924. Platz did not then know that the weight moment of the ailerons could be the source of the trouble; he thought it lay in lack of strength. The wing flutter was cured by fitting a mass balance to the aileron: this idea had not previously occurred to him, possibly because of his antipathy towards horn-balanced ailerons.

Another problem arose with the Fok. D.VIIIs, which had the Siemens–Halske Sh.3a engine. This was the most powerful German rotary engine, giving up to 220 b.h.p., but at an airscrew speed of only 900 r.p.m. The torque reaction was considerable, even when a four-blade airscrew of somewhat smaller diameter was tried; the ratio of wing-span to airscrew diameter was as low as 2·8 to 1 or 3 to 1. This placed heavy demands on the small ailerons.

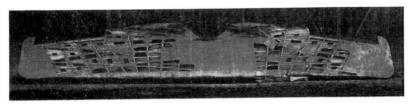

A Kruck experimental wing designed for the Fok. D.VIII, after being tested to destruction at Adlershof in January 1919.

In spite of this, the Adlershof test pilots reported favourably on the Fok. D.VIIIs. They found it pleasant to fly, particularly for aerobatics. The acceleration was greater and the manoeuvrability better than the other versions of the Fok. D.VIII with ungeared rotaries of approximately the same power. However, the landing was a little tricky if the blip-switch was used: if the aircraft and its engine were not intelligently handled, the intermittent torque reaction would make the aircraft touch down one wing low.

This was not, of course, peculiar to the Fok. D.VIIIs; it was present, though perhaps less pronounced, in any rotary-powered aircraft. The Siemens–Schuckert D.IV biplane, which also had the Sh.3a engine, had much the same tendency as the Fok. D.VIIIs.

It is doubtful whether any other single-seat fighter could better the Fok. D.VIII in terms of production costs. At the end of the war, the 1,800 workers at Schwerin were producing eight aircraft every day of the week. With a ten-hour working day, this meant only 2,250 working hours per aircraft. This compared with the average production time, in 1917, of 4,200 working hours per Fokker fighter. For the A.E.G. C.IV (Fok.) built at Schwerin, a production time of no less than 8,700 hours per aircraft was required, although this two-seater was only a trainer. In the Fok. D.VIII, Platz's objective of building the simplest and cheapest fighter had been achieved.

The third fighter trials

From October 15 to October 31, 1918, the third and last comparative trials for the selection of fighter aircraft were held at Adlershof. The object was the selection of types for quantity production during the winter in readiness for the offensives planned for the spring of 1919.

This time it was indicated that it would be preferable for prototypes to have the 185-h.p. B.M.W. IIIa engine. It was intended that in production aircraft this would be supplanted by the more powerful 240-h.p. B.M.W. IV, which was expected to start coming off the production line in December. It was hoped that fighters with engines of 240–350 h.p. would anticipate developments on the Allied side. This was an optimistic view, because the 300-h.p. Hispano-Suiza and the new, light 350-h.p. and 400-h.p. air-cooled radial engines developed in Britain would have made their appearance in Allied fighters. The aerodynamic and technological advances in German airframe design might not have compensated for the lack of engine power and engine development.

Prototypes with 145–220-h.p. rotaries were also admitted to the competition as secondary choices. No official decision on the production of further rotary-powered fighters had been taken, because there was insufficient evidence of the serviceability of these engines under operational conditions with the *ersatz* castor-oil lubricant. Moreover, the supply of this oil was still uncertain.

The *IdFlieg* therefore made it plain that there was little purpose in selecting a rotary-powered type at this time, except perhaps for the equipment of the home-defence fighter squadrons. These units had come to be increasingly important, owing to the increase of deep-thrusting bombing raids by the Allies.

For the initial selection, nine prototypes with the B.M.W. IIIa engine were presented. The V.36 (see pages 290–297) was one of Fokker's entries, the V.29 the other.

The Fokker V.29 was a parasol monoplane, generally similar to the Fok. D.VIII except in power-plant and size. Although larger than the D.VIII it was smaller and lighter than the V.27.

The Pfalz Works entered two high-performance biplanes, the Pfalz D.XVf and a "special Df" fighter experiment. Both were developments of the Pfalz D.XII, but they were cleaned up and had a minimum of external bracing. Like all Pfalz products, their workmanship and materials were impeccable.

From the L.F.G. came a parasol monoplane, the Roland D.XVII. This could not compare with the Pfalz or Fokker types. Albatros contributed the Alb. D.XII, a braced biplane of low structural weight and a promising come-back by this firm. It was the lightest of all the B.M.W.-powered types but did not look robust enough for front-line service.

Also very light and promising was the Rumpler D.I, now modified and improved and displaying excellent detail design. The Zeppelin D.I re-

The Fokker V.29.

appeared, its defective wing joints reinforced after the tragedy of the second trials. This all-metal cantilever biplane had passed a stiff structural examination at Adlershof. It now carried a jettisonable fuel tank externally under the fuselage.

Finally, there was the latest version of the Junkers D.I (by this time, Fokker and Junkers had separated). One or two of these Ju. D.Is had been sent to fighter squadrons for evaluation. They had been quickly returned as entirely unsuitable, with acrid comments on their peculiar flying qualities. Now the Dessau firm was trying again.

Six rotary-powered prototypes participated in the trials. Fokker's two entries were the Fok. D.VIIIe and the Fok. D.VIIIg. The Siemens-powered Fok. D.VIIIs did not appear, owing to either a lack of a suitable airscrew or engine trouble.

The Kondor Works submitted two versions of a cantilever parasol monoplane: the Kondor E.III with UR.III, and the Kondor E.IIIa with 200-h.p. Goebel Goe.IIIa. A strut-braced parasol, the Roland D.XVI, was entered by the L.F.G.; it had an Sh.3 engine. Also powered by the Sh.3 was the steep-climbing Albatros D.XI, a biplane. A special new Siemens type could not be completed in time, and the firm was represented by a standard Siemens–Schuckert D.IV biplane. This type was already in operational use on the Western Front and was proving successful.

The trials followed the pattern of the previous competition: the climbing tests were flown by the pilots of the firms, under the supervision of the Adlershof technicians. These were followed by the usual speed-comparison flights. Several "heats" were flown until a reliable assessment of speeds was obtained.

For the B.M.W.-powered types the first speed comparison was flown at 1·0 km. altitude and without use of the engine's mixture control. After this, the aircraft were raced between 3·0 and 5·0 km. altitude with full use of the mixture control. A Fok. D.VIIF was flown in this test, presumably for purposes of comparison.

At a height of about 4·0 km. (13,000 ft) the Fokker V.29 and Junkers

347

D.I were the fastest aircraft. The Junkers was slightly the faster below that height; above it, the V.29 was faster. The Fokker V.36 was next; it was rather slow at low altitudes but still better than the Fok. D.VIIF; at higher altitudes the V.36 was considerably faster than the Fok. D.VIIF. Following the Fokker V.36 in level-speed performance came the Rumpler D.I and Albatros D.XII with little to choose between them. Bringing up the rear, in descending order, were the Pfalz Df No. D.8364/17, Fokker D.VIIF, Zeppelin D.I, Pfalz D.XVf, and the Roland D.XVII.

Of the Siemens-powered fighters, the Roland D.XVI proved faster than the Siemens–Schuckert D.IV and, up to 4·0 km. altitude, faster than the B.M.W.-powered Fok. D.VIIF. At 4·0 km., the Roland D.XVI was as fast as the Fok. D.VIIF; above that altitude it was slower.

The Fok. D.VIIIe proved considerably faster than the Kondor E.III with the same UR.III engine.

In the climbing tests, the Rumpler D.I was unquestionably the best: it climbed to 7·0 km. (23,000 ft.) in 24·7 minutes. The next-best performance was put up by the Roland D.XVI, which needed 26·1 minutes to reach the same height. The Fokker V.36 took 31·1 minutes; for some reason the V.29 was unplaced (the barograph often froze, and this rendered climbs invalid). Both the Rumpler D.I and Albatros D.XII managed to reach nearly 8·0 km. (26,300 ft.) with their regulation military load.

In flying qualities the Fokker V.29 was rated to be about the best of the aircraft. Its manoeuvrability and behaviour when gliding and diving were judged to be superior to the corresponding characteristics of the Fok. D.VIIF. The take-off was regarded as good but rather long: this was attributable to the higher wing loading. For the same reason the landing speed was rather high, and the V.29's tendency to float was adversely criticized.

The Fokker V.36 was not so well liked, because its aileron control was rather heavy, but in general it was regarded as an improvement over the standard Fok. D.VIIF.

The Junkers D.I was cordially disliked. It was obvious that the Junkers works had failed to profit from Fokker's skill as a test pilot. This Junkers failing persisted: even ten or more years after the war, Junkers aircraft usually had flying characteristics inferior to those of contemporary Fokker types, despite extensive experimental work at Dessau.

In general handling qualities the Albatros D.XII was judged to be superior to the standard Fok. D.VII. However, the structure of the Albatros flexed too much in flight, giving an impression of insufficient strength.

The Rumpler D.I was thought to be good, on the whole, apart from a tendency to slip inwards and spin on steep turns. To save weight, its fuselage had been kept too short.

In the final assessment, the Fokker V.29 and Rumpler D.I shared top place; there was a tie for second place between the Fokker V.36 and the special Pfalz Df. The Roland D.XVI would have been placed third if its handling qualities had been better.

The Armistice was signed before the final choice was made; but both Fokker and Rumpler could have counted on receiving substantial contracts for the V.29 and Ru. D.I respectively.

And yet the supervention of the Armistice may have been a blessing for Fokker. Platz had won his fight for plain, unbalanced ailerons, but his latest products were on the verge of attaining critical speeds for wing flutter. If the V.29 had gone into operational use, wing flutter and failures would have followed inevitably. Equally inevitably, Fokker would have been under grave suspicion, yet this time he would have been innocent.

Fokker V.30 on display at the 1921 Paris Aero Salon.

A glider development

In December 1921 the Dutch Fokker works exhibited a small monoplane glider at the Paris Aero Salon. This glider's derivation from the Fok. D.VIII was at once apparent: the cockpit had been moved forward to the position occupied by the engine of the Fok. D.VIII, otherwise the aircraft was little changed. The glider, which was designated Fokker V.30, was equipped for aero-towing, having facilities for the release of the towing cable by its pilot. Fokker explained that he had built it for his own amusement.

The V.30 had exactly the same wing span as the Fok. D.VIII (8·34 m., or 27·5 ft.); its length was 5·86 m. (19·4 ft.), wing area 10·7 sq. m. (115 sq. ft.), and empty weight 150 kg. (330 lb.).

Despite the V.30's belated debut, its history went back to 1916. Both the Allies and Germany were then working secretly on tele-guided, unmanned aircraft for possible use as flying bombs and flying marine torpedoes.

In Germany the Siemens–Schuckert firm had been experimenting since 1914 with large gliders intended to carry bombs or torpedoes over

349

substantial distances after release from airships. These gliders were controlled by electric impulses passed through thin wires connecting the gliders to the airship. Distances of as much as 8 km. (5 miles) were successfully covered after release.

Fokker, always well informed about the activities of his competitors, learned about these experiments. He also gathered that the Admiralty were interested. The Admiralty had always been generous to him and he was anxious to work for them.

Quite separate from the Siemens development of wire-guided "stand-off" bombs, the Army Flying Corps had established a special command at Doeberitz to work on a similar idea, but using radio guidance, either from the ground or from aeroplanes. Several aircraft manufacturers were asked to interest themselves in the airframe aspect of the project. Fokker may have been one of those who were approached, for the *IdFlieg* knew him as a versatile manufacturer who was quicker than anyone else in carrying out new developments.

And so it was that during 1916, while a hectic development and production programme was running at Schwerin, Fokker began to take an interest in gliders. He made preparations for towing gliders by motor-cars and motor-boats, but no flying experiments were conducted at that time. Probably he received no development contract.

A year later, Junkers began to experiment with an "aerial torpedo"; that is to say, a gliding bomb to be released from aeroplanes. Automatic control and guidance devices were developed for such gliders. The firm were then building an armoured two-seater for infantry support duties, so their gliding bomb had prospects. When Fokker became co-owner and a director of the Junkers–Fokker Works, he learned about this project.

When the Doeberitz establishment had developed radio guidance and control devices to the point where flight experiments were possible, the need arose for an inexpensive, expendable and simple aeroplane, preferably one that could be developed from a mere test vehicle into the ultimate weapon. No firm was better able to supply such an aircraft than the Fokker Works. At this stage, the intention was that the winged bomb should be towed by, rather than carried in, the launching aircraft.

An order was given to Fokker to conduct appropriate experiments. He was promised substantial production orders if the idea proved practical; and his co-operation would later be sought in the development of a self-propelled, radio-controlled flying missile. These developments had become more pressing because the increasing effectiveness of the air defences of such places as London, Paris and the Channel ports had made bombing attacks, even by night, costly undertakings.

In the summer of 1918 Fokker began to experiment with gliders towed by a specially modified two-seat version of the Fok. D.VII. This aeroplane, apparently given the designation Fokker V.31, was fitted with a simple winch to wind in the cable after releasing the glider. Fokker feared that the cable might foul the tail controls, so Platz devised a semi-circular safety hoop that extended from one tailplane tip to the other, rising above the rudder. This hoop was braced by two struts.

Platz was never told the purpose of these experiments; he merely thought that Fokker was interested in gliding as a sport. At Fokker's request he redesigned a V.26 airframe as the V.30 aero-tow glider. Platz thought it a clumsy effort of little merit for sporting purposes. So, when left to carry on by himself at Schwerin after the Armistice, he designed a light flying-boat glider, the V.42, which would, he hoped, satisfy Fokker's sporting desires rather better than the improvised V.30. The V.42 had no military application of any kind. It is described in the following chapter.

Platz never learned whether the V.30 was ever aero-towed by Fokker. It may have been, but confirmation is lacking. If Fokker did this—and there is no reason why he should not have done so—he would almost certainly have done it in co-operation with de Waal. Fokker trusted de Waal and knew he could rely on him to keep his mouth shut whatever happened.

Only one V.30 was built. It was the original aircraft that was displayed at Paris in 1921. Fokker diplomatically omitted to explain that it was originally intended to be a flying bomb.

In 1922 Fokker obtained an American patent (USP. No. 1,418,783, from June 6, 1922) for an aero-towing arrangement. This incorporated the tail-protecting hoop devised by Platz in the summer of 1918, and envisaged the use of a long guide tube for the cable running from the cockpit to a point behind the rudder, the guide tube passing over the protective hoop. The tube could be fitted above or below the fuselage.

A year or so later, Fokker, by now regarded as an expert on military aircraft, read a paper before an audience of Dutch officers. In it he emphasized the tactical and strategical importance of airborne guided missiles. Fokker was right, but twenty years too early; and all that his advocacy of weapons of the future achieved was a brief notice in some of the aeronautical journals.

In a Press interview during 1919 Fokker disclosed that in 1916 the German Army had asked him to produce a cheap radio-controlled aeroplane to carry a bomb. Formations of these pilotless aircraft were to be controlled from a single command post in an aeroplane. He claimed that in the summer of 1918 he was given a "huge order" for the manufacture of these aircraft, and that he was "just prepared for production" when the war ended. No evidence to substantiate Fokker's "disclosure" exists, and the account is highly improbable.

CHAPTER XV

AFTER THE WAR

FOR TONY FOKKER the Armistice conditions were flattering: his Fok. D.VII was the only aircraft type mentioned by name. Apparently Allied intelligence had not yet discovered that the Fok. D.VII was already obsolescent and that the Fok. D.VIII was in service. During the immediate post-Armistice period in Germany, aircraft production ceased abruptly. For some time afterwards, owing to political unrest, the war administration was disorganized.

It is not now possible to quote exact figures of aircraft production by the Fokker works during 1914–18. Some statistics were compiled by the Inter-Allied Control Commission, apparently based on inquiries at the Fokker works. But as this Commission was not exactly popular in Germany, the figures extracted by its officers may not necessarily be correct.

Statistics that are likely to be more reliable are those contained in a secret memorandum that Oberstleutnant F. Wagenfuehr compiled after the war for use in the Service. Even these figures may not be complete. They are as follows:

	1914	1915	1916	1917	1918
Aircraft supplied	32	260	675	798	1,500
Estimated all-in production		315		820	
Working space	3,300 sq. m.				18,000 sq. m.
Workmen	95	430	850	1,250	1,650
Staff	15	50	100	150	200

In assessing statistics of output and production time, it should be remembered that the Fokker works bought few components ready-made. They made their own tanks, cowlings, undercarriages, controls, and so on, at Schwerin: only the engines, radiators, wheels and some minor accessories were bought out.

Apart from aircraft, the Schwerin workshops, and later the weapons firm at Reineckendorf, supplied 42,000 gun-synchronizing gears, in addition to modifying the guns themselves.

The total aircraft production at Schwerin, including all pre-war aeroplanes, licence-built and experimental types, has been put as high as 7,600 aircraft. This seems a considerable exaggeration. Wagenfuehr gives the total of Schwerin-built aircraft, including those made under licence, as 4,300. Of that total, 3,330 were supplied to the Army between 1914 and November 1918. The Allied Control Commission confiscated 492 aeroplanes, 539 engines and a large number of components at the Fokker works.

Backing out of Germany

In his autobiography, Fokker claims to have known beforehand that the war would end in a crushing defeat for Germany. He had certainly made thorough preparations for this eventuality, and had made plans for making a quick get-away with his money. He had made a cash profit of 30 million marks (£1,500,000 sterling) during the four years of war, quite apart from the money that he had sent to Holland while this was still legally possible. (Fokker had been granted special facilities for this, by a grateful German government.) His special long-range V.38 had been standing by at Goerries aerodrome.

The war over, Fokker now thought it time to discard the guise of a patriotic German. The great problem was how to liquidate his industrial empire of 6,000 employees as profitably as possible, and how to divest himself of the German nationality that would be a handicap to him abroad. He also wanted to save as many as possible of his aircraft: they had a good reputation and should be worth a good deal of money. All neutral countries wanted modern military aeroplanes: he, Fokker, was the man to satisfy their needs.

A week or so before the final collapse of the German war effort, Fokker made W. Horter deputy general manager of the Fokker Werke G.m.b.H., with comprehensive and unrestricted authority to act on Fokker's behalf. Horter had been the firm's discreet business manager and agent in Berlin.

From the day of the Armistice, Fokker gave instructions for all serviceable aeroplanes and engines to be hidden away outside the factory and aerodromes—in barns, cellars, unused buildings and other unlikely places. Little of this material was legally the property of the firm, but niceties of this kind troubled Fokker not at all.

Fokker was not popular with the workers at Schwerin; their opinion of him was not high. When on November 9, 1918, shop stewards were elected and workers' councils formed in all German factories, Fokker was at once at loggerheads with the Schwerin workers. He alleges that they were after the money he had accumulated; he also believed that they intended to murder him.

It is unlikely, however, that these staid Mecklenburg citizens and

M   353

tradesmen were after his money or his blood, half-starved and worn-out by hard war work though they were. At worst, they may have wanted to air grievances: they may have wanted to learn from Fokker what their future would be: perhaps they wanted to press for assurances that the firm would carry on, or that any necessary re-organization would be carried out in a fair manner. Whatever the truth of the matter, Fokker feared for his life and fled incontinently, never to return to Schwerin.

Fokker would have readers of his autobiography believe that he really stood in peril of his life in those troubled post-Armistice days. This sounds dramatic but is rather improbable. It is far more likely that he departed in such haste because he had "forgotten" to pay taxes on his vast profits: his income-tax liabilities alone stood at 14,250,000 marks (£715,000). The extraordinary thing is that the German authorities allowed such immense liabilities to accumulate—unless Fokker had been able to grease the right official palms.

However that may be, it seems that this tax debt was at last followed up, causing Fokker to depart in disguise. A month or so later, the Schwerin income-tax office made the matter public, quoting the sum mentioned above, and requesting all debtors of Fokker to pay their dues to the tax office instead of to Fokker.

At Goerries aerodrome, the special V.38 two-seater was already under guard, so that line of escape was closed. Platz conveyed the disguised Fokker by car to the distant Ludwigslust railway station: Fokker feared he might be recognized at the Schwerin station. He reached Berlin without being spotted, and took refuge in the Bristol Hotel. On his rare sorties into the streets he had a bodyguard of two hefty naval deserters who, when paid well enough, could be relied upon to deal with anyone, including policemen and bailiffs. After doing what he could to settle his affairs, Fokker left for Holland.

This time it was no sad young man who returned to his native country: it was a millionaire with a world-wide reputation, though burdened with the great financial problem of how to get the remainder of his wealth across the border.

Platz carries on

Platz found no difficulty in carrying on at Schwerin with the workers who were somewhat baffled by their boss's sudden disappearance. Platz was highly respected by his workers as a trustworthy man who was strict but just. He was therefore given full support when he re-organized the Fokker works on a reduced scale with a view to manufacturing products that promised orders and profits. Although not all attempts to obtain work for the Schwerin factory were successful, Platz found the shop stewards and workers' council eager to co-operate in keeping the factory going.

He retained a small aircraft section, staffed with thirty of the best aircraft workers. This small team built a number of new experimental aircraft, until a limited amount of production could be undertaken (which was later—for political reasons—claimed to be Dutch manufacture at Amsterdam). Until 1922 all Fokker transport monoplanes were in fact made at Schwerin. There was no contact between Fokker and the Schwerin factory until the first transport aircraft had flown. When Platz reported the success he was invited to Amsterdam.

When he set up the aeronautical department Platz had no idea what the future of aviation in Germany would be. He did not foresee that aircraft manufacture would be forbidden, and he carried on in the hope that Germany would be able to market aircraft. For the first time he had to carry the responsibility of deciding development policy. In the past, Fokker had indicated the purpose for which the next aircraft should be designed; but Fokker was now in Holland, cut off from his Schwerin firm and apparently indifferent to its fate. Platz wanted to keep the staff of aircraft workers and the Schwerin factory occupied.

He thought that orders would be most readily obtained by offering a variety of types to civilian customers. He therefore designed in quick succession two single-seat light aeroplanes, a two-seat trainer with side-by-side seating, a flying-boat glider for towing, a high-powered single-seat fighter, and, most important of all, a six-seat transport monoplane. All were high-wing monoplanes derived from the successful Fok. D.VIII that had proved to be so economical to produce. These types are discussed in more detail below.

The name of the firm was changed to Schweriner Industrie-Werke. Although Fokker was still the legal owner it was necessary, for political reasons, to drop his name. The new products included punts, dinghies, Canadian scullers, and motor-boats of various sizes, all marketed under the trade name Obotrit. This line was not very profitable, however.

Early in 1919 all assets of the Fokker firm were acquired by the Unie Bank voor Nederland & Kolonien of Amsterdam. This transaction prevented the German finance authorities from attaching Fokker's firm against their claims upon him. As the property of a Dutch bank the firm was now beyond the reach of the German authorities. Fokker had smuggled out his profits untaxed by employing his father-in-law, a former German general of high reputation, as an unsuspecting decoy. No smuggler had ever before thought of using Prussian generals as vehicles of their trade. Fokker's debt to the German tax-payer was further increased when he succeeded in smuggling enormous quantities of aircraft and material out of Germany.

Of the existing stock of aircraft at Schwerin—paid for by the Government—some were sold abroad direct, notably to Scandinavian countries. Hermann Goering was now Fokker's sales representative. On May 8, 1919, he flew one of the latest Fok. D.VIIF variants from Schwerin to Copenhagen. Goering managed to sell the aeroplane, but the "trading expenses" were excessive.

But most of the material at Schwerin went to Holland in six goods trains totalling 350 wagons, each train deliberately made too long to go into checking sidings for scrutiny. By this means, Fokker's railway manager, W. Hahn, aided and abetted by others, contrived to transport some 220 aeroplanes, over 400 engines, and an enormous amount of materials and accessories across the guarded German frontier into Holland.

Most of this material was the property of the German government, but had been condemned to destruction by order of the Allies. It included 120 Fok. D.VII, sixty Fok. C.I, twenty Fok. D.VIII, and various prototypes, apart from half-finished aeroplanes and components. Fokker admits that the removal of this loot cost him 20,000 guilders in bribes, but it was well worth it.

It seems not unlikely that certain German government authorities connived at this undertaking. It would not be unreasonable to assume, from an agreement between German defence departments and Fokker, that the removal of so much aviation equipment was not so much a daring act of Fokker's but an expression of high policy.

On September 29, 1921, a shareholders' meeting of the Schweriner Industrie-Werke decided that the managing director, Reinhold Platz, was to be replaced by H. G. von Morgen as sole director. Von Morgen was a young man—and Fokker's brother-in-law. This resolution set the seal on Fokker's greatest coup: he had completely severed all connexion with Germany. Platz was leaving Schwerin to join him at Amsterdam.

The Fokker V.39.

The light aeroplanes V.39 and V.40

Soon after the unrest of the early days of November 1918 Platz completed two new designs. Both were low-power single-seat monoplanes intended for sporting flying. Platz built them in the belief that there were people who liked to fly for fun. What he forgot was that

356

Fokker V.39.

people who are so inclined usually lack the money needed to buy aeroplanes.

The two new aircraft were scaled-down Fok. D.VIII single-seaters. In both, however, the wing was fabric-covered. This meant that torsional loads had to be resisted entirely by differential bending of the spars. These were designed accordingly. The ailerons were simplified, being no longer inset but extending to the wing tips; their hinge lines were slightly skewed, and they had no horn balance. The elevator was also a plain surface; the rudder was balanced, but there was no fin.

Although basically similar, the V.39 and V.40 differed in size and power units. V.39 was the larger of the two, with a wing area of about 9 sq. m. (97 sq. ft.); its engine was a Gnôme of 50 or 80 h.p., cowled in the same way as the engine of the Fok. D.VIII.

The V.40 was the smallest aeroplane ever built by the Fokker Works.

Harry Rother lends scale to the tiny Fokker V.40.

A sand-loading test on the V.40 wing.

Its wing span was only 5·9 m. (19·5 ft.), the area 7 sq. m. (75·5 sq. ft.); its length was 3·94 m. (13 ft.). The V.40 was powered by an old 35-h.p. Anzani inverted-Y air-cooled engine, and had a top speed of 111 km./hr. (69 m.p.h.).

Both aircraft flew well, and were liked by all pilots who tried them. The flight tests were done by Parge. Fokker seems never to have flown them, and it is doubtful whether they ever went to Holland. They failed to find a market and did not go into production.

A somewhat similar attempt to build a small edition of the Fok. D.VIII was made by Gabriel at Bromberg a year or so later. This aircraft, the Gabriel P.5, had a plywood-covered wing but had a plywood fuselage instead of the steel-tube structure of the Fok. D.VIII. It had a 30-h.p. Haacke two-cylinder engine and was even smaller than the Fokker V.40: its wing span was only 5 m. (16·5 ft.) and the length 4 m. (13·2 ft.). The empty weight was stated to be a mere 125 kg. (275 lb.).

The V.41 (Fokker D.X)

The V.41 was designed as a development of the V.29 with a more powerful engine, probably the high-compression 220 h.p. Benz Bz. IVü or the 220 h.p. Oberursel-Becker U.IVBe eight-cylinder engine that Fokker had had developed. In view of the heavier engine, the V.41 had to be larger than the V.27 and V.29. Its wing span was 14 m. (46·3 ft.), and its wing area was about twice that of the Fok. D.VIII. Its designed load was 335 kg. (740 lb.).

For obvious reasons, this prototype was not completed at Schwerin. The wing was half completed and not even partly skinned when the project was shelved. However, when Fokker completed his withdrawal from

The Fokker D.X.

Schwerin in 1921, the V.41 was taken to Amsterdam. There, it was completed with a 300 h.p. Hispano-Suiza and retractable side radiators, and was given the new designation Fokker D.X. Its total weight was 1,246 kg. (2,750 lb.).

Unfortunately, the engine was an American-made Hispano-Suiza, built under licence, and was neither so reliable nor so smooth-running as the original French engine.

The performance of the Fokker D.X was surprisingly good for its time: its top speed was 225 km./hr. (140 m.p.h.) and it climbed to 5·0 km. altitude (16,500 ft.) in 16 minutes.

In 1922, von Mallinckrodt demonstrated the prototype D.X in Spain. While diving the aircraft, he experienced serious wing flutter; before he could recover control and land, the wing failed. From the crash von Mallinckrodt escaped without serious injury. Platz thought that rain might have affected the wing structure while the aircraft was in transit

Fokker in the cockpit of the D.X.

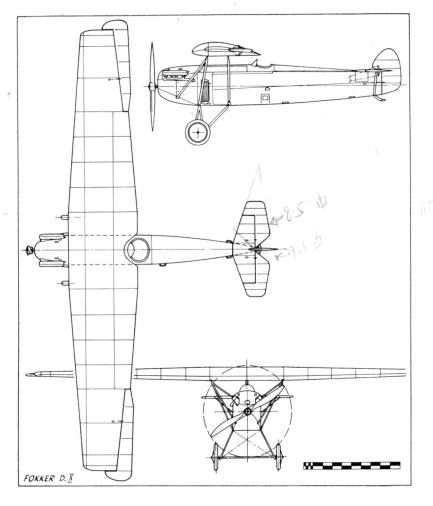

FOKKER D.X

from Holland; he had earlier suggested to Fokker that this wing should be scrapped.

The Fokker D.X was not alone in suffering from wing flutter. It had been preceded by another parasol monoplane assembled at Amsterdam: the Fokker F.VI. The F.VI, like the D.X, was powered by an American-built 300 h.p. Hispano-Suiza, but it had a frontal radiator. The forward portion of the fuselage was covered with armour plate, consequently it had more angular lines than the D.X. No attempt was made to protect the radiator, as had been done on the V.37; and despite the armoured fuselage there was a gravity petrol tank in the wing. The upper longerons were slightly cranked behind the cockpit.

The Fokker F.VI, an armoured single-seat fighter.

The cantilever, plywood-covered wing was similar to that of the Fokker D.X but was somewhat smaller. The arrangement of the cabane struts was different from that of any other Fokker parasol monoplane. Horn-balanced ailerons were fitted.

There was no fin, and the rudder was a balanced surface. The original Fokker F.VI had plain elevators. The sturdy undercarriage had three struts on each side and double cross bracing.

By the time the F.VI appeared, the Fokker F series was well established as a line of transport aircraft. The armoured single-seat fighter was out of place in it, and no satisfactory explanation of its inclusion in the F series has yet been given.

Ten Fokkers F.VIs were supplied to the U.S. Army Air Service in 1922. They were given the official designation PW-5. The production PW-5s had horn-balanced elevators, and at least one (A.S.64231) had the trailing edge of its ailerons collinear with the wing trailing edge: the original F.VI and other PW-5s had ailerons with compound taper.

One of the Fokker PW-5 fighters delivered to the U.S. Army Air Service in 1922. This aircraft, A.S.64231, crashed on March 13, 1923, at Dayton. Its pilot, Lt. Weider-meyer, was killed.

361

One of these aircraft suffered a wing failure similar to that of von Mallinckrodt's D.X. Other incidents of this kind had been experienced elsewhere; for example, with the Dornier *Falke* parasol-wing fighter. Wind-tunnel experiments in England and Holland, complemented by German theoretical work, showed that the ailerons were to blame. Lack of mass-balance about the hinge axis, especially if the aileron control cables were slack, could induce serious wing flutter of increasing amplitude, and ultimately cause structural failure. Aero-elasticity had become an important consideration for aircraft designers.

Horn-balanced ailerons embodying counterweights were then fitted to the Fokker D.X. Grasé, Fokker's experimental pilot at Amsterdam, made daring test flights with a modified aircraft. Even in a terminal-velocity dive, flutter no longer occurred. From 1925 onwards, all Fokker aircraft, including even the slow transport monoplanes, were fitted with mass-balanced ailerons.

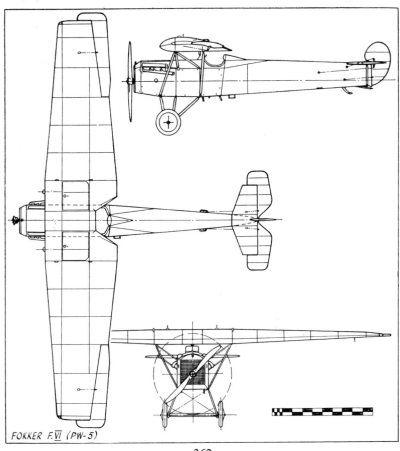

FOKKER F.VI (PW-5)

The unfortunate experiences with the D.X and PW-5 led Platz to abandon the parasol-wing arrangement for fighter aircraft. All subsequent Platz-designed fighters were biplanes, with the sole exception of the D.XIV low-wing monoplane.

The V.42 glider

Platz was a persistent man. Once he was certain that a suggestion of Fokker's was impractical, he did not rest until he could prove that his own way was the better one. The V.30 experiment had annoyed him. When Fokker had asked him to convert a Fok. D.VIII for towing, Platz had proposed designing a more suitable glider, but Fokker would not have it. Now Platz would show Fokker how it should be done.

The V.42 glider in its flying-boat form.

In Platz's view, a glider should be able to operate from land or water. The V.42 was therefore designed to have either a simple, ply-skinned box-like float attached directly to the lower longerons, or a simple V-type wheel undercarriage. The fuselage was a welded steel-tube structure, covered with fabric. The cantilever wing was also fabric-covered, and was attached directly to the upper longerons. Its area was 10·2 sq. m. (110 sq. ft.). The cockpit was in the leading edge of the wing. This was an unfortunate feature, for the cut-out and the pilot's head spoiled the airflow over the wing.

All controls were plain, unbalanced surfaces. There was a triangular fin in the tail unit, and the ailerons reached to the wing tips.

A release for the towing cable was fitted to the upper longeron joint at the nose. This device was, in its simplicity, typical of Platz: it consisted simply of a pair of pliers and parts of a turnbuckle.

The V.42 glider was not flown at Schwerin. It was sent to Amsterdam and was tested on the Ymuiden Canal in 1919. Parge was the pilot, and Fokker towed it from a motor boat. The glider handled well, but its performance was limited by the short towing cable, which restricted the altitude to 150 ft. But Fokker was no longer interested in gliders.

The V.43

Platz thought that a modern two-seater specifically designed as a trainer might be a selling proposition. During the war no special training aeroplanes had been designed in Germany; all trainers were merely obsolete operational types converted for instructional purposes. A few aircraft, such as the L.V.G. B.III, were simplified and redesigned for cheaper materials for production as trainers.

For his training two-seater Platz chose side-by-side seating. He thought this would be better for demonstrating control movements than the conventional tandem arrangement. Because the parasol wing arrangement combined stability with an unobstructed field of downward vision he chose this configuration.

The only available engine of less than 100 h.p. was an old 75-h.p. Mercedes, a six-cylinder engine of 1913 vintage with a dry weight of 146 kg. (322 lb.). It had a flat, square nose radiator.

The prototype was test-flown by Parge at Schwerin early in 1919. It was later taken to Amsterdam, where it was painted green. It was flown a good deal at Schiphol until it was crashed by Meinecke in October 1921 while attempting an emergency landing.

The V.43 was resuscitated as the Fokker S.I with modern water-cooled engines of 80 to 90 h.p. In 1922 Fokker took to the U.S.A. an S.I with a Curtiss OX-5 engine. The U.S. Army Air Service bought it and gave it the designation TW-4.

Fokker S.I

In certain aspects the Fokker S.I resembled the Fokker F.VI; in particular, its upper longerons were cranked upwards behind the cockpit. The nose radiator was 76 cm. (30 in.) high and 54 cm. (24 in.) wide; its total cooling surface was 8·9 sq. m. (96 sq. ft.). Shutters were fitted behind the radiator to regulate the engine temperature. The petrol tank was installed between the engine and the cockpit, and fuel feed was by pressure.

With the official Project No. P245, the Fokker TW-4 was tested by the McCook Field Engineering Division of the United States Army Air Service. The report was critical of the aircraft's taxying characteristics:

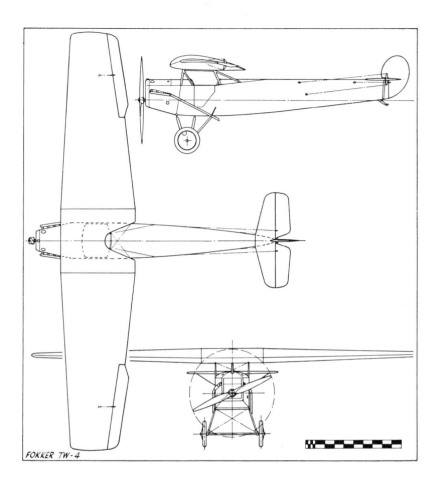

FOKKER TW-4

Fokker TW-4

365

the rudder was too small for adequate ground control. Take-off was easy, but the run was rather long; landing was also easy, but the TW-4 floated a long way after the round-out and would need an experienced pilot to get it into a small field or aerodrome. Laterally and longitudinally the aircraft was stable; it was slightly tail-heavy at full throttle, slightly nose-heavy in the glide. The field of view was excellent downwards and sideways, but extremely poor upwards and sideways. Accessibility for maintenance was good.

In his summing-up, the test pilot stated that the lack of upward visibility was a serious drawback in a military trainer, which would have to be used at aerodromes where numbers of aircraft would be in the air at the same time.

The transport monoplane, V.44 and V.45

The post-war development of air transport in Germany had been foreseen in 1917. In that year the Deutsche Luftreederei, a transport enterprise, had been founded by a powerful shipping combine in conjunction with the A.E.G. This company announced that passenger and mail transport services would be organized immediately after the war ended.

When the Armistice was signed, Platz at once started work on the design of an aeroplane specifically intended for passenger transport. In the early post-war months, most of the would-be transport companies in Germany and elsewhere were content to convert the plentiful unwanted bombers or reconnaissance aircraft by adding seats, ashtrays and, occasionally, a cockpit canopy. However, a few of the less conventional German designers shared Platz's opinion that transport aeroplanes had to be specifically designed for their purpose. These were Junkers, where Mader and Reuter developed an excellent all-metal monoplane, Dornier, Dorner, and Sablatnig. All these firms had constructed aircraft with enclosed cabins; all but the Dorner were monoplanes. The Sablatnig product was a parasol monoplane designed by Seehaase.

The Fokker V.45 or F.II at Schwerin.

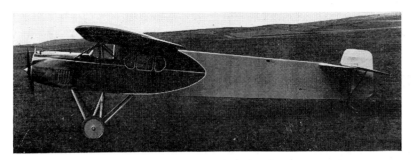

The prototype F.II at Schwerin.

Platz's first project was the V.44, a parasol monoplane rather like an enlarged Fok. D.VIII with a 185-h.p. B.M.W. IIIa engine. It had seats for six passengers arranged in three side-by-side pairs; the passengers were expected to climb over the fuselage side to enter the cockpit.

While the V.44 was under construction Platz discovered one morning that some practical joker had put into the nearly-completed fuselage a sign-board announcing "Facklam's Sight-seeing Excursions". Facklam was the alcoholic proprietor of a modest transport undertaking at Schwerin; he operated an antique horse-drawn char-à-banc with open seats. This vehicle spent most of its time as the transport for proletarian pub-crawls, and had a reputation all its own.

Platz was dismayed to see his new passenger transport treated with such facetiousness. But on reflection he realized that the unknown wag had done him a service: this aircraft was too primitive for its purpose. The V.44 was abandoned without more ado. It was replaced by a new design, the V.45, which had a completely enclosed cabin for the passengers. The wing of the V.44 was adapted for use on the V.45. The V.44 fuselage was subjected to a series of strength tests and then scrapped.

In the V.45 the rear spar of the mainplane rested on the upper longerons, but the front spar was supported by two typical tripods of struts. This arrangement facilitated access to the pilot's cockpit, which was open; there was no connecting door to the passenger cabin.

Work on the V.44 had begun in December 1918. Owing to various

The prototype F.II with the V.40.

circumstances of a non-technical nature, nearly a full year elapsed before Parge made the first test flights of the V.45. The V.44 was to have been named Fokker I or F.I; the V.45 was therefore designated Fokker F.II.

Parge was delighted with the new aeroplane and was soon at home in it. He took up nine passengers on one occasion, a considerable load for the 185-h.p. B.M.W. IIIa.

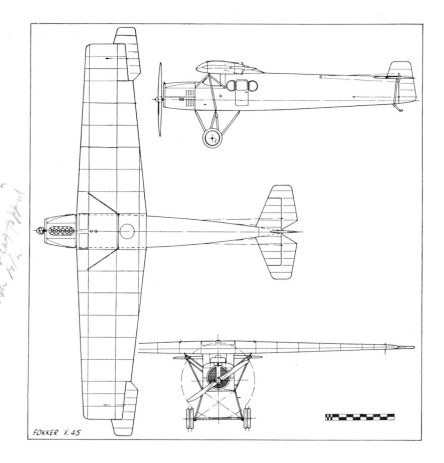

FOKKER V.45

Platz suggested he should try to loop the F.II when flying it solo. Parge tried several times but failed. The aircraft would begin each attempted loop in normal response to the controls but, instead of going over the top, it would put the nose down on its own and dive gently out, even with the stick held firmly back.

On the next flight Platz accompanied Parge to try for himself, using the dual controls. Platz was more muscular than Parge, but even their combined forces on the stick failed to coax the F.II over the top.

Under the new regulations, passenger-transport aeroplanes had to obtain a Certificate of Airworthiness, after being technically approved by the D.V.L. (the German Research Establishment for Aeronautics) at Adlershof. The D.V.L. were prepared to accept a comprehensive stress analysis in lieu of a test to destruction in their laboratory. Platz was reluctant to submit his own stressing: he thought the D.V.L. would ridicule his home-made methods and reject his stress analysis. He therefore cautiously suggested that the D.V.L. send one of their experts to prepare the necessary stress analysis at the firm's expense. Hoff, now director of the D.V.L., readily obliged, and sent Dipl. Ing. Bethge.

As has been related in Chapter X, Bethge was surprised to discover that the Fokker F.II was not only of adequate strength with a comfortable factor of safety, but also economically designed; that is to say, no component was unnecessarily large. However, he raised two minor objections related to the adequacy of the undercarriage structure, and told Platz that it might be necessary to redesign part of it. He was nonplussed when Platz proved conclusively from his own stress assumptions that his calculation was at fault: the central inverted-V members of the four-strut undercarriage legs were, contrary to Bethge's assertion, sufficiently strong. Before they could buckle, the landing impact would be dissipated into the other struts of the structure, consequently the central connexions to the lower longerons were adequate.

Bethge reported his findings to Hoff, who was so surprised that the Fokker designer now possessed more reliable stressing methods than the D.V.L. that he urged Platz to write a paper on the subject. This was too much for Platz: overwhelmed by the suggestion, he hastily declined.

After its approval by the D.V.L., the prototype F.II was flown to Holland by de Waal. A second aircraft was already under construction. De Waal had arrived at Schwerin in disguise, and members of the Workers' Council helped him to get away in the F.II. On the way to Holland he had three emergency landings owing to engine trouble; Fokker saw the F.II for the first time after it had been damaged by de Waal in making yet another forced landing, this time on Dutch soil.

When de Waal told him about the F.II's excellent flying qualities and remarkable performance, Fokker became enthusiastic. The business-man in him was quick to see the possibilities that lay before this latest creation by Platz. He sent Platz a most flattering testimonial: this was the only testimonial or expression of appreciation that Platz ever received from Fokker.

In his autobiography Fokker wrote:

"But while I was still in Germany, *we* built the first really commercial cabin aeroplane, the F-2 (*sic*), and had it secretly flown over to Holland by de Waal."

Apart from the fact that Fokker was not in Germany while the F.II was being built, it is necessary to add that the aircraft was by no means the first "really commercial cabin aeroplane". In England, the B.A.T. F.K.26 had flown in April 1919. Nearer at hand and more directly comparable was the Junkers F.13, powered by a 185-h.p. B.M.W. IIIa, which had flown on June 25, 1919; on September 13, 1919, in an officially observed flight, it climbed to 6·75 km. (22,200 ft.) with eight people on board.

The Deutsche Luftreederei soon became interested in the Fokker F.II; their pilot Harry Rother was asked to try the aircraft. In Holland Fokker found it easy to introduce the new transport aeroplane. The Koninklijke Luchtvaart Maatschappij, now internationally known as K.L.M., began operations on May 17, 1920. On the same day, Fokker personally demonstrated the F.II before the Press and the public with all his brilliant showmanship. Afterwards Parge made passenger flights with various highly-placed personages aboard. The occasion was a great success.

Orders for F.II aeroplanes were immediately placed with the Dutch Fokker firm; these were executed at Schwerin. By September 1920, the K.L.M. had taken delivery of two F.II aircraft. One was flown to Croydon on September 30 by W. G. R. Hinchliffe, K.L.M.'s chief pilot; his passengers were Albert Plesman, later to become President of K.L.M., Henri Hegener, and S. Elleman, a Fokker works mechanic. In addition, the aircraft carried fuel for seven hours. The flight to Croydon took just over three hours; fuel consumption was 118 litres per hr. (26 gals. per hr.). In England the F.II was much admired.

The prototype V.45 was later acquired by the Dutch Rijksstudiedienst voor de Luchtvaart (Aeronautical Research Establishment) as a flying laboratory. It was extensively used by Dr. van den Maas for his im-

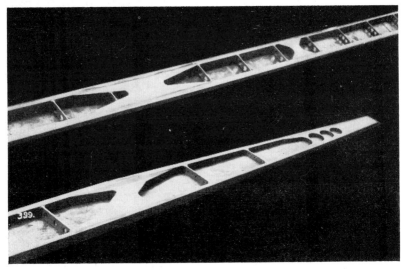

Wing spars of the Fokker F.II.

portant experimental work. This historic aircraft was still flying up to the outbreak of the Second World War.

Description of the Fokker F.II

In some of its features the F.II wing was identical with that of the Fok. D.VIII. It was covered entirely with plywood. The ailerons originally had no horn balances but were modified at an early stage, before the prototype was flown to Holland.

The spars by themselves had a load factor of 7 in Case A; the plywood skin raised this to 9 for the whole wing. The maximum wing thickness was 63 cm. (24·8 in.); and the wing weighed 350 kg. (775 lb.). It was secured by only four steel bolts.

Side-by-side seats for two pilots and dual control were provided in the crew's cockpit, which was a short distance aft of the engine. For the ailerons Platz provided wheel control, as had been used on all heavier German military aeroplanes at the end of the war. The pilots' cockpit was open and was entered from the outside via external steps. A small window in the bulkhead wall provided a means of communication with the passenger cabin.

This cabin was underneath the wing. It had seats for four passengers, two of whom sat facing rearwards with their backs against the bulkhead behind the pilots' cockpit. There were three Triplex-glass windows in each side of the cabin; all could be opened. The door was in the port side.

Fuselage stern and tailplane of the Fokker F.II.

The stern of the fuselage was deep, and no fin was required; the rudder was a squat, balanced surface. The tailplane was braced to the lower longerons, and horn-balanced elevators were fitted.

In designing the fuel system, Platz avoided pressurized tanks to minimize trouble with leaks and the risk of fire in the event of a crash. The main tank, of 330-litres (73-gals.) capacity, was situated under the front seats of the passenger cabin but insulated by a fume-proof bulkhead. From this tank, fuel was transferred by a small hand-operated Allweiler petrol pump to the 50-litre (11-gal.) gravity tank just behind the engine. The pump could be operated from either seat in the pilots' cockpit, and the contents of the gravity tank could be read from a stand glass. This arrangement was simple but perfectly reliable.

The undercarriage had four struts on each side to distribute the landing loads into the fuselage structure. To prevent the wheels from sinking into soft ground Platz fitted a form of double wheel. In this, two standard rims placed side by side were spoke-braced to a common hub. Existing accessories and components could therefore be used, and the double wheel created little more drag than the more conventional wheel. Fokker was very pleased with this idea.

In 1925 a batch of modified Fokker F.II aeroplanes were built under licence arrangements in Germany for the Deutsche Aero Lloyd airline company. The wings were made by the Albatros Works, while the fuselage construction and final assembly were undertaken in the workshops of the Deutsche Aero Lloyd at Staaken aerodrome. Modification design work was in the hands of Karl Grulich, designer of the Harlan types and many Gotha aeroplanes. The workshops were under the supervision of H. Jeannin, formerly of the Argus Engine Co.

The Aero Lloyd F.IIs had the 230-h.p. B.M.W. IV engine. They had no cabane struts and were genuine high-wing monoplanes. The crew compartment was neatly incorporated in front of and below the wing, and access to it was via a door from the passenger cabin. The undercarriage had only three struts on each side, and more substantial wheels were used. The speed of this version was 125 km./hr. (77·5 m.p.h.) with a load of 794 kg. (1,750 lb.).

These Fokker F.IIs and some F.IIIs were extensively flown in the service of the Deutsche Lufthansa on German internal routes. No pilot was promoted to be captain of a passenger aircraft unless he had airline experience on the Fokker F.II.

The Fokker F.III

Good though it was, the F.II could still be improved upon. A redesign with a more powerful engine was needed to compete against the speedier D.H.16. The pilots' cabin with accommodation for a crew of two seemed unnecessary. Fokker's mechanic Kuerth suggested that the pilot should be seated beside the engine. Fokker thought this an excellent idea and requested Platz to incorporate it in the new aircraft; he even went so far

Fokker F.III of the Russo-German company Deruluft.

as to patent this extraordinary idea (German patent DRP No. 375,857 of March 23, 1921, by A. H. G. Fokker of Amsterdam).

Platz did not like this idea at all. Fokker argued that the aircraft would be more economical and manoeuvrable, and seemed to think that it would be possible for the pilot to handle the engine better and, if necessary, remedy trouble. In fact, pilots hated the arrangement, and said so.

The position of the pilot was such that a large cut-out had to be made in the wing leading edge. This affected adversely the airflow over the wing and tail unit, a drawback that was aggravated by the presence of the pilot's head and windscreen.

Platz designed the F.III, but washed his hands of the cockpit design.

Detail of the Fokker F.III undercarriage.

Fokker F.III of the Deutsche Aero-Lloyd A.-G.

He would have provided access to a conventionally placed cockpit through a door from the passenger cabin, and declined to modify his design in the way demanded by Fokker. The original Fokker-Kuerth cockpit was therefore made independently at Amsterdam.

The F.III dispensed with the cabane bracing of the F.II: the top longerons extended sufficiently far forward for them to be directly connected to the front spar of the mainplane. The engine was a 230-h.p. Siddeley Puma. The use of a six-cylinder in-line engine was virtually inevitable; the cockpit arrangement precluded V-type engines.

While the F.III was under construction Platz was still working at Schwerin, completing the first batch of F.IIs. As Fokker did not dare to show up at Schwerin, Platz had to pay regular visits to Amsterdam. Subsequently a batch of Fokker F.IIIs were built at Schwerin. They were tested by Parge and Rother before being flown to Schiphol, whereupon they became "Dutch-built" aircraft, products of Fokker's Amsterdam workshops.

The Fokker F.III was extensively used by the K.L.M. and on the 1,220-km. (760-mile) Koenigsberg–Moscow airline.

During a test flight in gusty weather with nine passengers aboard, Rother turned over when landing at Goerries, fortunately without injury to anyone. When the aircraft was righted it was found to be completely undamaged. The exhaust stack had stuck in a patch of sand, some of which had got into the engine. The power unit had to be cleaned, but this was the only work that had to be done on the aircraft; it was fit to fly again on the following day.

Fokker in Holland

After his return to Holland late in 1918, Fokker collaborated with the motor-car firm of Spijker at Trompenburg, who had aviation interests. During the war, Spijkers had produced Clerget rotaries and a few prototype aeroplanes.

Fokker had some of his aircraft modified and reconditioned in the Trompenburg works, notably a Fok. D.VIII that was fitted with a 130-h.p. Spijker-Clerget, and the old M.17E biplane, which now had an 80-h.p. Thulin Le Rhône engine. These two Fokker types were demonstrated during the E.L.T.A. exhibition at Amsterdam, the Fok. D.VIII by Lieutenant Versteegh of the Dutch Air Service, who gave a daring display of aerobatics.

As early as April 1919 the U.S. Army Air Service detached two officers to Amsterdam for the purpose of studying Fokker types. They encouraged Fokker to start up his business again in Holland, for the U.S. Army's experience of Fokker aircraft had been so satisfactory that they were prepared to buy more of them. The U.S. Navy, too, was seeking new prototypes.

In August 1919, Fokker founded his Dutch firm at Amsterdam with a capital of 1½-million Dutch guilders. The firm was named Nederlandsche Vliegtuigenfabriek; Fokker's name was not at first embodied in the title, but he was the manager of the new company. During the E.L.T.A. exhibition, held during that same month, Fokker made it known that he had relinquished his German nationality.

In 1920 Fokker went to Dayton, Ohio, where the Technical Center of the U.S. Army Air Service was situated at McCook Field. His intention was to offer aircraft and to discover what the Army's future requirements were likely to be. Fokker met with little resentment against his wartime activities, and found that his prospects were better than he had hoped. He soon returned to the U.S.A. with some of the Schwerin prototypes which, as has been related, had been adapted in accordance with American requirements.

The American visit brought orders for small batches of such types as the Fokker D.IX, D.X, F.IV, C.III and so on, and prototypes like the Fokker D.XII and naval aircraft were suggested. Fokker also secured an order to rebuild 100 American-built De Havilland D.H.4 biplanes; these aircraft were to have welded steel-tube fuselages of the Fokker type. The fuselages seem to have been made at Amsterdam, but the final conversion and assembly were done in the Witteman–Lewis factory at Hasbrouck Heights, New Jersey, by personnel from Holland and Germany. From this arose the Atlantic Aircraft Co. as Fokker's American subsidiary.

When Fokker next visited the U.S.A., he took with him a Fokker F.VI (as PW-5); an improved Fok. D.VII (Fokker D.IX), which acquired the American designation PW-6; a modified Fokker C.I, which became the XCO-4; and the re-engined V.43 (Fokker S.I) as TW-4.

It seems that some sort of settlement was made in 1922 between the German government and Fokker with regard to his financial liabilities in Germany. Rumour had it that a German minister[1] had taken the matter in hand.

The outcome of the negotiations was a secret undertaking, given by Fokker in writing, that he would offer his firm's technical services to the German Republic in the event of a war. In such an eventuality, Germany

[1] In his autobiography Fokker names Mathias Erzberger, Minister of Finance. Erzberger was later murdered by the Nazis when he was leader of the Catholic Party.

would be offered all Fokker designs for military aeroplanes for un-restricted production under licence. Fokker would produce exclusively for German needs if called upon to do so, and would give such other assistance as might be needed to support a German war effort. The one and only copy of this comprehensive agreement was in the files of the German Reichswehr Ministry and treated as top secret.

Now that he could return freely to Germany, Fokker found it useful to renew acquaintances there. To his surprise, he found no resentment when he visited the Rhoen gliding competition: on the contrary, he was treated like an old friend.

To the U.S. Army Air Service the Fokker F.IV was known as the T-2.

Platz's transport aircraft development in Holland

The Fokker F.IV was the first Platz transport type to be wholly designed and built in Holland. It was much larger than the F.II and F.III. Only two aircraft of the F.IV type were built, and both were supplied to the U.S. Army. One was the Army transport, designated T-2; the other was equipped as the Army ambulance A-2.

Long-range and endurance records were set up by the T-2. In April 1923 Lieutenants John A. Macready and Oakley G. Kelly established a world record by flying for 36 hours without refuelling. On May 2–3, 1923, they flew from Roosevelt Field, New York, to Rockwell Field, San Diego, in 26 hours 50 minutes; the total distance flown was about 2,500 miles. For this flight the Fokker T-2 carried 745 gallons of fuel, and its loaded weight was 10,850 lb.

The corpulent Fokker F.V could be flown as a biplane or as a high-wing monoplane. It was powered by a 360-h.p. Rolls-Royce engine. In the vicinity of the cabin the steel-tube fuselage had plywood stiffening in place of wire cross-bracing. This feature was the subject of a Fokker patent (German patent: DRP No. 404,060, of August 22, 1923).

The original design of the Fokker F.VII was by Rethel. Its main feature was that the entire nose of the fuselage, complete with the engine in its

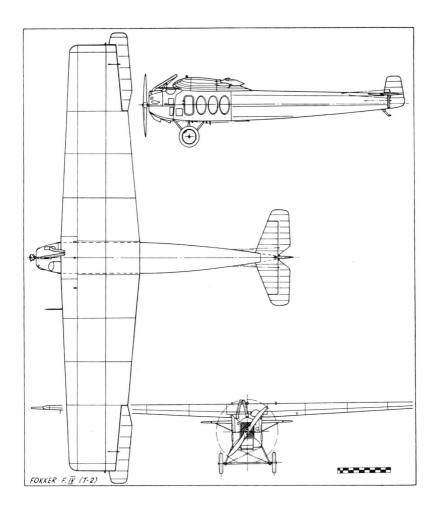

FOKKER F.IV (T-2)

mounting, could be detached. This greatly facilitated maintenance. The
F.VII was redesigned as the F.VIIA with a reduced span and a simplified
undercarriage that gave better shock absorption. It was a great success.

At this time, early 1925, Fokker was living in America. Learning of
the Ford Reliability Tour, a competition for transport aircraft, he
instructed Platz, by telegram and letter, to convert the F.VIIA into a
three-engine aeroplane with three 200-h.p. Wright Whirlwind radial
engines, for participation in the contest. With his instructions Fokker
sent a rough sketch of the engine arrangement he wanted, with the outboard engines mounted on the wing.

Platz found Fokker's proposal quite impossible and declined to execute
it. Instead of complying with Fokker's request, Platz designed and built

377

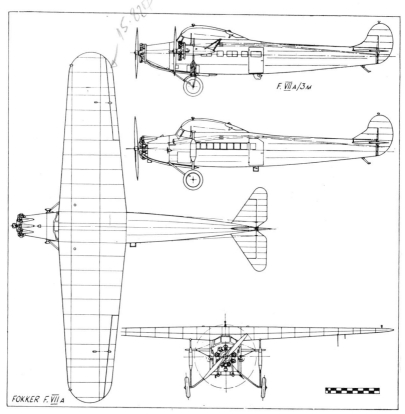

F. VIIA/3M

FOKKER F. VIIA

the first F.VIIA/3m, which had the outer engines installed under the wing. Fokker found the prototype ready for flight-testing when he returned to Amsterdam.

Three weeks after the receipt of Fokker's instructions, the prototype was shipped to the U.S.A. to participate in the Ford Reliability Tour. Before it left Holland, Fokker demonstrated it on September 7, 1925.

The original Fokker F.VIIA/3m.

He also flew it for five hours at full load to satisfy himself about the effectiveness and reliability of the engine installation that was so contrary to his wishes. In the U.S.A. Fokker won the Ford contest. Later he gave Platz a bonus for the trouble he had taken over the F.VIIA/3m.

The F.VIIA/3m and its derivative the F.VIIB/3m proved most successful, and large numbers of these aircraft were built. Even Britain ordered one for research purposes, powered by three Armstrong-Siddeley Lynx engines. It was carefully investigated, and finally confirmed a belated suspicion that cantilever wings of thick aerofoil section might, after all, be practical. An official report of the findings was published as R. & M. No. 1096 of April 1927.

The Fokker trimotors made a number of historic long-distance flights; and several developments were produced. Commercially it was one of the most successful aircraft in the world.

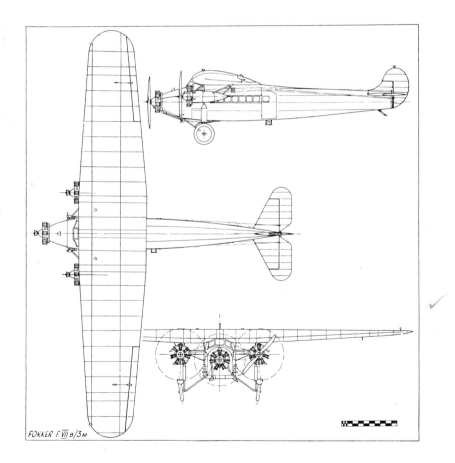

FOKKER F.VII B/3M

379

Fokker D.XI.

The development of military aircraft

The supply of aircraft for military and naval use was still one of the principal fields of activity for the transplanted Fokker firm. Fokker himself read a paper before a select audience of Dutch ministers, generals

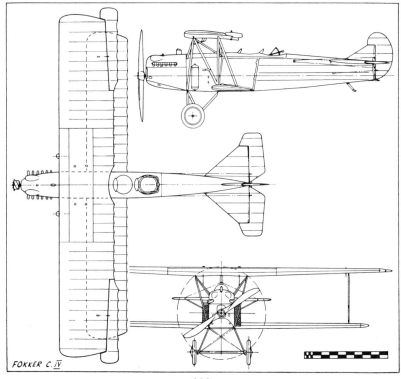

FOKKER C. IV

and other high-ranking officials on February 27, 1923. He pleaded with them that Holland should become a strong air power with an offensive air force (of Fokker aircraft, of course). He told them how cheaply this could be accomplished: the defence of Dutch Indonesia required no more than 100 fighters, 100 reconnaissance aircraft, fifty bombers and fifty flying-boats. Such an air arm would cost just as much as a single cruiser (and all its equipment could be obtained from the Fokker Works).

In August 1923, Fokker displayed the D.XI fighter at the International Air Exhibition at Gothenburg in Sweden. It shared the Fokker stand with the C.IV, a two-seater developed from the C.I. The C.IV was pro-

Fokker PW-7.

duced in numbers and was used by several countries. The D.XI was a biplane powered by a 300-h.p. Hispano-Suiza engine. The cantilever, plywood-covered wings were tapered; to give the larger upper wing greater stiffness in torsion, a V-type interplane strut was fitted. The undercarriage incorporated Platz's new design with the axle floating in a ring-shaped member at the apex of each leg, instead of lying in slots.

This new fighter attracted much admiration at Gothenburg, and proved to be highly successful, both in performance and handling qualities. It was then far in advance of contemporary fighters with the same engine. The U.S. Army Air Service ordered three of these fighters, which were delivered in 1923 under the American designation PW-7. These aircraft had the 440-h.p. Curtiss D-12 engine and a modified undercarriage; the second and third aircraft had N-type interplane struts; at one time, the first machine had an enlarged fin and rudder. This type was used by James Doolittle in daring experiments designed to determine the maximum stress to which a fighter aircraft could be subjected in flight. The results of these experiments were of great significance and importance. The D.XI was built in some numbers and was used by several countries, notably Russia.

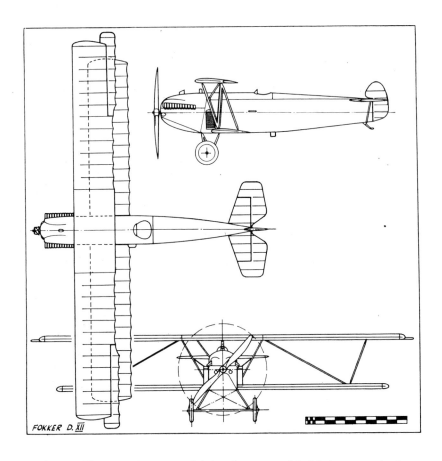

FOKKER D. XII

The D.XII was an unsuccessful development with fabric-covered wings. It did not progress beyond the prototype stage.

At the request of the German Reichswehr Ministry of Defence, the 450-h.p. Napier Lion was fitted to the Fokker D.XI. The result was given the new designation Fokker D.XIII and was in its day the fastest fighter in the world, with a top speed of 272 km./hr. (160 m.p.h.). World records for speed with load were set up by the D.XIII, and it was ordered in substantial quantities by Germany and Soviet Russia. The type gave excellent service, and was in use until 1929, latterly as an operational trainer.

The Fokker D.XIV was a special request by Tony Fokker. Platz, who had (and still has) an aversion from low-wing monoplanes, did not like it at all. It was a semi-cantilever monoplane, braced by lift struts from the ends of the rigid axle. Special wheels provided a measure of shock absorption. The engine was a 350-h.p. Hispano-Suiza.

This clean low-wing monoplane was very fast and highly manoeuvrable.

German experimental officers of the Reichswehr who flew the one and only specimen praised it highly for its outstanding performance and its steadiness as a gun platform. A German order for the D.XIV might have been forthcoming, but the prototype crashed in an uncontrollable flat spin, and its pilot was killed. It would probably have been a simple matter of patient experimenting to cure the D.XIV's trouble, but both Fokker and Platz were content to write off monoplane fighters. All succeeding Fokker fighters designed by Platz were more or less variations on the D.XI theme.

Platz also designed a twin-engine torpedo-carrier for the U.S. Navy, and a low-wing monoplane floatplane. Much of the design work on other Fokker naval types was done by W. Rethel, who later left Fokker to become chief designer to the new Arado Aircraft Works at Warnemuende. The Arado concern was established by H. Luebbe, Fokker's weapons expert, with money received from the German government for his new engine-operated machine-gun for use in aircraft.

Earlier interesting designs by Platz included two gliders. These were designed at Fokker's request; he wanted a glider of low structure weight

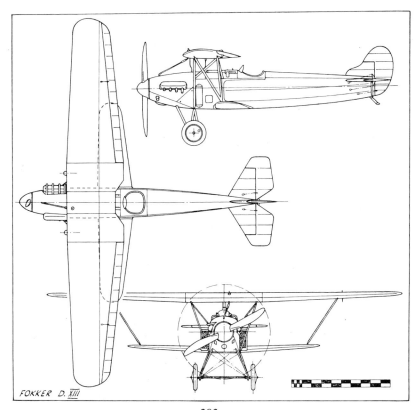

FOKKER D. XIII

Fokker D.XIII.

and large wing area, preferably a braced biplane with open seats. Platz designed two gliders, one a single-seater with a span of 9 m. (29·6 ft.), the other a two-seater with a span of 12 m. (39·4 ft.). Both were braced as single-bay biplanes and had the tail unit supported on booms. The two-seater had a nacelle enclosing the tandem seats; the single-seater was open.

Fokker took these gliders to the 1922 Rhoen gliding contest. On the two-seater, with F. M. Seekatz as his passenger, he set up a world gliding record by staying airborne for 13 minutes on August 26, 1922. In the same year he took the gliders to Itford Hill in England, where the first British gliding competition was held. Fokker's flying skill evoked great admiration.

In his spare time Platz also designed and constructed what may well

384

Fokker D.XIV in its original form.

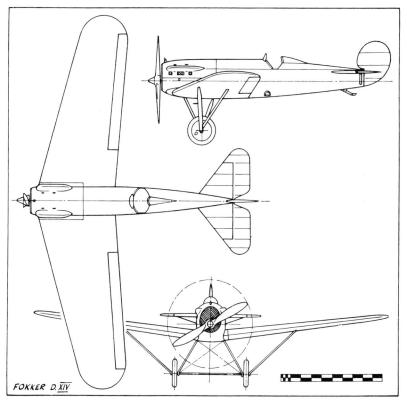

FOKKER D.XIV

Fokker's two-seat glider.

Platz's cruciform glider. (*Photos: Peter M. Bowers*).

have been the world's simplest winged aircraft. It consisted simply of two beams or tubes arranged crosswise with sailcloth stretched between them: in effect, it was the fore-sail and main-sail of a yacht used for gliding. Control was maintained by the differential movement of the divided forward surface. Trials were carried out with the glider tethered and carrying sand ballast. When these tests proved successful, short glides were made from dunes in Holland. Platz was too pre-occupied with work on other designs to be able to pursue the development of this rudimentary glider, but Hoff made him publish details of the experiment in a German scientific journal. Platz complied, under protest.

Production in Holland

When Platz settled in Holland, he took over the production side of the Fokker factory. Most of his Schwerin staff accompanied him; some others who had previously left the Fokker works rejoined to work under him. In Holland, Platz developed a further forty aircraft types, in addition to the forty-five V-types of the Schwerin period and his contribution to the M-series. The work in Holland was spread over eleven years, consequently more time was available for the preparation of new designs than in the hectic 1916–1919 period.

This work was carried on at Veere and at Amsterdam, where the Fokker concern was primitively housed in the more-or-less temporary buildings that had been erected for the E.L.T.A. exhibition. The aircraft types came in great variety: fighters, trainers, bombers, torpedo-carriers, transports, floatplanes, reconnaissance types, the B.IV flying-boat, and gliders and sailplanes. These appeared in almost every configuration except triplanes: biplanes; low-wing, high-wing and parasol-wing monoplanes; pushers; tractors; one, two, three or four motors; fuselage or tail-booms. The production quality was, of course, higher than it had been at Schwerin before Platz became works manager.

Fokkers were used by twenty-five countries, and many of the aircraft were built under licence abroad.

Platz developed at Amsterdam sound production methods for light-alloy floats and hulls, requiring only single-curvature forming of the metal. Adequate tooling and production facilities were lacking, however. Platz realized that his mixed wood-and-steel-tube construction methods were approaching the end of their usefulness, and aircraft built in accordance with them would soon cease to be competitive in the world market. He therefore suggested that the Fokker factory should be re-equipped for modern production methods.

However, Fokker and his financial adviser Elekind were unwilling to make the kind of investment that Platz's suggestions would necessitate. "The *dubbeltje* [a small Dutch coin] can be spent only once" was the reply that Platz was given.

In these frustrating circumstances, Platz could see no possibility of modern developments in the Fokker firm, and withdrew from it. He left, so he says, "as soundlessly as I had entered Tony Fokker's service, and as silent as I had had to remain during twenty-five years with him". During this time he had been a welder, metalworker, sheetmetal worker, body-builder, chargehand, foreman, designer, chief of experimental department, chief designer, and production manager. He left as the technical director of a firm with a world-wide reputation. Yet virtually no-one knew that that reputation was founded upon his designs.

EPILOGUE

IT is the late summer of 1923. In the study of Fokker's home in Amsterdam, four men are sitting round a table in earnest discussion; they have known each other for many years. There is Fokker, older and better fed than he was ten years ago. There is Felix Wagenfuehr, once the powerful man of the *IdFlieg* who had threatened Fokker with criminal proceedings, but now a director and right-hand man of the financier and industrial magnate Hugo Stinnes. There is Walter Hormel, a pre-war pilot and former naval officer; he is now Wagenfuehr's assistant. And there is a quiet man of pleasant manners, round-faced and with a rather high-pitched voice, who chews his cigar while the others discuss the deal: Fokker has known him as Hauptmann Kurt Student when he was in charge of experimental fighter work at Adlershof; he met him again in 1922, flying a clumsy glider, on the Rhoen. Wagenfuehr explains that Student has been brought along as an expert on fighters. Fokker gives him a friendly greeting, for he has known Student since 1915, when he was a successful pilot of the early Fokker single-seaters.

Under discussion is an agreement for the supply of Fokker D.XI and D.XIII fighters: Wagenfuehr is going to buy them on behalf of Stinnes. Fifty aircraft of each type are required as soon as possible. The acceptance tests are to be performed by a pilot provided by Stinnes. Fokker looks quizzically at Student, but Student shakes his head: he will not be that pilot.

Following acceptance, each aircraft is to be dismantled and crated for sea transport. Their shipping will be a matter for Wagenfuehr; Valparaiso is mentioned. The fighters are wanted urgently, and Fokker is required to pledge secrecy on the deal. Should anything leak out, Stinnes would cancel the agreement at once. To all this Fokker agrees.

The purchase of the engines in France and Britain is discussed. Wagenfuehr has all the prices and delivery dates at hand. Another clause

One of the D.XIIIs of the "Stinnes order", with two LMG.08/15 guns installed.

provides that, eventually, fifty more Fokker D.XIII may be required in place of the fifty D.XI. Fokker again agrees.

The aircraft are to be supplied fully armed: Wagenfuehr and Stinnes will supply the machine-guns. Fokker wants to know what type of gun is to be installed, as this affects the design; at present he is installing Browning guns for the Americans. Wagenfuehr's reply puzzles Fokker: the weapons will be German LMG. 08/15, the gun Fokker knows well. Valparaiso and the LMG. 08/15? Queer!

Fokker does not quite know what to make of this mystery order. Might it be for the German government? The only regular officer among Fokker's visitors could be Student. Fokker decides to make some discreet enquiries: for the moment, he puts on a bland countenance. The possibilities of rearming Germany with his aircraft would be enormous. Wagenfuehr has already indicated that more orders may follow, provided Fokker plays the game.

Fokker had guessed right: the order was indeed the first post-war aircraft acquisition by the German Reichswehr. Student was actually representing the German Defence Ministry on behalf of the government of the Reich. Wagenfuehr and Hormel were there merely to camouflage the nature of the transaction.

Student, nominally in charge of a somewhat mysterious department within the ministry's Inspectorate of Arms and Equipment, allegedly concerned with the development of railway engines and tractors, had been sent to Amsterdam on the express orders of the chief of the army, General von Seeckt. His mission had been suggested by the air chief, Major H. Wilberg.

Student had been given full powers. He was to check on available Fokker fighter types. If he found them suitable for combat under modern conditions, he was to order a hundred of them immediately.

What lay behind this sudden, clandestine rearmament, coming so soon after, and contrary to, the Treaty of Versailles, the terms of which forbade Germany to possess aircraft, tanks and heavy guns? The matter had its roots in the Treaty of Rapallo between Germany and Soviet Russia, and in the occupation of the Ruhr by the French.

The Rapallo Treaty was concluded between Dr. W. Rathenau,[1] German Foreign Minister, on the one side, and Lenin and Trotsky on the other. It contained a secret clause for mutual assistance in the event of Polish aggression. At that time Poland was a bitter enemy of Russia, and it was believed in Germany that she was persistently encouraged by France to invade Germany and seize more German territory. The Rapallo Treaty was designed to be a safeguard against such an eventuality.

During 1922 the French Army invaded the Ruhr under the pretext that Germany had not fulfilled her obligation to supply coal to France. The truth was that Germany was unable to deliver coal owing to a series of strikes in the coal-mines, and German industry itself was jeopardized by the acute shortage of coal. It was believed in Germany that the strikes had been fomented by French-paid agitators.

All political parties in Germany demanded immediate military counter-measures against this invasion. The Defence Minister Gessler and General von Seeckt replied that, without aircraft or tanks, any such action would be suicide, and they could not accept responsibility for this. The German cabinet resigned and was replaced by politicians who were prepared to treat with the French.

At the same time as France's march into the Ruhr, Polish infantry made a concerted attack on the eastern borders of Germany. They were repulsed by formations of ex-soldiers, deployed along the border by the Reichswehr. The German formations of thinly-disguised "civilians" sent the invaders flying back across the border with considerable losses. Both sides found it politic not to publicize the fighting, the Germans because it had involved soldiers that ought not to exist, the Poles because they were sent packing by what appeared to them mere farm yokels.

Faced with these developments in foreign affairs, the leading German politicians—including the Socialist leaders—were compelled to reconsider the situation created by the Treaty of Versailles. The French and Polish incursions without the formality of a declaration of war were occurrences that could not be tolerated. The Treaty of Versailles did not guarantee the integrity of German territory and therefore provided no remedy. A Reichswehr unable to defend German territory was of no use.

[1] Murdered by the Nazis as a Jew.

The German government was therefore empowered by agreement of all political parties, including the Socialists, to take all necessary steps to provide Germany with adequate means of defence, notwithstanding the restrictions of the Treaty of Versailles. The German view was that the French themselves had violated that Treaty.

The Russians offered facilities for the training of fighter and reconnaissance squadrons on Russian soil. In consideration of this, the Germans undertook to assist the Russians in the reorganization and training of their air force. A German Air Staff was established in Moscow with Colonel Thomsen, the one-time *Feldflugchef*, in command. For camouflage, Thomsen used only part of his full name, being known in Moscow as von der Lieth. His staff included the best-qualified officers, in terms of aviation experience, that Germany could provide.

The Germans saw to it that the Red Air Fleet was equipped with modern aircraft. It was at their suggestion that the U.S.S.R. acquired Fokker fighters and reconnaissance aircraft. They also tried to establish a Junkers factory in Russia, but the attempt failed dismally.

A batch of the Fokker D.XIIIs despatched to "Traugott Müller", Valparaiso, that arrived at Lipezk in Russia.

The hundred Fokker fighters that the Germans had ordered for their own immediate requirements were consigned to a firm of Traugott Müller, Valparaiso. They never reached this destination: Traugott Müller never received them. But Traugott Müller did not complain. By some mischance, the crates containing these aircraft were "misdirected" to Stettin, reshipped from there, and finally arrived at—of all places—Lipezk in the U.S.S.R. There, by an extraordinary coincidence, German Service personnel were waiting for them.

And so the wheel of fate had turned full circle—from the first Spider that Fokker had landed at Doeberitz, to the first Fokker D.XIII that was taken from its crate at Lipezk aerodrome in Russia: Fokker was again delivering aeroplanes to Germany's air arm.

APPENDIX I

LIST OF FOKKER AIRCRAFT TYPES UP TO THE V.45

Type	Engine(s)	Date	Notes	Text reference (page nos.)
Fokker–von Daum monoplane	50-h.p. Argus	Oct. 1910	(a) without elevator or rudder; (b) with elevator and rudder.	12–14
Fokker–von Daum Goedecker mono-plane	50-h.p. Argus	Spring 1911	Ailerons.	16–17
Fokker–Goedecker monoplane	50-h.p. Argus	Aug. 1911	No ailerons. The Haar-lem Spider.	18–24
Fokker monoplane	50-h.p. Dixi	1912		25
Spider	50-h.p. Argus	1912	Cockpit fairing added, block radiator fitted.	24
Spider	60-h.p. Argus	1912	Alternative engine.	29
Spider	70-h.p. Argus	1912	Alternative engine.	29
B-1912 Spider	100-h.p. Argus	1912	Belly fairing added, sup-plementary fuel tank fitted.	30, 34–36
Spider	100-h.p. Argus	1912	For Ljuba Galantschi-koff. Cockpit fairing; Garuda airscrew.	33
Spider	50-h.p. Gnôme	1912	Experimental engine change.	33
Spider	70-h.p. Renault	1912	Alternative engine.	21, 35
W.1	70-h.p. Renault	Feb. 1913	Flying-boat. Develop-ment projected with 100-h.p. Renault.	37–40
M.1 Spider	100-h.p. Argus	Feb. 1913	For Prussian Army.	39
M.1 Spider	95-h.p. Mercedes	March 1913	A.38/13. For Prussian Army.	39–40
M.1 variant	70-h.p. Renault	1913	Modified fuselage and cabane.	42
M.2	95-h.p. Mercedes	1913	Built for military aircraft competition. Stream-lined fuselage built up on Jeannin welded structure. Originally with single rudder, di-vided elevator; later two-piece rudder, en-larged one-piece eleva-tor.	46–50

393

Type	Engine(s)	Date	Notes	Text reference (page nos.)
M.3	95-h.p. Mercedes	Sept. 1913	First flew 26.9.13. Wrecked November 1913.	51–54
M.3A	70-h.p. Renault	1913	Engine from W.1. Sold to Worobieff. Crashed 7.9.14.	54, 55, 83, 84
M.4 Stahltaube	100-h.p. Mercedes	1913	Underwent various modifications. Unsuccessful.	55–57
W.2	100-h.p. Mercedes	1913	Abandoned after few flights. Fuselage and floats converted into hydroplane with 70-h.p. Renault.	57–58
M.5K	50-h.p. Gnôme later 80-h.p. Oberursel-built Gnôme	April 1914	Single-seat monoplane derived from Morane–Saulnier Type H.	65–74, 78, 79, 96, 104
M.5L	70-h.p. Gnôme, later 80-h.p. Oberursel-built Gnôme	April 1914	As M.5K, but with increased span.	73–79, 81, 83–85, 100, 126
M.6	80-h.p. Oberursel	June 1914	Two-seat semi-parasol monoplane for military reconnaissance. One only; crashed July 1914.	79–83
M.7	80-h.p. Oberursel	Jan. 1915	Two-seat biplane designed for Admiralty.	81, 83, 84, 132–136, 138
M.8, Fok. A, later Fok. A.I	80-h.p. Oberursel	Oct. 1914	Two-seat shoulder-wing monoplane for reconnaissance.	81, 84–92, 100, 109
M5K/MG	80-h.p. Oberursel	1915	Armed with Parabellum machine-gun. Factory No. 216.	96–99, 102, 403
M5K/MG	80-h.p. Oberursel	1915	LMG. 08 machine-gun. Factory No. 258.	99, 102, 403
E.I	80-h.p. Oberursel	1915	Armed with LMG. 08 gun. Quantity production.	99–102, 104–116, 128, 130, 403
W.3	80-h.p. Oberursel	1915	Fuselage of M.7, floats of W.2, fitted with new wings. Twin-float seaplane.	137–138
M.9	Two 80-h.p. Oberursel	1915	Twin-fuselage, three-seat biplane. Intended to be a fighting aircraft.	138–141
M.10	80-h.p. Oberursel	1915	Two-seat military biplane. Prototype was Factory No. 169.	89, 136, 141–146

APPENDIX I—continued

Type	Engine(s)	Date	Notes	Text reference (page nos.)
M.10	100-h.p. Mercedes	1915	Experimental engine change.	143
M.10E	80-h.p. Oberursel	1915	Single-bay interplane bracing; modified cabane.	143–144
M.10Z	80-h.p. Oberursel	1915	Two-bay bracing.	143–146
E.II (M.14)	80-h.p. Oberursel	1915	Single-seat fighter; development of E.I.	114–116, 403
E.II	100-h.p. Oberursel	1915		114–116, 130
E.III	100-h.p. Oberursel	1915	Single-seat fighter, increased span. Armed with one or two machine-guns.	116–119, 125, 127, 130, 403
	80-h.p. Le Rhône			117, 403
	100-h.p. Goebel Goe. I		Experimental engine. Factory No. 520.	116–117, 403
	90-h.p. Siemens–Halske Sh.I		Experimental engine.	117
E.IV (M.15)	160-h.p. Oberursel	Nov. 1915	Single-seat fighter monoplane. Ultimate development of Fokker monoplane.	103, 120–124, 127, 130, 403
E.IV	100-h.p. Oberursel, later 160-h.p. Le Rhône	Dec. 1915	Aircraft E.189/16, Factory No. 385, for Max Immelmann, with three guns. Designed for 160-h.p. Le Rhône; engine not at first available.	123, 403
	160-h.p. Oberursel		Engine changed owing to lack of spares for the 160-h.p. Le Rhône.	123–124
M.16E Karausche	100-h.p. Mercedes	1915	Single-seat fighter with single-bay wings.	147, 151
M.16Z	160-h.p. Mercedes	1916	Two-seat, two-bay biplane.	148, 151
M.16ZK	185/200-h.p. Austro–Daimler	1916	Factory No. 435. For Austria. Built in numbers in Austria.	148–153
M.17E	80-h.p. Oberursel	1916	Single-seat fighter. Deep fuselage.	150, 153
	80-h.p. Thulin Le Rhône	1919	Engine change in Holland, after the war.	374
M.17 (two-bay)	80-h.p. Oberursel	1916	Original deep fuselage, two-bay wings.	150

395

Type	Engine(s)	Date	Notes	Text reference (page nos.)
M.17E modified	80-h.p. Oberursel	1916	Modified fuselage of reduced depth, staggered wings. Factory No. 499.	155–158
			Similar aircraft with two guns (1 Schwarzlose, 1 Mannlicher) and strengthened undercarriage.	155–156
	80-h.p. Oberursel	1916	For Austria. Supplied in numbers. Comma rudder.	155–156
	100-h.p. Oberursel	1916	Experimental engine change.	158
M.17Z	80-h.p. Le Rhône	1916	Pointed stern, small straight-sided rudder, two-bay wings.	156
	100-h.p. Oberursel	1916	Officially tested at Adlershof, 17.4.16. Became prototype Fok. D.II.	157–159
D.II (M.17ZF)	100-h.p. Oberursel	1916	Warping wings. Comma rudder. Production single-seat fighter.	159–161, 163, 404–405
D.II (M.17ZK)	100-h.p. Oberursel	1916	As M.17ZF, but with ailerons.	159–161, 404–405
M.18E	100-h.p. Mercedes	1916	Single-seat fighter. Single-bay wings.	150, 161–163
M.18Z	100-h.p. Mercedes	1916	Single-seat fighter, two-bay wings. Pointed stern, parallelogram rudder set forward.	150, 162–164
M.18	160-h.p. Mercedes	1916	Experimental engine change.	
D.I	100-h.p. Mercedes	1916	As M.18Z but with comma rudder and elongated radiator blocks.	164–166
D.I (M.18ZF)	120-h.p. Mercedes	1916	Production aircraft with warping wings.	165–168, 404–405
D.I (M.18ZK)	120-h.p. Mercedes	1916	Production aircraft with aileron control.	167–168, 404–405
D.I (Austria)	160-h.p. Austro–Daimler	1916	Austrian-built version with large fin.	166, 168–169
D.III (M.19)	160-h.p. Oberursel	1916	Development of D.II with twin guns. Early aircraft had warping wings; later machines had ailerons.	170–174, 404–405
D.IV (M.20)	160-h.p. Mercedes	1916	Modified D.I with more powerful engine.	174–179
D.IV	160-h.p. Mercedes	1916	Experimental version with spinner and modified engine cowling.	177

Type	Engine(s)	Date	Notes	Text reference (page nos.)
D.IV	160-h.p. Mercedes	1918	Experimental version with long-span wings.	178, 275
M.21	100-h.p. Oberursel	1916	Single-seat fighter.	180–182
M.22	100-h.p.	1916	Basically similar to M.21, but fuselage faired out. Prototype of D.V.	181–182
D.V	100-h.p. Oberursel	1916	Single-set fighter, produced in quantity.	181–185
"D.VI"	100-h.p. Oberursel	1916	M.22 developed, in no way connected with later Fok. D.VI. Modified wing and centre-section bracing.	186
M.22 development	100-h.p. Oberursel	1916	Generally similar to the so-called "D.VI", but with different fuselage fairings and cable arrangement. Faired front legs on undercarriage.	187
M.22ZF	100-h.p. Oberursel	1916	Two-bay warping wings with Fok. D.V fuselage. No guns.	187, 189
M.22ZF	110-h.p. Siemens–Halske Sh.II	1916	Experimental engine change. Guns fitted. Single front legs in undercarriage.	187, 188, 190
V.1	100-h.p. Oberursel	Dec. 1916	Experimental single-seat cantilever biplane, armed with two LMG. 08/15 guns at one time.	197–203, 213
V.2	120-h.p. Mercedes	Jan. 1917	Experimental single-seat cantilever biplane. Later fitted with revised fin and rudder, mainplane raised to improve pilot's view.	203–204, 213
V.3	110-h.p. Le Rhône	1917	Single-seat fighter triplane with cantilever wings. Middle and bottom wings of equal span; plain ailerons and elevators.	224–226, 237
V.4	110-h.p. Le Rhône	1917	Development of V.3 with new wings of increased span, horn-balanced ailerons and elevators, and interplane struts. Later numbered F.101/17.	226–228, 312
F.I	110-h.p. Le Rhône	1917	Two aircraft, 102/17 and 103/17, only. As V.4, but with modified elevator balances.	228–233, 411

Type	Engine(s)	Date	Notes	Text reference (page nos.)
Dr.I	110-h.p. Le Rhône	1917	Production triplane. As F.I, but with wing-tip skids.	195, 233–247, 273, 275, 310, 312, 406–412
	110-h.p. Oberursel UR.II	1917	Alternative standard engine, exchanged whenever possible for the Thulin-made Le Rhône.	347
	110-h.p. Rhenania Le Rhône			
Dr.I (V.5)	160-h.p. Goebel Goe.III	1917	First installed in 108/17; about thirty Fok. Dr.I supplied wih this engine.	249–250
Dr.I (V.7)	160-h.p. Siemens–Halske Sh.3	1917	Aerofoil not fitted to undercarriage axle; also with lengthened fuselage.	247–249
Dr.I	Siemens–Rhemag		Experimental engine installation.	
Dr.I	Goebel-built Gnôme		Experimental engine installation, aircraft No. 416/17.	
Dr.I	145-h.p. Oberursel UR.III	1917	Remained experimental only. Flown at first fighter aircraft comparative trials, January 1918.	250
Dr.I	200-h.p. Goebel Goe.III	1917	Flown at first fighter trials, January 1918.	250
Dr.I	130-h.p. Clerget	1917	Three experimental aircraft only (485/17, 527/17 and 562/17).	250
Dr.I	Super-charged Oberursel UR.II		Engine fitted with Schwade compressor.	250–251
Dr.I	160-h.p. Gnôme	1918	Aircraft No. 100/18, fitted with captured 160-h.p. Gnôme.	
V.6	120-h.p. Mercedes	1917	Single-seat triplane.	251–252
V.8	120-h.p. Mercedes	1917	Quintuplane. Failure.	252–254
V.9	80-h.p. Oberursel	1917	Single-seat fighter biplane.	257
	110-h.p. Le Rhône	1917	Engine change after first flight.	257–258, 275
	110-h.p. Oberursel UR.II	1917	Flown in first fighter trials, January 1918.	266

Type	Engine(s)	Date	Notes	Text reference (page nos.)
V.11	160-h.p. Mercedes	1917	Flown at first fighter trials, January 1918. Underwent various modifications and became prototype of Fok. D.VII. First V.11 had Fokker Factory No. 1883.	258–264, 265–271, 276–277, 290, 413
D.VII	160-h.p. Mercedes D.IIIa 160-h.p. Mercedes D.IIIaü	1918 1918	Standard production Fok. D.VII.	270, 273, 275–280, 280–299, 302–308, 310, 319, 344, 348, 352, 356, 375, 413–416
D.VIIF	185-h.p. B.M.W. IIIa	1918		281–282, 286, 290, 292, 321–322, 347–348, 355
D.VII	160-h.p. Mercedes D.IIIa	Apr. 1918	Fok. D.VII (Alb) 541/18. Plywood fuselage; one aircraft only.	296, 322
D.VII	210-h.p. Austro–Daimler	1918	Production by MAG for Austria.	290
D.VII	160-h.p. Mercedes	1918	Experimental installation of 12-mm. TuF gun.	416
			Experimental installation of Siemens motor-driven gun.	416
			Interplane struts removed; flown as cantilever biplane.	289
			Experimentally fitted with full cable bracing.	289
1D7 2D7 3D7 4D7 5D7 6D7 7D7			Fok. D.VII aircraft modified in various ways by the Flugzeugmeisterei.	290
D.VII	230-h.p. Liberty 6		Post-war modifications made in the U.S.A.	304–305
D.VII	270-h.p. Packard 1A-1116			
D.VII two-seat			Various two-seat D.VIIs were built, both during and after the war.	302

Type	Engine(s)	Date	Notes	Text reference (page nos.)
V.13/I	110-h.p. Oberursel UR.II	1917		262, 272
	145-h.p. Oberursel UR.III	1918	Flown at first fighter trials, January 1918.	264, 266, 269, 270, 275
V.13/II	160-h.p. Siemens–Halske Sh.3	1918	Flown at first fighter trials, January 1918.	262, 264, 269, 272
D.VI	110-h.p. Oberursel UR.II	1918	Produced in quantity.	270–273, 290, 310, 324, 329
	200-h.p. Goebel Goe.III	1918	Intended as ultimate production version of Fok. D.VI. Few delivered.	271
	145-h.p. Oberursel UR.III	1918	Few supplied.	272
V.17	110-h.p. Oberursel UR.II	1917	Cantilever shoulder-wing monoplane. Flown at first fighter trials, January 1918.	215, 262–263, 266–267, 312–313, 317
V.18	160-h.p. Mercedes D.IIIaü	1917	Generally similar to V.11. For first fighter trials.	261–262, 264, 266–267
V.20	160-h.p. Mercedes D.IIIa	1918	Cantilever mid-wing monoplane built within a week for first fighter trials, January 1918.	216, 266, 313–314
V.21	160-h.p. Mercedes D.IIIaü	1918	Factory No. 2310. V.11 development with tapered wings, for second fighter trials, June 1918.	276, 320
V.22	160-h.p. Mercedes	1918	V.11 development with dihedral on mainplanes, four-blade airscrew.	276
V.23	160-h.p. Mercedes D.IIIa	1918	Factory No. 2443. Midwing monoplane, flown in second fighter trials, June 1918.	314–316, 320
V.24	240-h.p. Benz Bz.IVü 185-h.p. B.M.W. IIIa	1918	Factory No. 2612. Flown in second fighter trials, June 1918. Engine change.	261, 280–281, 319–320
V.25	110-h.p. Oberursel UR.II	1918	Low-wing monoplane. Flown in second fighter trials June 1918. Factory No. 2732.	316–318, 320, 323
V.26	110-h.p. Oberursel UR.II	1918	Parasol monoplane. Prototype of Fok. E.V/ D.VIII.	319, 320, 321, 323–324, 327 351

Type	Engine(s)	Date	Notes	Text reference (page nos.)
V.27	195-h.p. Benz Bz.IIIb (direct drive)	1918	Parasol monoplane. Flown in second fighter trials June 1918. Factory No. 2734.	319, 320, 325, 346
	195-h.p. Benz Bz.IIIb (geared)	1918	Fitted with armour plate around engine and cockpit, later redesignated V.37.	325
V.28	200-h.p. Goebel Goe.IIIa	1918	Parasol monoplane.	321, 323–324
	145-h.p. Oberursel UR.III		Flown in second fighter trials, June 1918.	319–320, 324, 327
Fok. E.V	110-h.p. Le Rhône 110-h.p. Oberursel UR.II	1918	Production single-seat fighter from V.26. Alternative engine.	273, 299, 323–324, 327–339, 342
D.VIII	110-h.p. Oberursel UR.II		As E.V but with new (i.e., properly made) wings.	251, 328, 339–346, 349, 352, 355–356, 358
D.VIIIe	145-h.p. Oberursel UR.III		Production aircraft with new engine.	341–342, 347–348
D.VIIIg	200-h.p. Goebel Goe.IIIa		Production intended.	341–342, 344, 347
D.VIIIs	220-h.p. Siemens–Halske Sh.3a		Experimental installation.	345, 347
D.VIII	130-h.p. Spijker–Clerget	1919	Post-war modification by Spijker company.	374–375
V.29	185-h.p. B.M.W. IIIa	1918	Parasol monoplane. Third fighter trials, October 1918.	346–349
V.30	Nil	1918	Glider embodying some V.26 components.	349–351
V.31	160-h.p. Mercedes	1918	Two-seat glider-towing development of Fok. D.VII.	350
V.33	100-h.p. Oberursel 110-h.p. Le Rhône	1918	Late V.9 development, originally with V-type, later N-type, interplane struts.	274–275, 290
V.34	185-h.p. B.M.W. IIIa	1918	Single-seat fighter developed from Fok. D.VII.	290
V.35	185-h.p. B.M.W. IIIa	1918	Two-seat conversion of D.VII. Undercarriage fuel tank fitted.	297–298, 302

APPENDIX I—continued

Type	Engine(s)	Date	Notes	Text reference (page nos.)
V.36	220/240-h.p. Benz Bz.IVü	1918	Factory No. 2656. Further development of V.34.	289, 290–297, 346, 348
	185-h.p. B.M.W. IIIa	1918	Engine change. Flown in third fighter trials, October 1918.	290–291
V.37	195-h.p. Benz Bz.IIIb (geared)	1918	Armoured development of V.27 with large armoured spinner.	326
V.38	185-h.p. B.M.W. IIIa	1918	Two-seat fighter-reconnaissance biplane, put into production as so-called Fok. C.I but never ordered officially.	282, 298–302, 356, 375, 381
V.38 (Special)			One special machine with enlarged tankage for Fokker.	299, 353–354
V.39	50-h.p. or 80-h.p. Gnôme	1918	Single-seat light sporting monoplane, built after Armistice.	213, 356–357
V.40	35-h.p. Anzani	1918	Single-seat sporting monoplane, built after Armistice.	213, 357–358
V.41	300-h.p. Hispano-Suiza	1922	Single-seat parasol monoplane fighter.	358–363
V.42	Nil	1919	Glider. Could be flown as flying-boat or with wheel undercarriage.	351, 363
V.43	75-h.p. Mercedes	1919	Parasol monoplane; two-seat trainer with side-by-side seating. Revived as S.I.	364
S.I	90-h.p. Curtiss OX-5	1922	To U.S.A. as TW-4.	364–366, 375
V.44 (F.I)	185-h.p. B.M.W. IIIa	1919	Abandoned parasol-wing monoplane transport. Wing used on V.45.	366–368, 376
V.45 (F.II)	185-h.p. B.M.W. IIIa	1919	High wing monoplane developed from V.44. Cabin for four passengers.	367–372, 376
Fokker F.VI F.III				361–363 372–374

402

APPENDIX II

NOTES ON INDIVIDUAL FOKKER MONOPLANES

Factory No. 216: M.5K fitted with Parabellum machine-gun. Returned to Schwerin for repair in August 1917, then sent back to a training unit.

Factory No. 258: M.5K fitted with an LMG. 08 machine-gun.

E.2/15: Flown by Parschau; first Fokker fighter to see operational service.

E.3/15: Boelcke's first single-seat fighter.

E.13/15: Immelmann's first Fokker monoplane, on which he scored five victories. This aircraft was preserved and exhibited in the Berlin Zeughaus, but was destroyed by bombing during the Second World War.

E.8/15 and E.37/15: also flown by Immelmann, the latter during October and November 1915.

E.I, E.33/15: flown by O. Kissenberth of the Bavarian Feldfliegerabteilung 9.

E.I, E.36/15: Buddecke's first Fokker, believed to have gone to Turkey with him.

E.65/15: tested to destruction at Adlershof on October 9, 1916, after Immelmann's fatal crash. No structural weakness found.

E.II, E.86/15: shot down in Flanders.

E.IV, E.125/15: Factory No. 374, accepted January 16, 1916. First M.15-type aircraft for structural investigation at Adlershof during February 1916. It was subsequently repaired and went to the front late in March 1916.

E.IV, E.174/15: First standard E.IV with two guns and 160-h.p. Oberursel. Taken over by Boelcke on December 19, 1915.

E.IV, E.189/15: The so-called "Immelmann Aeroplane" with three guns. Flown by Immelmann, also tried by Boelcke. Not satisfactory.

E.III, E.210/15: Factory No. 309. Accepted October 3, 1915; was repaired at Schwerin on June 21, 1916, after a crash, and fell into British hands soon afterwards.

E.III, E.419/15: Factory No. 401. Accepted January 1, 1916; was selected as representative of the M.14 and subjected to a type test at Adlershof. Single machine-gun. Later experimentally fitted with a captured 80-h.p. Le Rhône engine. Returned to Schwerin in July 1916 for repairs.

E.I, E.327/15: Factory No. 420. Accepted February 1, 1916. On October 20, 1916, landed intact near Plessis-Belleville in the French sector after interrupter-gear failure led to airscrew breakage.

E.III, E.210/16: Factory No. 509. Despatched to the front, April 1, 1916. Shot down near St. Omer on April 8, 1916, and captured by the French.

E.III: Factory No. 520. Accepted April 8, 1916. Experimental installation of 100-h.p. Goebel Goe. I nine-cylinder rotary engine.

E.III: Factory No. 613, 100-h.p. Oberursel U.I engine. Captured by the French near Chalons, summer 1916.

THE STRUCTURAL TESTS OF THE FOKKER D.I, D.II AND D.III

The structural tests of Fokker biplanes conducted at Adlershof in the summer of 1916 covered the three types D.I, D.II and D.III. The load factors were calculated for all three types from a single loading, since all stress-carrying elements (spars, struts, cables, etc.) and their field lengths were practically identical. Engines and all-up weights were assumed as follows:

Fok. D.I   120-h.p. Mercedes. Weight 671 kg. (1,480 lb.)
Fok. D.II   100-h.p. Oberursel U.1. Weight 576 kg. (1,270 lb.)
Fok. D.III   160-h.p. Oberursel U.3. Weight 699 kg. (1,540 lb.)

The Fok. D.III was so much heavier because of its twin guns and 2,000 rounds of ammunition, a load of 274 kg. (600 lb.).

Three loading cases were experimentally investigated:

Case A: flattening out from a steep glide;
Case B: gliding, with resultant air force acting rather far aft;
Case D: condition of inverted flight.

As was usual at that time, Case C (torsional strength in a terminal-velocity dive) was not investigated.

For Case A a load factor of $n_A = 5$ had to be achieved. The first sand loadings produced the following results:

	Rigged for wing warping	Rigged for ailerons
Fok. D.I $n_A =$	4·90	5·17
Fok. D.II	5.85	6·15
Fok. D.III	4·68	4·92
Cause of collapse	Buckling of centre-section tube connecting upper front spars.	No damage; no permanent deformation.

The steel tubular inter-spar member that failed in the 880-mm. wide centre section was of 28-mm. external diameter and 1-mm. wall thickness. It was replaced by a steel tube of the same gauge but of 30-mm. diameter.

The second test was for Case D (inverted flight); the required factor was $n_D = 3\cdot 0$. The results, for wings rigged for warping control, were:

Fok. D.I $n_D = 3\cdot 15$ ⎫
Fok. D.II   3·75 ⎬ No permanent deformation
Fok. D.III   3·00 ⎭

The required strength was therefore achieved without destruction.

In Case B (gliding) the requirement was $n_B = 3\cdot5$. The tests caused minor deformations, and yielded these results:

$$\begin{array}{lll}\text{Fok. D.I} & n_B = & 3\cdot55 \\ \text{Fok. D.II} & & 4\cdot25 \\ \text{Fok. D.III} & & 3\cdot39\end{array}$$

Subsequently the Case A loadings were repeated to destruction. The enlarged tube member in the centre section again failed, this time at its welded joint. At the same time, one of the spar coupling bolts, of 6-mm. diameter, sheared. The ultimate strength still remained below the required minimum for the Fok. D.I and D.III. The broken tube was replaced, and spar coupling bolts of 8-mm. diameter were fitted.

Repeated sand loadings proved that the cross tube was still not strong enough; it was again replaced, this time by a tube of 1·5-mm. gauge. The following ultimate load factors for Case A were finally achieved:

$$\begin{array}{lll}\text{Fok. D.I} & n_{Au} = & 5\cdot87 \\ \text{Fok. D.II} & & 7\cdot00 \\ \text{Fok. D.III} & & 5\cdot60\end{array}$$

Failure occurred with the buckling of the spars of the port upper wing. The wing weight had been 84 kg. (185 lb.), all included.

Dr.-Ing. W. Hoff (in civilian life, chief of the aircraft department of the D.V.L.) certified that the aircraft was structurally cleared for flight, subject to the incorporation of all the modifications that the tests had shown to be necessary.

Structural tests of the tail control surfaces were also made. These revealed that the main tubular spar of the elevator was of thinner-gauge metal than that of the Fok. E.IV, with which it was otherwise identical in size and loading. Fokker was unable to explain why this was so. The control column failed under a pull of 50 kg. (110 lb.) applied at the grip: the acceptable minimum was 80 kg. (177 lb.).

Fokker was asked to submit strengthened components, and these proved to be satisfactory. He was thus shown that his aircraft had been made safe by the addition of no more than one kilogram of structure weight. This additional weight also included the enlargement of the elevator area from 1·49 to 1·68 sq. m., a modification that the Army test pilots had found necessary.

The rudder did not require modification; its area remained unchanged at 0·56 sq. m., its gearing at a ratio of 0·65. Control friction in the circuit was, at 19·5%, almost the acceptable maximum (20%). All controls were found to be heavy owing to friction in the cable circuits, and Fokker was asked to improve this aspect of his products.

The strength of the fuselage structure, engine mountings, tanks, seats, safety belts, etc., was not examined: surprisingly, it was assumed that the results of corresponding tests on the monoplanes were valid for the biplanes. In this respect, Fokker was let off lightly, for no Fokker monoplane had had a stationary engine.

In all, seven complete wing loadings, three elevator-control loadings and one rudder loading, were carried out during one week of intensive testing by the structures department under Dr. Hoff. The tests cost Fokker nothing: he was even paid for the test airframes.

DESCRIPTION OF THE CONSTRUCTION OF THE FOK. DR.I

Wings

The construction of the spar box is described in the text (see pages 198 and 225). The flange members were identical in all wings, as were the spar webs, which were made of 1·5-mm. birch plywood. Splices of the flanges had to be in length twelve times their thickness; in plywood, the length had to be ten times its thickness and its outer veneers had to overlap, giving greater local thickness. To brace the plywood covering between the spars, bulkhead-like frames were glued between the spars in line with the ribs.

While production of the Dr.I was under way, but before the wing failures occurred, it seems to have been found desirable to provide local protection of the wing spars where they passed through the fuselage: two additional plywood strips were applied to the top and rear of the spar box. This modification seems to have been made to the bottom wing and possibly to the middle wing. Platz says he never authorized this modification, for it was unnecessary from the standpoint of structural strength. It may have been required by the Adlershof experts as a protection against damage by pilots, mechanics or armourers.

The rib webs were of 1-mm. three-ply with circular lightening holes. Cap-strips of lime wood and rectangular cross-section were fitted to the top and bottom of each rib. These cap-strips were originally grooved to fit over the web, but, as described on page 236, they were replaced by pairs of rib-contour runners between which the rib web was sandwiched. All subsequent Fokker aeroplanes retained this feature.

Each rib was an integral component extending over the full chord. For assembly, the ribs were slid over the spar box and anchored to it on both sides of the rib webs by vertical members of triangular cross-section. The nose contour of the aerofoil section was preserved by a strip of 1·2-mm. plywood along the leading edge. The wing trailing edge consisted of a steel wire attached to the rib tails, but in the top wing the outer portions had a wooden spar member that carried the aileron hinges. In the modified wing, triangular ply-wood gussets were fitted to reinforce the attachment of the ribs to this spar.

The ailerons were simple structures welded up from steel tubing attached to a main spar tube; this was connected to the wing by three hinges. The Adlershof experts recommended four hinges, but this modification was never implemented. It is not clear why the additional hinge was thought necessary. The control horn was mounted immediately inboard of a stout box rib (formed by gluing two ordinary wing ribs together) and close to the central aileron hinge.

Simplicity was the essential characteristic of the fittings by which the wings were attached to the fuselage and cabane struts. They were made of very ordinary commercial-quality mild steel sheet and other materials of similar quality, yet none ever failed in service. They would have remained serviceable after thousands of hours of flying, if necessary.

The interplane struts were not one-piece components running through the middle wing as on the Sopwith triplane: there was a separate short strut in each wing gap. Each strut was little more than a lath of streamline section; it was incapable of transmitting major compression loads. The strut attachment fittings were simple and effective.

It is not clear why wing-tip skids were fitted under the lower wings. An aircraft of such short span and with such a tall undercarriage would be unlikely to touch the ground with a wing tip in all but the most exceptionally adverse operating conditions. Platz thinks the skids may have been requested by units at the front; but it is equally possible that they were asked for by Adlershof after the undercarriage was found to be of less than regulation strength, in the hope that they might minimize damage in the event of undercarriage failure.

Fuselage and Controls

The fuselage structure was basically similar to that of the V.1: it consisted of steel tubing welded into a structure of rectangular cross-section with a vertical sternpost. The longerons were of 20-mm. outside diameter and 1-mm. gauge; .04" the lugs for the wire cross bracing were of 2-mm. steel tubing with an outside diameter of 8 mm. The lower longerons were shaped to pass over the spar of the bottom wing, the contour of the lower line of the fuselage being preserved by a sub-structure of lighter-gauge steel tubing. This is clearly shown in the illustration (see page 249) of the V.7 fuselage. The upper longerons were straight and horizontal as far aft as the cockpit; behind that point they curved downwards to the sternpost, with a small "step" to accommodate the tailplane.

In front of the cockpit a triangulated system of spacers obviated the need for wire cross bracing. To the front of the fuselage was welded a three-quarter circle of light steel tubing; this provided the attachment for the engine cowling. On each side of the fuselage a plywood fairing piece helped to blend the circular engine cowling into the rectangular cross-section of the rear part of the fuselage.

As in all Fokker types of the war period, there was no dashboard; the instruments were mounted somewhat haphazardly wherever attachment points could be found. The aluminium bucket seat could be adjusted for height. The triangular supports carried sleeves that could travel on the appropriate fuselage uprights, the upper sleeve of each pair being slotted and fitted with a bolt and wing nut by which it could be clamped in any desired position.

The control arrangements were typical of Fokker practice. The stick was pivotally attached to a longitudinal rocking shaft that bore two control horns to which the aileron cables were attached; the elevator cables were attached direct to the control column. The stick was surmounted by a two-handle grip. Between the two handles was the engine blip-switch, below it two trips for firing the guns; these were later replaced by von Richthofen's twin-trigger arrangement. The left handle of the grip was an auxiliary throttle lever, the movement of the throttle grip being transmitted by a Bowden cable to the actual throttle lever (the Le Rhône permitted a certain amount of throttling, in addition to its mixture control). This innovation was popular with pilots, because it allowed them to keep both hands on the stick in combat. It was used on subsequent Fokker fighters.

Some triplanes had a simple lever that depressed both gun trips for continuous fire from both guns. This was rarely used: fighter pilots had by then learned to aim properly, to fire only at close range, and to use as few rounds as possible. The long bursts of Immelmann's and Boelcke's time were now out of fashion.

A clamping device was provided to enable the elevator to be locked. This was commonly fitted to German aircraft with fixed machine-guns and was intended to facilitate the clearance of stoppages by letting the pilot use both hands.

The rudder bar was a piece of steel tubing with welded-on stirrup-type footrests. The cables were attached to clips on the tube between the foot-rests.

Engine installation

A most interesting and novel feature of the Fok. Dr.I was that the engine mounting could be taken out of the aircraft with the engine in place, by removing four easily accessible bolts. This greatly facilitated engine changing, which was a major operation in aircraft with plywood fuselages, such as the Albatros, Pfalz and Roland fighters.

As noted in Chapter XI, most Fok. Dr.I were powered by the Thulin-built Le Rhône, always carefully coded as *Beute* (captured) engines. A few Fokker triplanes had the Oberursel copy of the Le Rhône, the UR.II; it took an expert to distinguish between the two types. But, much to Fokker's chagrin, experienced pilots were unpatriotic enough to prefer the foreign-built engines.

The Le Rhône was carried on an overhung mounting that consisted of a ring-shaped main plate anchored by four struts to the corners of the front frame of the fuselage. A rear mounting was provided by the apex of a pyramid of four steel tubes, their other ends being anchored to the same front-frame corners. At first sight this eight-strut mounting seemed somewhat complicated, but it was in fact a simple and straightforward job, being welded up in a plain jig. The ends of the eight struts bore strong lugs: these registered with bushes in the corresponding corner joints of the fuselage front frame. Four high-grade steel bolts secured them. By withdrawing these bolts the engine and its mounting could be withdrawn from the fuselage. These attachment bolts also held the aluminium cover plate that separated the engine from the fuselage interior.

Units in the field greatly appreciated the ease with which the Fok. Dr.I could be serviced and kept ready for use at short notice, despite the greater care that its rotary engine required. Small wonder that German mechanics liked the triplane, for in its contemporaries the engine and all its accessories were very difficult to deal with.

The fuel system, like the rest of the aircraft, was simple. Just behind the engine there was a large tank with a longitudinal division inside. The port compartment held 73 litres (16 gals.) of petrol, the other 18 litres (4 gals.) of castor oil, or castor-oil substitute. This gave an endurance of just over two hours when the mixture was economically adjusted. The carburettor was fed by gravity; no pump or internal pressure was needed.

An amusing example of hardy historical myth originated in the U.S.A. some twenty-five years ago and survived until recent days. According to this, the Fok. Dr.I was fitted with an ammeter. It seems that no-one wondered why such a simple aircraft, whose only piece of electrical equipment was its magneto, should have such an instrument, much less what its purpose might have been. The source of the mystery is the simple fact that the standard Bosch ignition switch (used in every German aircraft since 1913) had been at some time hastily misinterpreted as an ammeter.

The undercarriage

The V-struts were made of steel tubing, connected spanwise at their apices by two spreader bars, also of steel tubing. The spreader bars had at each end a welded steel frame around which the rubber-cord shock absorbers were wound. The axle lay within an aluminium housing that gave it a reasonable amount of upward travel.

With the exception of a few experimental variants, all Fokker triplanes had an aerofoil fairing over the axle. This aerofoil was of the same section as the mainplanes and of similar construction, but plywood covered. With a chord of 800 mm., its area was 24% of that of the bottom mainplane, consequently it contributed appreciably to the total lift of the aircraft, especially when landing, and virtually made it a quadruplane.

The upper ends of the V-struts were ball-shaped and fitted into corresponding sockets on the longerons. They were held in place by relatively weak pins. When a sudden abnormal load on the undercarriage occurred, the pins sheared and damage to the fuselage structure was reduced.

Some form of emergency break-away attachments for undercarriages was in fact one of the standard requirements of the BLV. Platz had never heard of the BLV and its requirements, but he produced a thoroughly workmanlike fail-safe attachment that earned Fokker great praise for such a clever solution of the problem. At best, Fokker may have told Platz that the undercarriage should break off in a heavy landing.

The tail-skid was of ash, fitted with a steel shoe that quickly wore away. It was pivoted at its point of attachment, and was sprung by rubber cord. The tail-skid support, relieved of the need to provide a hinge for the rudder that arose in the earlier Fokkers with Morane-type fuselages, was a simple affair.

The tail unit

The tailplane was a welded steel-tube surface, triangular in plan and of flat-plate aerofoil section. It was braced to the lower longerons by one steel strut on each side. The tips of the tailplane were cut off to accommodate the horn balances of the elevators.

There was no fin, the rudder being of the comma shape that had characterized most earlier Fokker types. It was hinged to the sternpost.

The elevator-control gear ratio (lever length of control column to lever length of elevator horn) was 550 to 100, or 5·5 to 1. For the rudder the ratio was 210 to 100, or 2·1 to 1.

With little variation, the lay-out of the Fok. Dr.I tail unit was repeated in all subsequent Fokker fighters of the war period, especially those with rotary engines.

Armament

All operational Fokker triplanes carried the standard armament of two LMG. 08/15 machine-guns; no experimental variations are known. Each gun was

409

carried on two adjustable forked brackets. The front bracket was fitted to the top of a shallow tripod structure in a form of pivot bearing that allowed the gun a small amount of movement during adjustment. Each rear bracket was fastened to a cross tube between the top longerons; it could slide on the cross tube for the lateral alignment of the gun, and it could be raised or lowered for adjustment in elevation. This gun mounting proved to be simple and practical in the field, for all pilots insisted upon individual gun alignment to suit their personal combat tactics.

The Fok. Dr.I was equipped with the Zentral-Getriebe gun synchronizing gear designed by Luebbe. In this improved gear, flexible shafts were employed to transmit the impulses that actuated the gun triggers. The gear itself was mounted close to the engine oil pump and the magnetos. As required by current regulations, each gun had a veeder counter that indicated to the pilot the number of rounds fired since take-off. This useful device helped pilots to know when it was necessary to break off a combat owing to lack of ammunition.

The gun butts were so close to the pilot that the clearing of stoppages was made easy, and the loading lever needed no system of linkage. Servicing the guns was more easily accomplished than in other German fighters of the period. However, the arrangement had one serious disadvantage.

For maximum manoeuvrability all masses should be as close together as possible. These masses, in an aircraft like the Fok. Dr.I, were the engine, fuel tanks, armament and pilot. In the Fok. Dr.I the tank was larger than in earlier Fokker fighters because there was no second tank behind the cockpit. By virtue of its size the tank made it necessary to keep the ammunition boxes fairly well aft; this in turn brought the guns rather closer to the cockpit than was desirable. Accessible though the guns were, they protruded well back into the cockpit and were dangerously close to the pilot's face. As indicated above, this arrangement had its advantages, but in the event of a crash the pilot's head and face were exposed to serious injury.

The BLV requirements specified liberal padding of exposed gun butts for protection. But on all production Fokker triplanes only a pretence of padding had been made: such as was fitted was shoddy and flimsy, and should never have been allowed by the officials who were responsible for the acceptance of the production triplanes. It consisted of little more than a strip of patent leather holding an inadequate piece of felt against the sharp metal. It was easily torn, and frequently was not replaced in the field.

This deplorable feature caused injuries to pilots in what would have otherwise been minor landing incidents. Matters were made worse by pilots' disdain of seat belts: few would wear proper seat harnesses for fear of being thought faint-hearted, and no fighter pilot wore the regulation crash helmet (which was quite effective but clumsy). Some pilots, like Udet, would even do without a helmet of any kind whenever they could, partly because they thought it smart, partly because their head movements were not impeded in combat.

This type of bravado, coupled with Fokker's cheap and nasty production standards, was responsible for many fatalities and permanent injuries.

APPENDIX V

NOTES ON INDIVIDUAL FOKKER TRIPLANES

101/17		V.4 prototype. Tested to destruction at Adlershof.
102/17	F.I	Accepted at Schwerin, August 16, 1917. To Jagdgeschwader I, August 21, 1917. Flown by Manfred von Richthofen, September 1, 1917. Oblt. Kurt Wolff shot down, September 15, 1917.
103/17	F.I	Accepted at Schwerin, August 16, 1917. To Jagdgeschwader I, August 21, 1917. Flown by Werner Voss, who scored 21 victories on it. Voss was shot down while flying this F.I by Second Lieutenant A. P. F. Rhys Davids, No. 56 Squadron, Royal Flying Corps, on September 23, 1917.
104/17	Dr.I	Acceptance test at Goerries, September 13, 1917. To Jagdgeschwader I, October 1917.
106/17	Dr.I	Acceptance test at Goerries, September 13, 1917. To Jagdgeschwader I, October 1917. Leutnant Bahr (Jasta 11) crashed fatally, March 6, 1918.
107/17	Dr.I	Delivered to Jagdgeschwader I, October 1917.
108/17	Dr.I	To Adlershof as test-bed for 160-h.p. Goebel Goe.III engine.
109/17	Dr.I	To Jagdgeschwader I, October 1917.
110/17	Dr.I	To Jagdgeschwader I, October 1917. Leutnant Erich Just, Jasta 11, shot down wounded, March 1, 1918.
111/17 112/17 113/17	Dr.I	To Jagdgeschwader I, October 1917.
114/17	Dr.I	To Jagdgeschwader I, October 1917. Flown by Manfred von Richthofen. Wrecked in emergency landing, October 30, 1917.
115/17	Dr.I	To Jasta 15. Leutnant Heinrich Gontermann crashed fatally, October 29, 1917.
116/17 118/17 119/17	Dr.I	To Jagdgeschwader I, October 1917.
121/17	Dr.I	To Jagdgeschwader I, October 1917. Leutnant Pastor, Jasta 11, killed October 31, 1917.
122/17 123/17 125/17	Dr.I	To Jagdgeschwader I, October 1917.
127/17	Dr.I	To Jagdgeschwader I on October 29, 1917. Flown by Manfred von Richthofen.

132/17	Dr.I	To Jagdgeschwader I, October 1917.
141/17		Used for official performance tests, November 10, 1917.
144/17		Leutnant Stapenhorst, Jasta 11, brought down in British territory, aircraft almost intact. Examined in England. Factory No. 1856. British No. G.125.
152/17		Flown by Manfred von Richthofen. This Dr.I was returned to Schwerin for the fitting of the modified wings required by the Flz.
155/17		To Jasta 11. Crash-landed by Leutnant J. Wolff on February 3, 1918, after wing failure.
188/17		Fitted with Oberursel-built Le Rhône engine.
195/17		Fitted experimentally with Rhenania-built Le Rhône, also with the Siemens–Rhemag and the original 160-h.p. Siemens–Halske Sh.III engines.
216/17		Flown by Hauptmann Ritter von Tutschek.
404/17		Originally fitted with 160-h.p. Goebel Goe.III engine; officially accepted January 10, 1918. Flown by von Tutschek, who was killed on this aircraft.
405/17		Delivered to Manfred von Richthofen as reserve aircraft on January 23, 1918.
416/17		Fitted with Goebel-built Gnôme engine.
425/17		Factory No. 2009. Acceptance test by Weidner at Goerries on January 8, 1918. Flown by Manfred von Richthofen, who met his death in this aircraft on April 21, 1918.
469/17		Trial installation of 145-h.p. Oberursel UR.III.
485/17		Fitted with captured 130-h.p. Clerget No. 953.
527/17		Fitted with captured 130-h.p. Clerget No. 1072.
545/17		Leutnant Weiss killed, February 5, 1918.
562/17		Fitted with captured 130-h.p. Clerget No. 1503.
591/17		Leutnant Scholz (Jasta 11) killed, May 2, 1918.
100/18		Fitted with captured 160-h.p. Gnôme. Acceptance test by Matthias at Goerries on April 26, 1918.

STRUCTURAL DESCRIPTION OF THE FOKKER D.VII

Wing structure

Unlike the wings of the triplane, the mainplanes of the V.11 were not designed as full-cantilever structures. Each spar could resist all bending loads as an individual cantilever, but the wing frames were not torsionally stiff enough to be full cantilevers. In the triplane, with its narrow-chord wings, the interplane strut transmitted little load; it was more or less an afterthought, useful but not absolutely necessary.

This was not so in the V.11: the N-strut was essential to the torsional stiffness of the structure. A Fok. D.VII was experimentally flown without interplane struts (see page 289). Platz was not aware of this experiment at the time: had he been, he would have objected because he did not consider it to be safe.

Fokker claimed the N-strut to be his invention, but this is demonstrably untrue. A patent applied for on March 29, 1918 (German patent D.R.P. 460076), but published ten years later, claimed protection for the use of N-shaped interplane struts in biplanes with cantilever wings and continuous spars extending from wing tip to wing tip. Such N-struts would merely prevent the wings from twisting under torsion loads. According to the claim, this permitted the wings to be thinner than if they were full cantilevers.

The aerofoil sections were similar to those of the triplane. The ribs had divided cap-strips like those of the later Fok. Dr.I; they were of 5×5-mm. lengths of pine. The web was of 1·2-mm. birch plywood, but elm plywood may have been used as a substitute later on (which may account for the inferiority of plywood on which the Flz. commented). The vertical rib stiffeners were again used; they were of triangular cross-section, 10×10 mm., and were of pine. Pine gusset strips, also of triangular section, secured the ribs to the spars by bradding and gluing. All ribs in both wings were spaced equidistantly, 300 mm. apart. They were consecutively numbered through both wings: for example, No. 50 rib was the starboard tip rib in the upper wing.

The plywood strip along the leading edge was of 1·2-mm. birch plywood. It was supported by a spanwise wooden member that was attached to the rib noses and formed the leading edge proper. The plywood also rested on two light stringers, 5×10 mm., that ran parallel to the leading edge.

Both wings had two separate box spars with inter-spar drag bracing. In the D.VII wing Platz took into account the difference in the compression and tension strengths of wood, and the spar flanges were not of equal thickness as they had been in the triplane. In the D.VII wing each flange was composed of two laminations; the webs were of 1·5-mm. birch plywood. At strut-attachment points, tapering internal filler blocks were glued in. Care was taken to ensure that all fixing bolts went through the neutral axis of the spar.

Each wing tip consisted of a wooden former that was built up from four curved laminations. After gluing the whole former was spindled out for lightness. It was rigidly attached to the tips of the spars and reinforced with two plywood strips, each 65 mm. wide. The trailing edge consisted of a length of 1-mm. steel wire, clipped to the rib tails in the manner employed on the Fok. Dr.I. There was a spanwise stringer a short distance ahead of it.

The cut-out in the trailing edge of the upper wing was formed by a substantial member made, like the wing tips, by gluing five laminations together and spindling out the resultant component. This was 25 mm. wide and 30 mm. deep, and was strong enough to support the rear-view mirror that fighter pilots found increasingly necessary.

There were no compression struts. Instead, each wing embodied two box ribs, one at the root or cabane pick-up points, the other at the interplane-strut attachment points. The outer panel of each wing and its centre portion had only one pair of crossed drag cables. Thus there were only eight metal fittings in the lower wing; the upper wing additionally had four pulley brackets for the aileron controls attached to the front spar. The basic material for all fittings was 1-mm. and 2-mm. mild-steel sheet. Welding was extensively used in their fabrication, thicker parts being built up of several layers of sheet.

In the standard version of the Fok. D.VII the axis of each aileron was slightly skewed. Fokker thought this improved the flying qualities.

Fuselage and tail

The fuselage was a welded steel-tube structure, of which the two engine bearers and their supporting members formed an integral part. The tripod that supported the front spar of the upper wing was also welded to the fuselage; the front strut was welded to the engine bearer on each side. The rear-spar supporting struts were detachable and their length could be adjusted.

Whereas the lower longerons of the Fok. Dr.I had been angled upwards to pass over the bottom wing, those of the Fok. D.VII were cut to provide a recess large enough to accommodate the central portion of the lower wing. An arrangement of steel tubes bridged this gap; when the wing had been bolted in place, the cut ends of the longerons were connected by detachable lengths of tubing. This feature of a removable portion of the lower longerons was the subject of a German patent, D.R.P. No. 325930 of March 29, 1918, under the name of A. H. G. Fokker.

The rear part of the fuselage was generally similar to that of the Fok. Dr.I, with the exception of the triangular fin and the method of attaching the rudder, which was connected by four simple hinges to the fin and sternpost. A turtledeck fairing that tapered down towards the tail was fitted on top of the fuselage.

The complete fuselage structure, with this top decking, weighed 47·5 kg. (105 lb.). A further 45 kg. (99 lb.) were added by the seat, control gear and other fixed installations.

As in other Fokker aeroplanes, the cockpit was characterized by spartan simplicity. There was no dashboard, for it would have hampered access to the ammunition boxes. The two fuel pressure gauges were mounted on the rear wall of the petrol tank itself; below them were the fuel and pressure cocks. The r.p.m. indicator was carried on the steel-tube bridge piece that supported the guns. The starter magneto and Bosch ignition switch were on the port side, together with an ignition timing lever (the Bosch magneto had no provision for automatic timing). There was no air-speed indicator, but some pilots installed such instruments, for they found them useful when flying through cloud.

Fuel delivery to the carburettor was by pressure feed, for which the engine drove a small air pump. In addition, to restore the pressure when necessary, the pilot had a hand pump on the starboard side of the cockpit. This seldom had to be used, except in emergency and after long glides.

A total of 90 litres (19·5 gals.) of fuel and 8 litres (1·75 gals.) of oil were carried; this load weighed nearly 66 kg. (146 lb.). Acceptance tests had to be carried out with tanks two-thirds full; that is, with a fuel load of 43 kg. (95 lb.). The single tank was divided into three sections: the starboard for oil, the central as an auxiliary petrol tank of 30 litres (6·5 gals.) capacity, the port the main tank of 60 litres (13 gals.). This fuel load gave an endurance of 1½ hours at full throttle at ground level. The fuel was usually a mixture of 60% petrol and 40% benzene.

As noted in Chapter XIII (page 279) the tank attachments were not officially approved, and their replacement by steel straps was demanded.

The left handle of the control grip was an auxiliary throttle; this permitted pilots to keep both hands on the stick in combat. Even in 1918, most German pilots were not happy flying with only one hand on the stick: this legacy of the days when wheel control was compulsory on German army aeroplanes died hard.

At the lower end of the control column was a forked bush that was hinged to a rocking shaft. The forward extension of this shaft carried two staggered levers to which the aileron control cables were attached. The levers had to be staggered because the control cables were crossed. The elevator cables were attached directly to the bush of the control column.

The rudder bar was a steel tube with stirrup-type foot-rests welded on. The control cables were attached to it by shackles.

It may surprise present-day designers to learn that no part of the Fok. D.VII airframe or control system embodied a single roller or ball bearing. In spite of this, the controls gave no trouble whatever, even after twenty years of intensive flying.

The triangular tailplane had a span of 2·32 m. (7·67 ft.) and a chord of 2·44 m. (8·04 ft.). It was of a thin symmetrical section and its angle of incidence was 3°. The complete tail group weighed 15·5 kg. (34·3 lb.).

The characteristic radiator was made by Tewes & Braun, and was specially made to meet Platz's wishes. He wanted a tidy, compact arrangement instead of the remote installations, with their long water tubes, that were used on so many contemporary German aeroplanes. Behind the radiator was a shutter that was intended to regulate the water temperature during flight. It was not very effective, however, and there was trouble with engine temperatures being too high or too low.

Thirteen litres (2·88 gals.) of water were held by the radiator; the total quantity of water in the whole cooling system was 27 litres (6 gals.). Only water was used, and some trouble was experienced in freezing conditions if the radiator and water pump were not properly drained.

The mounting of the radiator on the forward ends of the engine bearers prevented relative movement between engine and radiator. It required only short water tubes, consequently leaks were rare on Fok. D.VII aircraft. In fact, the installation was regarded as the best in use on German aircraft when the war ended.

In accordance with current German opinion, the engine was attached directly to the engine bearers. No German military aeroplane had any kind of elastic or shock-absorbing connexions between the engine and its mounting; these were in fact regarded as unnecessary and somewhat harmful. A rigid installation gave no trouble as long as balanced engines such as six-cylinder in-line types were used; but when eight-cylinder V-type engines came into use in 1918, rigid mountings began to manifest vibration troubles. Nevertheless, elastic engine mountings were not tried until much later.

In its general features the Fok. D.VII undercarriage did not differ materially from that of the Dr.I. It had the aerofoil over the axle, and the same ball-and-socket attachments that were supposed to fail in shear if the landing was unduly rough. The struts were streamline steel tubes of 65×32-mm. cross-section.

Like most Fokker undercarriages, that of the D.VII did not wholly satisfy the BLV strength requirements, and Flz. technicians repeatedly reminded Fokker that the D.VII undercarriage was not regarded as serviceable. However, no serious trouble was experienced in service, so it is likely that the D.V.L.'s testing method was not altogether realistic.

Rubber shock-absorber cord was no longer obtainable, even for front-line fighters. It was replaced by steel coil springs in a fabric covering. Externally, these resembled rubber cord, but were a poor substitute and responsible for many landing incidents.

At the apex of each V-strut of the undercarriage was a sheet-steel casing. This had a slot for the axle that permitted a maximum travel of 100 mm. (4 inches); the casing also housed the shock absorbers, which were wrapped round the axle and the two spreader bars. The axle travel was too little when the aircraft was flown from the uneven fields that were used as front-line aerodromes, and avoidable damage resulted.

The undercarriage wheels were of the standard 760×100-mm. type, with a hub width of 160 mm. (6·32 in.); the wheel track was 1·8 m. (5·92 ft.). Wider wheel tracks were tried experimentally but were never used on the standard Fok. D.VII.

Armament

The regulation armament consisted of two LMG. 08/15 machine-guns, synchronized by the Fokker *Zentralsteuerung*. They could be aligned on the ground by adjustment of the two-fork mountings.

Two 500-round hemp ammunition belts were usually carried. The ammunition box was of aluminium sheet. Unfortunately, it was too close to the engine and grew hot during flight, especially on hot days. This caused the incendiary (phosphorus) ammunition to explode, and was the most serious defect of the Fok. D.VII.

Experimental installations of other weapons were made, among them the first specimen of a heavy 12-mm. machine-gun named TuF (Tank und Flieger; that is, for use against tanks and aeroplanes). The Siemens motor-powered gun was also fitted. This had some initial success operationally but needed further development.

INDEX